Advances in

THE STUDY OF BEHAVIOR

VOLUME 8

Contributors to This Volume

ROBERT A. HINDE
BERT HÖLLDOBLER
JERRY A. HOGAN
MICHAEL LEON
FRANK MCKINNEY
T. J. ROPER
ELIZABETH STEEL

Advances in
THE STUDY OF
BEHAVIOR

Edited by

JAY S. ROSENBLATT
Institute of Animal Behavior
Rutgers University
Newark, New Jersey

ROBERT A. HINDE
Medical Research Council
Unit on the Development and Integration of Behaviour
University Sub-Department of Animal Behaviour
Madingley, Cambridge, England

COLIN BEER
Institute of Animal Behavior
Rutgers University
Newark, New Jersey

MARIE-CLAIRE BUSNEL
Laboratoire de Physiologie Acoustique
Institut National de la Recherche Agronomique
Ministère de l'Agriculture
Jouy en Josas (S. et O.), France

——————— VOLUME 8 ———————

ACADEMIC PRESS   New York   San Francisco   London   1978
A Subsidiary of Harcourt Brace Jovanovich, Publishers

ACADEMIC PRESS, INC.
111 Fifth Avenue, New York, New York 10003

United Kingdom Edition published by
ACADEMIC PRESS, INC. (LONDON) LTD.
24/28 Oval Road, London NW1 7DX

LIBRARY OF CONGRESS CATALOG CARD NUMBER: 64–8031

ISBN 0–12–004508–7

PRINTED IN THE UNITED STATES OF AMERICA

Contents

Comparative Approaches to Social Behavior in Closely Related Species of Birds
FRANK MCKINNEY

The Influence of Daylength and Male Vocalizations on the Estrogen-Dependent Behavior of Female Canaries and Budgerigars, with Discussion of Data from Other Species
ROBERT A. HINDE AND ELIZABETH STEEL

Ethological Aspects of Chemical Communication in Ants

BERT HÖLLDOBLER

Filial Responsiveness to Olfactory Cues in the Laboratory Rat

MICHAEL LEON

A Comparison of the Properties of Different Reinforcers

JERRY A. HOGAN AND T. J. ROPER

List of Contributors

Numbers in parentheses indicate the pages on which the authors' contributions begin.

ROBERT A. HINDE, *M.R.C. Unit on the Development and Integration of Behaviour, University Sub-Department of Animal Behaviour, Madingley, Cambridge, England (39)*

BERT HÖLLDOBLER, *Department of Biology, Harvard University, Museum of Comparative Zoology Laboratories, Cambridge, Massachusetts (75)*

JERRY A. HOGAN, *Department of Psychology, University of Toronto, Toronto, Canada (155)*

MICHAEL LEON, *Department of Psychology, McMaster University, Hamilton, Ontario, Canada (117)*

FRANK MCKINNEY, *Department of Ecology and Behavioral Biology, University of Minnesota, Minneapolis, Minnesota (1)*

T. J. ROPER,* *Department of Experimental Psychology, University of Cambridge, Cambridge, England (155)*

ELIZABETH STEEL, *M.R.C. Unit on the Development and Integration of Behaviour, University Sub-Department of Animal Behaviour, Madingley, Cambridge, England (39)*

*Present address: School of Biological Sciences, The University of Sussex, Falmer, Brighton, Sussex BN1 9QG, England.

Preface

The study of animal behavior is attracting the attention of ever-increasing numbers of zoologists and comparative psychologists in all parts of the world, and is becoming increasingly important to students of human behavior in the psychiatric, psychological, and allied professions. Widening circles of workers, from a variety of backgrounds, carry out descriptive and experimental studies of behavior under natural conditions, laboratory studies of the organization of behavior, analyses of neural and hormonal mechanisms of behavior, and studies of the development, genetics, and evolution of behavior, using both animal and human subjects. The aim of *Advances in the Study of Behavior* is to provide workers on all aspects of behavior an opportunity to present an account of recent progress in their particular fields for the benefit of other students of behavior. It is our intention to encourage a variety of critical reviews, including intensive factual reviews of recent work, reformulations of persistent problems, and historical and theoretical essays, all oriented toward the facilitation of current and future progress. *Advances in the Study of Behavior* is offered as a contribution to the development of cooperation and communication among scientists in our field.

Announcement

Beginning with this volume of *Advances in the Study of Behavior*, Dr. Evelyn Shaw is no longer serving as an editor. The publishers and editors express their appreciation to Dr. Shaw for the original idea for this serial publication, which has grown to be an important contribution to behavioral scientists.

Dr. Marie-Claire Busnel of France has been invited to be an editor and we are pleased that she has accepted the position, thus adding another European editor to the editorial board of *Advances in the Study of Behavior*. We hope to maintain the international representation amongst both readers and contributors established by earlier volumes.

Contents of Previous Volumes

Advances in

THE STUDY OF BEHAVIOR
VOLUME 8

Comparative Approaches to Social Behavior in Closely Related Species of Birds

FRANK McKINNEY

DEPARTMENT OF ECOLOGY AND BEHAVIORAL BIOLOGY
UNIVERSITY OF MINNESOTA, MINNEAPOLIS, MINNESOTA

I. INTRODUCTION

Attempting to understand why each animal species has evolved its uniquely characteristic behavior is an endless task. We can never identify all the factors that have molded the behavior of the extinct ancestors of living animals or the precise sequence of events that determined the course of evolution. Partial explanations for species-characteristic behavior are possible, however, and confidence in the correctness of interpretations can increase as additional pieces in the puzzle fit together. From time to time a key observation or idea can unlock the door to new ways of posing questions, and for a while progress is rapid. We are in the midst of an explosion of new ideas on how behavior evolves and the reorganization in thinking is having many repercussions. This is especially the case with regard to the evolution of social behavior in animals, and comparative research is once again in the limelight.

The word ''comparative'' is used in a variety of ways in the behavior literature. In the ethological sense ''applying the comparative approach'' implies a search for explanations of similarities and differences in species-characteristic

1

behavior in terms of phylogenetic history and the operation of natural selection. Two complementary methods are used: (1) studies of adaptive radiation of behavior in groups of closely related species and (2) comparisons of similar behavior, in distantly related species, presumed to have evolved through parallel or convergent evolution. In psychology, the term *comparative* has often been used to refer to any research on nonhuman animals, but, in response to provocative critiques (e.g., Hodos and Campbell, 1969; Lockard, 1971), deliberate comparison between species is now often involved and a blending of ethological and psychological viewpoints is in progress (Dewsbury, 1973; Dewsbury and Rethlingshafer, 1973; Tobach *et al.,* 1973).

At the same time, development of a theoretical framework for thinking about the evolution of social behavior has been progressing rapidly (Hamilton, 1964; Williams, 1966, 1975; Crook, 1970a; Crook and Goss-Custard, 1972; Trivers, 1972, 1974; Maynard Smith and Price, 1973; Alexander, 1974; Parker, 1974a, b; Maynard Smith, 1976), and a number of new texts treat the overlapping fields of ecology, ethology, and evolutionary biology in exciting ways (Ricklefs, 1973; Emlen, 1973; Alcock, 1975; Brown, 1975; Wilson, 1975). Much adjustment in thinking about behavior evolution is underway, and the implications are important for all students of behavior.

From time to time, proponents of the comparative zoological approach to behavior have tried to explain how it can be used (e.g., Lorenz, 1950; Hinde and Tinbergen, 1958; Baerends, 1958; Wickler, 1961a, 1967; Alexander, 1969; Hailman, 1976a), and a large body of literature is available to illustrate the method. Concepts have been changing, however, and comparative studies—even tentative explorations of previously unstudied groups—no longer need be carried out in the rather haphazard, intuitive ways that used to be acceptable. Much old ground needs to be retraced with new questions in mind and even the best-studied groups must be reexamined. Different kinds of information are needed, and new techniques are called for.

The basis for the approach still lies in comparative observational studies in a phylogenetic context (Lorenz, 1941) and studies of adaptive function of behavior in single species (Tinbergen, 1953, 1967). By studying a number of closely related species, the "ground plan" for the whole group begins to emerge. If evolutionarily conservative characteristics can be distinguished from plastic ones, the nature and extent of variations on the phylogenetic theme become clearer. Ideas on the particular balance of selective forces that have shaped the evolution of behavior in each species then can be developed. In striving for a better grasp of how natural selection has worked our conception of each species changes. We begin to understand not only the forces that shaped its behavior but also the roles that behavior has played in its evolutionary history. Gradually, by comparing and contrasting, each species can be placed with increasing conviction in a special "evolutionary perspective." Eventually the point may be reached when all evidence points to one interpretation, and alternative hypotheses become highly improbable.

Comparison of closely related forms is discussed here as though it can stand alone as a scientific method. I have done this deliberately to draw attention to special features of the approach and implications of using it. Obviously it is only one of many approaches, and, in tackling evolutionary questions, it is complemented by other methods (e.g., experimental demonstration of adaptive value of behavior patterns, genetic analysis, developmental studies, theoretical model building, and especially by studies of behavior resulting from convergent evolution). I hope to show, however, that comparison of closely related forms remains a natural and essential component of research on ultimate causal factors. Further, it is often the best way we know to tackle a host of interesting problems relating to behavioral phenomena that are peculiar to particular populations, species, or groups.

One of the consequences of proliferation of specialized interests among students of behavior has been a widening of gaps between fields organized around topics or problems and those defined by taxonomic groupings. The links between ethology and ornithology have continued to be strong, however, notably among field workers interested in ecological, evolutionary, and functional problems. Nevertheless, the research orientation appropriate for comparative studies on closely related species is often misunderstood. In evolutionary studies, it may be essential to view the group itself, and each species in turn, as the "problems" of primary interest. As Geist (1971) has expressed it, the study of behavior can become a tool in understanding a species. Identifying key factors in specific cases of behavior evolution—cliff nesting (Cullen, 1957), cooperative hunting (Schaller, 1972; Kruuk, 1972), glacial retreat (Geist, 1971), the difficulty of mollusk predation for a shorebird (Norton-Griffiths, 1969)—not only can influence all future research on these species but can also lead to concepts and viewpoints of wide significance.

To illustrate the problems faced by comparative ethologists seeking these elusive perspectives I will review some of the main concepts that have guided research on avian social behavior. Although birds provide few examples of highly developed "sociality," they show a wide range of social systems and are especially appropriate for studies on mating systems involving pair bonding. The waterfowl (family Anatidae), my own study group, have been especially thoroughly investigated, and I will use the ducks to illustrate most points.

II. Captives versus Field Studies

The earliest comparative behavior studies on groups of closely related animals were carried out in zoos or private collections. The classic work on waterfowl

(Heinroth, 1911; Lorenz, 1941, 1953), pigeons (Whitman, 1919), and cichlid fishes (Baerends and Baerends van Roon, 1950) illustrate this method, and many similar studies have followed. By observing semiwild, free-flying birds (Lorenz, 1935) or by "enriching" the enclosures in which captives are held some improvements are possible in the naturalness of the setting. With some animal groups, however, captive breeding is very difficult, and artificiality of captive conditions is often unavoidable.

The value of "living with your animals" as advocated by Lorenz (1952) continues to be widely recognized in comparative studies. By collecting and keeping animals of different species, living at close quarters with them, handling them, and encouraging them to breed, much can be learned about their behavior and their needs. In becoming a competent aviculturist, in the tradition of Oskar Heinroth and Derek Goodwin, it becomes impossible to ignore individual differences in behavior, and, in time, rare behavioral events are observed. Sensitivity to both of these aspects of behavior is essential to balance the tendency to stress the most common, conspicuous, most easily quantified kinds of behavior when compiling ethograms.

Studies on captives allow side by side comparison of many species from different parts of the world, observations can be made at close range, and manipulations of groupings and other kinds of experiments are often possible. Conditions for observation can be standardized, increasing the precision of quantifying specific differences, as Dewsbury (1975) has done in his elegant laboratory studies of copulatory behavior in rodents. However, the limitations of working with captives have often been underestimated, and to proceed beyond the stage of making preliminary descriptive inventories of behavior repertoires, field studies must be made.

Studies of behavior evolution in birds entered a new phase with the first attempts to carry out extensive comparative work in the field (Tinbergen, 1959, on gulls; Crook, 1964, on weaverbirds). The fruitfulness of these studies on birds is apparent from the research they have stimulated on relationships between ecological factors and social behavior in other animal groups (e.g., primates, Crook and Gartlan, 1966; Crook, 1970b; Eisenberg *et al.*, 1972; Clutton-Brock, 1974; ungulates, Jarman, 1974).

A prime consideration in selecting a study group is often feasibility of field observations. It is no accident that many of the bird groups that have been worked on to date are colonial nesters (gulls, sulids, penguins, herons, weaverbirds, and many icterids) or birds in which social gatherings provide opportunities to accumulate data rapidly (lek grouse, ducks), or those that are easily observed because they use open perches (flycatchers, bee-eaters). Although it may be possible to work quite easily with some species in captivity, it may be virtually impossible to complement the observations with field study (e.g., many rails). Thus, although social behavior has been studied in many species of birds, there are still only a few families, subfamilies, and large genera for which comparative knowledge is both extensive and thorough.

The size and diversity of the group are very important. The strength of the method depends in part on the number of species available to constitute the sample. In birds, a family including dozens of species has obvious advantages over one with only a few. While some of the most intriguing evolutionary problems are posed by the ratites, anhingas, loons, kiwis, painted snipes, phalaropes, and finfoots, these groups do not include enough living species to permit studies of the adaptive radiation of behavior, no matter how instructive they may be as illustrations of specialization and/or evolutionary convergence.

Accessibility, aesthetic qualities, and availability of research funds often influence ethologists in selecting their first species for intensive study. If evolutionary questions are of primary interest, however, suitability for applying the comparative approach should also be considered carefully. Time spent becoming familiar with the behavioral repertoire of one species is an investment which may not pay off until some of its close relatives are also studied.

Many field observers are uneasy about working with captives and many lab workers begrudge the time needed for field studies, but the two approaches are complementary and there are advantages in combining them. Some kinds of behavior (e.g., quiet calls) can be extremely difficult to record in the field, and to answer certain questions about complex social interactions it may be essential to have all individuals marked. For example, the social courtship of dabbling ducks is impossible to analyze properly under field conditions where all individuals are not identified. By filming long sequences of courtship in groups of full-winged captives held in flight pens, interactions can be analyzed on the individual level necessary to interpret them (Weidmann and Darley, 1971; Simmons and Weidmann, 1973; McKinney, 1975; Laurie-Ahlberg and McKinney, in press). Comparative studies of breeding behavior can also be made in large flight pens, providing opportunities to analyze interactions rarely observed at close range in the field (McKinney, 1967, 1975). One of the best examples of the method is provided by the long-term comparative and experimental field and aviary program on weaverbirds carried out by Collias and Collias (1964, 1967) and their collaborators (e.g., Collias *et al.,* 1971a,b).

III. Behavioral Homologies and Taxonomic Characters

Most early comparative studies on closely related species emphasized similarities in their behavior. By adopting the concept of homology from comparative anatomy, attempts were made to establish that the "same" behavior had been present in a common ancestor. Although many ethologists have become convinced that this is possible, especially for highly stereotyped displays in closely related species of birds, the difficulties have been stressed by Atz (1970) and Klopfer (1973). The concept of homology and its application to behavior have been reviewed recently by Campbell and Hodos (1970) and Hailman (1976b), while Beer (1973) and Baerends (1975) have responded to the critique by Atz.

In theory, there is no reason to doubt that certain behavior patterns have remained relatively unchanged during speciation and there must be many examples if we can just identify them. The big problems are with the notoriously plastic processes of behavior development, the criteria to be used in identifying homologies, and the dangers of confusing homologous features with similar behavior patterns evolved convergently. The task is easiest where (1) the behavior patterns concerned are very distinctive in form and inherently unlikely to have evolved this particular form more than once, (2) they occur in many closely related species, and (3) there is independent evidence on the closeness of relationships between the species (Tinbergen, 1962).

These criteria are met by many of the display movements and vocalizations of waterfowl (Heinroth, 1911; Lorenz, 1941, 1953; Delacour and Mayr, 1945; Johnsgard, 1965). Taxonomic relationships within the Anatidae have been worked out mainly by using adult body shape, duckling downy plumages, wing speculum color and pattern, tracheal anatomy, and certain behavioral characters. In general, the conclusions agree with those reached by Woolfenden (1961) on the basis of postcranial osteological features, and there is now widespread agreement among specialists on the major groupings of species within the family. There are still many practical problems of nomenclature (e.g., whether to recognize *Mareca, Dafila,* and *Spatula* as separate genera or to place all dabbling ducks in the one genus *Anas*), but these are matters of convention and they do not affect the basic arrangement of species.

Johnsgard has used behavioral characters to correct mistakes in the classification of a number of duck species where morphological and other features (sometimes behavioral ones) had misled earlier taxonomists. These studies on *Marmaronetta angustirostris* (Johnsgard, 1961), *Callonetta leucophrys* and *Lophonetta specularioides* (Johnsgard, 1965), and *Thalassornis leuconotus* (Johnsgard, 1967) provide convincing evidence that behavior patterns can be even more helpful than morphological features to indicate phylogenetic affinities in this group of birds. (The correctness of Johnsgard's judgments cannot be established with certainty, of course, but his conclusions are supported by much stronger evidence than earlier views.)

Some kinds of behavior (including some displays) are less useful as taxonomic characters since they could easily have evolved independently many times. Preening is an everyday activity in birds of all kinds and, judging from the erratic distribution of ritualized preening movements within the various duck tribes (McKinney, 1965), these displays have probably evolved several times in the

Anatidae. This is supported by the widespread occurrence of ritualized preening movements in other bird groups of diverse origins (e.g., grebes, herons, albatrosses). Similar arguments apply to other comfort movements and to the open-bill threatening and head-up postures adopted by many kinds of birds during hostile encounters (see the illustrations in Tinbergen, 1959, and Marler, 1961).

When used with caution, some general behavioral features (e.g., diving and perching abilities) can help to confirm affinities in the waterfowl but they can also be misleading. For instance, early attempts to use "quarrelsome temperament" as an indicator of affinities with the shelduck group (Tadornini) now appear to have been incorrect in placing *Lophonetta*, and apparently "social demeanor" can vary widely among close relatives, associated for example, with various degrees of territoriality. Movements involved in body care can vary little within whole families of birds (McKinney, 1965; Storer, 1969), but even head-scratching methods, once considered very stable characteristics, have evidently changed a number of times during the evolution of the birds (Wickler, 1961b).

Some vocalizations are very valuable taxonomic characters in waterfowl. Perhaps the best example is the "decrescendo call" of *Anas* ducks—a distinctive series of descending notes known to be given by females of all living species that have been well studied and not known outside this group (see Table I). The same kind of pattern consistency is found in the evenly spaced "repeated calls" of males in the blue-winged duck group (McKinney, 1970) although the quality of the notes varies greatly between species ("tooks" in *Anas clypeata*, "pews" in *A. discors*, "rrars" in *A. cyanoptera*). In birds in general, however, vocalizations are of little value in tracing relationships above the generic level (Thorpe, 1961; Thielcke, 1964; Lanyon, 1969).

Apart from close similarity in form, the social situations where they are given and their positions in display chains often support judgments on homology of duck displays. This is the case, for example, with the attention-getting sequence grunt–whistle + head-up–tail-up + turn-back-of-head found in a number of *Anas* species.

Instances of probable convergence have also been detected in duck displays. Movements involving tossing the head backward while delivering a call are found in a number of distantly related groups, for example, but there are differences in form and timing (e.g., among *Aythya, Bucephala, Somateria*), indicating that these have had separate origins.

Knowledge about waterfowl displays is now so extensive that it is possible to pursue these methods further. In some cases, we may be able to deduce how display repertoires have probably changed during evolution and perhaps even why they have changed in certain ways. For example, species with "missing" displays (based on expectations from the repertoires of their close relatives) provide opportunities to search for factors that could have caused such evolutionary changes (see Section IV).

TABLE I
Selected Displays of Dabbling Ducks (genus *Anas*) Believed to Be Reliable Taxonomic Characters[a,b]

	Precopulatory pumping	Decrescendo call	Grunt–whistle	Head-up–tail-up	Down–up	Postcopulatory bridling	Independent bridling	Lateral dabbling
Wigeons								
Anas penelope	×	×						
Anas americana	×	×						
Anas sibilatrix	×	×						
Anas falcata	×	×	×	×	?R			
Anas strepera	×	×	×	×	×			
Anas formosa	×	×	●	●	●			
Green-winged teals								
Anas crecca	×	×	×	×	×	×	×	
Anas flavirostris	×	×	×	×	●	×	×	
Anas capensis	×	×	●	×	●	×	●	
Austral teals								
Anas gibberifrons (*Anas bernieri*)	(×)	×	×	×	×	(×)	×	
Anas castanea (*Anas aucklandica*)	×	×	×	×	×	×	×	
Mallards								
Anas platyrhynchos	×	×	×	×	×	×		
Anas rubripes	×	×	×	×	×	×		
Anas melleri	×	×	×	×	×	×		

	1	2	3	4	5	6	7	8
Anas undulata	×	×	×	×	×	×		
Anas poecilorhyncha	×	×	×	×	×	×		
Anas luzonica	×	×	×	×	×	×		
Anas sparsa	×	×	×	×	●	×		
(Anas waigiuensis)								
(Anas specularis)		×						
Anas specularioides	×	×	×	×				
Pintails								
Anas acuta	×		×	×	●	×		
Anas georgica	×		×	R	●	×		
Anas bahamensis	×		●	×	×	×	R	
Anas erythrorhyncha	×		●	●	●	×	R	
Silver teals								
Anas versicolor	×	×						
Anas punctata	×	×						
Blue-winged ducks								
Anas querquedula	×	×						×
Anas discors	×	×						×
Anas cyanoptera	×	×						×
Anas platalea	×	×						×
Anas smithi	×	(×)						×
Anas rhynchotis	×	×						×
Anas clypeata	×							×

[a] The absence of "expected" displays in certain species (●) requires explanation. × = present, (×) = almost certainly present, R = rare.
[b] Based on Johnsgard (1965), and personal observations.

As Atz (1970) and Klopfer (1973) have rightly stressed, the problems increase as soon as comparisons extend beyond very closely related species. The difficulties are obvious from the attempts that have been made to trace display homologies at the ordinal level (e.g., in Pelecaniformes by van Tets, 1965; in charadriiform shorebirds by Maclean, 1972). Families such as the grouse (Tetraonidae) are very difficult also (Hjorth, 1970; Wiley, 1974) because the living species are so diverse (17 species usually placed in five genera). Even within a single genus, homologies may be very uncertain, as with the complex vocal and aerial repertoires of tyrannid flycatchers (Smith, 1966). Nevertheless, the waterfowl, gulls (Tinbergen, 1959), and sulids (Nelson, 1970, 1972) provide convincing evidence that the method can work well. In general, birds seem much easier to study in this way than fish which have limited possibilities for posturing in distinctive ways.

In summary, any attempt to trace the evolutionary history of behavior and to identify the factors that have influenced its course depends on a sound taxonomic understanding of the study group. Behavior patterns that can be homologized confidently can provide very valuable evidence on relationships and their use as taxonomic characters should not be neglected (see Cullen, 1959). If many kinds of nonbehavioral characters are also used, the dangers of circular reasoning can be minimized. Although groups vary in their suitability for applying the method, a search for homologies among closely related species can be fruitful not only in leading to improved understanding of taxonomic relationships but also in revealing new and interesting problems requiring study.

IV. PHYLOGENETIC TREES AND THE DIRECTION OF EVOLUTIONARY TRENDS

No matter how general the agreement is on the taxonomic arrangement of living species within a family or genus, this does not mean that we understand the time scale and positioning of the branches in the family tree. The construction of a diagram representing one taxonomist's views on the past history of the group, combining fossil evidence (if available) with evidence from living forms, is a heuristic device only. It is bound to be incomplete, likely to be inaccurate, or it may be totally incorrect. Phylogenetic interpretation constantly changes as new evidence accumulates, and its chief value is in presenting an author's views unambiguously so that future work may improve on them. Problems involved in constructing phylogenies have recently been reviewed, especially in relation to higher taxa of birds, by Cracraft (1972).

The problem, in trying to work out how behavior has changed during evolution, is to decide which of the species living today is closest in its behavior to the ancestral form from which the group arose and which species represent recently derived offshoots from this stock. If we can decide on the direction in which evolution has proceeded, we may be able to deduce some of the factors that promoted the changes in behavior. Hazardous as it may seem, this is not necessarily a hopeless task. In several mammal groups, where there are rich, well-worked fossil histories, a start has been made (e.g., Geist, 1971, on sheep; Kleiman and Eisenberg, 1973, on carnivores; Kaufmann, 1974, on kangaroos). In birds, where the fossil evidence is scanty, information from functional anatomy, comparative morphology, biogeography, and ecology has rarely been integrated with behavioral information, and there are promising areas for future research in these fields (see Mengel, 1964; Zusi, 1971; Keast, 1972; Mayr, 1972; Vuilleumier, 1975). Unfortunately few avian ethologists have shown an interest in exploring these fields, but much ornithological research appears to be heading in this direction.

One of the most obvious ways of deducing the direction of evolutionary changes is through the use of biogeographic evidence, for example, by studying island forms where the supposed ancestral type still persists on the adjacent mainland (e.g., Lack, 1947; Snow, 1974; Gill, 1973). Other possibilities are to search for preadaptations and constraints, factors that could have favored evolution in one direction rather than another. The common practice of distinguishing "generalists" from "specialists" and assuming that the latter have evolved from an ancestor resembling the former is a risky procedure, however, and convincing evidence (e.g., on the relative age of "simple" and "complex" signal repertoires) is often difficult to obtain. An illustration of one way in which comparative studies of social behavior may provide clues to the dispersal potential and ecological adaptability of different species is provided by the African black duck (*Anas sparsa*) (see Section VII).

One of the important ways in which evidence on behavioral homologies can play a role in comparative research is by drawing attention to species lacking behavior patterns which we expect them to exhibit. By stimulating the question "How do they manage without . . . ," we are led to a new line of inquiry. Among the dabbling ducks, for example, the male courtship repertoires of the four species in the "pintail" group vary strikingly in the number of displays they include (Table I) although, so far, no obvious differences have been detected in the overall process of competitive pairing. Apparently, in this case, displays have been lost from the repertoire of some species, judging from their wide distribution within the genus *Anas*. The absence of expected displays in *A. formosa*, *A. capensis,* and *A. sparsa,* is also indicated in Table I and the repertoires of these species are now being analyzed in search of explanations.

In making deductions such as this, some conception of the phylogenetic history of the group is necessary. Within a genus, for example, it may be possible to reach conclusions on the probable behavioral repertoire of the ancestral type. For whole families, the task may be much more difficult, although many proposals have been made (e.g., see Hjorth, 1970, on the argument for a forest-dwelling ancestry for the grouse). Comparative behavioral studies are likely to contribute increasingly to the development of theories on group ancestry in the future.

V. Conflicting Tendencies and Display Functions

Ethologists traditionally distinguish between four kinds of questions about behavior (causation, development, function, and evolution) and they insist that all are important (Tinbergen, 1963). Comparative studies on species-characteristic behavior are so broad in scope that they inevitably lead to questions in all four areas, but, in practice, priorities have to be ranked and decisions must be made on the level of the approach to be taken. Usually descriptions have been compiled and interpreted using both functional and causal concepts simultaneously and this has posed many difficulties.

One of the most influential ideas in ethological research on social behavior in birds has been the view that displays are products of conflict between incompatible motivational systems (e.g., attack and escape). A thorough up-to-date review of the history of this "conflict hypothesis" and a discussion of its merits is given by Baerends (1975).

An especially ambitious attempt to interpret specific differences in bird display repertoires in terms of variations in absolute and relative strengths of tendencies to behave in different ways was that by Moynihan (1955a, 1958a, b, 1962) in studies of gulls. Similar approaches were tried in interpretations of duck displays (Lind, 1959; McKinney, 1961) and variations on the FAM (flee–attack–mate) concept (Morris, 1956)—viewing courtship as an outcome of conflict between fleeing, attacking, and mating tendencies—have been used by many ethologists.

Application of the conflict hypothesis to studies of duck displays was especially helpful in drawing attention to the presence of latent hostility in social courtship. This elaborate social activity, involving a group of males performing displays around a female, usually while swimming, had not been well understood until we began to search for signs of conflicting motivation among the males. By concentrating primarily on the displays themselves, it was easy to miss the jockeying for position by the males, signs of threat and avoidance, and the occasional occurrence of chasing and fighting. Some duck displays are associated closely with hostility but others are not, and interpretations of their causation in terms of motivational conflict are possible. On the other hand, displays occur in social contexts, and it is easy to imagine the presence of conflicts of one sort or another in all such situations. Possibilities for circular reasoning and unjustified interpretations abound. These are painfully apparent to me now in looking back on my eider analyses (McKinney, 1961).

A major difficulty in applying these motivational concepts is that they call for increasingly detailed and penetrating causal analysis and yet they remain untested until they can be translated into physiological terms. If many species are to be studied, investment of effort in motivational analysis can lead to neglect of other approaches. Furthermore, in my eider duck studies I came to a frustrating impasse in trying to account for differences in the display repertoires of two subspecies. Certain displays, for which I had assembled evidence on the underlying motivation, were more frequent in one race than in the other. This might be explained by supposing that either (1) there had been a change in the FAM ratios controlling the display as the races diverged; (2) there had been more fundamental changes in the absolute levels of certain tendencies (e.g., one race could be "more aggressive" than the other) and that the display frequencies reflected this; (3) there had been changes in the signaling needs of the birds favoring changes in the repertoire; (4) two or all of the above had been involved. Although I had been able to work out correlations between varied social situations and the displays performed in each of them, I could say little about the signal functions served by each or how these functions might vary between races.

A particularly disturbing aspect of the motivational conflict approach to duck displays has been the temptation that it provides to account for puzzling behavior in terms of a presumed motivational state of the bird. This is illustrated by an early idea on the significance of postcopulatory displays. As in gulls and various other animal groups, either the male or both sexes perform one or a series of displays immediately after dismounting. In some species, the displays are the same ones as those used in courtship, where they are thought to be controlled in part by hostile motivation. The idea that these displays are expressions of hostility, "released" immediately after sudden exhaustion of sexual motivation, was a· conceivable "explanation" for their occurrence in terms of energy models of drive states. I suspect that less blatant use of motivational explanations still sometimes leads to unbalanced interpretations for behavior that we do not understand, perhaps especially displays. Part of the problem may be with the use of the term "expression movements," which can carry with it the notion that behavior inevitably reflects the physiological state of the animal and that animals are victims of their inner urges, which require "expression."

The concept of displacement activities, once used loosely and frequently, is now widely recognized as a fuzzy one, to be used cautiously (Hinde, 1970) if at all. It is still used in the comparative literature but is often avoided because of the confusion it can cause. Although used descriptively as a label for unexpected, out-of-context, "irrelevant" actions, displacement activity is a loaded term inseparable from the problems discussed above in respect to motivational conflict.

The discovery, after my eider studies, that I had still very little idea of the signal functions that duck displays were serving and the realization that it was essential to find out, illustrates one of the major problems that ethologists have had in striking a fruitful balance between the four levels of explanations for behavior. To think clearly about signal functions, questions have to be asked on a different plane from that involved in motivational analysis. This leads to deliberately focusing on problems of adaptive value of behavior patterns and the selection processes that have molded the behavioral repertoire of each species. These are the kinds of questions that have interested Tinbergen (e.g., 1972) in so much of his recent work, and this approach has had an increasingly strong influence on research on avian social behavior.

In practice, for example in studies of displays, this so-called "functional approach" places emphasis on displays as evolved mechanisms for signaling rather than as "expression movements" resulting from drive states. Individuals exhibiting inefficient signaling are expected to compete less well for mates, territories, and copulations and so will reproduce less well and so their genes will be less well represented in the population. In principle, all aspects of behavior can be expected to be under pressure, promoting efficiency in accomplishing the vital achievements involved in individual survival and reproduction, and displays are means to these ends. Thus, if "doing nothing" is a more efficient way for a bird to behave in a situation promoting say attack and escape, we may not expect it to perform preening or feeding actions; if we observe that preening or feeding actions occur in these situations, however, we postulate that these are somehow advantageous. This sets the question in a way likely to lead to ideas on why it is advantageous to the performer. As Brown (1975, p. 290) puts it, "The selective advantage of threat displays and various other displays seems to be that they tend to tip the balance in the viewer in favor of the performer."

On the other hand, whatever we call them and however they are represented in neural circuitry and hormonal systems, behavior patterns must be mediated by organizational systems of some sort. Evolutionary changes in these systems must occur, and we should be prepared to encounter motivational constraints and preadaptations that have influenced the direction in which behavior has evolved. For example, strong selection for aggressiveness favored in many species by strong competition for mates or territories has evidently posed special problems for individuals in coping with other aspects of their social life (Nelson, 1975; Section VII).

The search for a fruitful balance between causal and functional approaches to the analysis of bird behavior seems to have been thwarted by the ideas that displays are arbitrary "conventions" (Lorenz, 1941) and that their primary function is to promote species isolation (Sibley, 1957; Johnsgard, 1963). These ideas have been particularly deep seated in the comparative literature on duck behavior, especially while the focus of research was primarily taxonomic. The view that species-characteristic display repertoires have evolved their present form largely by chance and that selection for diversity per se has been the main factor producing species differences was challenged by Hinde (1959) and Crook (1964), and it is now widely recognized that many factors have to be considered. This does not mean that arbitrariness and isolating mechanism function have not been involved, but rather that we should not invoke them uncritically. If applicable, they may help to explain why specific differences exist but they throw no light on the nature of the differences. At worst, they may tempt us to explain away differences, and inhibit search for relevant selection pressures.

I have argued (McKinney, 1975) that duck displays cannot be regarded merely as devices to prevent hybrid matings. There is abundant evidence that they are primarily signaling devices and that they are serving diverse functions in helping individuals to succeed in their social interactions. Different blends of selective forces have evidently molded movements, vocalizations, and plumage patterns to serve the needs of individuals, and these needs are likely to be somewhat different in each species.

By concentrating attention on the possible role of display movements, vocalizations and plumage patterns as isolating mechanisms, there has been a tendency to think of "species" as inviolate units that are constantly "threatened" by the dangers of hybridization. As Orians (1971) has pointed out, this can divert attention from the individual level at which selection is operating. Thus, by thinking about displays as devices evolved to serve the needs of individuals, the relative constancy of specific signaling repertoires is explained rather in terms of the constraints imposed by species membership. Individuals deviating beyond the "accepted norms" for the species will be penalized by being at a disadvantage in competing with conspecific rivals in social situations.

In recent years, increasing attention has been given to the role of sexual selection in the evolution of social behavior in birds (Selander, 1972). The relevance of competition between males in interpreting the behavior observed at courtship arenas (leks) is now firmly established (e.g., Hogan-Warburg, 1966; Hjorth, 1970; Kruijt et al., 1972; Wiley, 1974) and the social courtship of ducks is now viewed as a result of competitive mate-selection activities rather than an infectious "gathering" for the purpose of "displaying." By focusing on what the individuals stand to gain by engaging in such group activities, considerable elaboration of earlier views on the functions of courtship (e.g., Tinbergen, 1954) is now possible. This has come mainly from different ways of viewing the processes of communication and deeper probing of the implications of intraspecific competition.

The application of ideas from semiotics to the study of animal communication has stimulated new ways of thinking about bird displays (Marler, 1961; Smith, 1965; Sebeok, 1968). In particular, Smith (1968, 1977) has argued the need to distinguish between messages, meanings, and functions, and his analyses of communication in tyrannid flycatchers have drawn attention to the importance of the context in which signals are delivered and the likelihood that displays have different meanings in different situations. Increasing attention is now being paid to possible multiple functions of displays (Beer, 1975) and also to ways in which information is given to conspecifics other than by displays.

In general, the task of integrating the concepts of motivational conflict and communication processes is still one of the most difficult confronting comparative workers. It is being faced in a variety of ways. Some prefer to ignore these concepts as much as possible, concentrating on describing species-characteristic behavior and making comparisons. Others have tried to use the conflict hypothesis and have criticized it (e.g., Brown, 1964a; Willis, 1972; Andrew, 1972). Many have chosen to direct the main focus of their attention away from motivational interpretations toward communication processes and questions of adaptive function.

In pursuing comparative studies beyond the preliminary descriptive-taxonomic level toward a more penetrating "analysis of differences" (Brown, 1975), some reordering of traditional ethological priorities seems desirable. Thinking primarily in terms of motivational concepts can be distracting if it diverts attention from the achievements of individuals. If the objective is to understand behavior evolution, it is essential to determine the short-term and long-term goals toward which individuals are working since it is on the outcomes of behavior that natural selection operates. In spite of the interest that ethologists have had in the functions of displays in terms of advertisement, threat, appeasement and so forth, it is clear from Smith's (1977) penetrating review that we still have a long way to go toward understanding social behavior from this viewpoint.

VI. Display Origins and Ritualization

The display movements of ducks provide some of the classic examples of the derivation of signals from nonsignal actions through the evolutionary process of ritualization (Lorenz, 1941). While the nature of the changes that have apparently accompanied this process agree closely with those identified in other birds (Morris, 1957; Tinbergen, 1952, 1959; Blest, 1961), there is room for doubt about the original sources. Intention movements and "displacement activities" still tend to be singled out by many authors as the prime sources for avian signal movements, but it has been realized for some time that this is an oversimplification (see Moynihan, 1955b; Hinde, 1970; Cullen, 1972; Smith, 1977).

Among the most easily identified sources for the signal movements of ducks are a variety of actions used in preening, bathing, stretching, and shaking (McKinney, 1965), several feeding movements (McKinney, 1970), and a great variety of locomotory actions used in swimming, walking, diving, flying, drinking, and looking from alert postures. In most cases, displays derived from these movements simply show exaggeration of certain components and performance from a particular body orientation with respect to the recipient. The actions have changed very little, and the term "intention movement" is inappropriate since the complete movement is performed. Some displays are evidently derived from open-bill threats (e.g., in *Anas flavirostris* and *Netta peposaca*), threat pointing with the bill (e.g., "inciting" in many species), or mounting actions (e.g., precopulatory head pumping in *Anas* species), and it is possible to view these as having evolved from intention movements.

There seems to be little value in trying to invoke the concept of displacement activities when speculating on the early stages of evolution in the case of relatively weakly ritualized signals derived from comfort movements. If the criterion is to be their performance "out of context," the argument is unconvincing in most cases. They are not strikingly inappropriate for the situations in which they are performed and often they grade into similar actions (e.g., preening) lacking any signs of ritualization. The main clue to the signal role that these movements are serving comes from evidence of "awareness" by one bird of the presence of another usually by adjustment in body orientation. If motivational conflict is supposed to have been present when ritualization began, this also poses problems since signs of conflict can be detected in virtually all social situations.

The problems are much greater in the case of complex, highly ritualized displays performed during social courtship (see illustrations in Johnsgard, 1965). Some are widely distributed within genera and are presumably very ancient (e.g., grunt–whistle in *Anas,* head-throw in *Aythya*). Components from different sources could have been superimposed, including head actions involved in producing simultaneous vocalizations. I am not convinced that we will ever be very sure of the origins of these displays; in fact, little progress seems to have been made since the early suggestions of Lorenz (1941) and Daanje (1951).

In other bird groups, progress continues to be made in identifying display sources, the most valuable conclusions coming from workers who have made long-term comparative studies on whole groups. As in the waterfowl, many displays of the flamingos (Phoenicopteridae) can be derived confidently from comfort movements and other postures adopted in everyday activities (Studer-Thiersch, 1974, 1975; Kahl, 1975). The tree-nesting storks (Ciconiidae) (Kahl, 1966, 1972a, b, c, d, 1973) and herons (Ardeidae) (Meyerriecks, 1960; Mock, 1976) appear to have a number of displays derived from aggressive intention movements, related to the enforced proximity of mates on small nest platforms. Nelson (1970, 1975) derives many of the displays of gannets and boobies (Sulidae) from aggressive and nest-building movements also, and again in this group the nest site is the center of social activities. In the grouse (Tetraonidae), male courtship includes terrestrial and aerial components, which Hjorth (1970) believes have evolved from different phases of offensive and defensive attitudes involved in actual fighting. In general, these authors have made little use of "displacement activities" in envisaging how displays have evolved and Hjorth (1970, p. 546), for example, has difficulty classifying any grouse activity seen in displays or during duels between males as "out of context." "Redirection" of aggression, an interpretation developed especially in gull studies (Bastock *et al.*, 1953), continues to be widely used (e.g., Nelson, 1975).

These examples are highly selective, and the literature in this field is now very large. It is a difficult topic to review critically, since so much depends on the judgements of specialists. The concept of ritualization remains of central importance and many authors find the idea of intention movements useful. The view that certain displays occur in situations involving incompatible responses (notably attack and fleeing), calling for resolution by some form of compromise or ambivalent action, continues to be convincing in explaining the form of the movements. Beyond this point, however, opinions differ on the validity and usefulness of invoking motivational conflict in interpreting how displays might have evolved. In particular, there seems to be increasing doubt about the "out of context" interpretation of display origins through the displacement phenomenon, and this whole subject remains controversial. Although new evidence continues to accumulate through comparative studies, this topic is perhaps of less immediate interest to many workers than it used to be. In many cases it seems that we will never be confident about how displays originated, but we may be able to make considerable progress in deciding why they have done so.

VII. ECOLOGICAL CORRELATION AND SOCIAL SYSTEMS

In many ways, the potential value of comparative studies on closely related species did not become clear until they were carried out in the field. Although anticipated by a number of workers, it was mainly through the extensive research by Tinbergen and Crook on gulls and weaverbirds that the possibilities for explaining many of the specific differences revealed in early studies of captives became widely recognized.

The method entails contrasting the behavior of closely related species living under diverse ecological conditions and searching for correlations between behavior and ecological factors. Such correlations are to be expected on the theory that changes in behavior have occurred during speciation and that these changes have been adaptive responses to meet the demands of different ecological conditions. Species experiencing similar blends of selective forces (e.g., living in similar habitats or eating the same food) may be expected to show similarities in their behavior in at least some ways. The difficulty, of course, is that every species has a unique evolutionary history, stocks have diverged at different places and times, and to a greater or lesser extent each species may be expected to have evolved unique ways of solving its particular problems.

In spite of these complications, the method is being applied in a number of bird groups, and the results are encouraging (see Section IX). Selection of a distinctive specialist within a group, as in Cullen's (1957) study of the cliff-nesting kittiwake (*Rissa tridactyla*), seems to be an especially rewarding approach, if the species has very close relatives within the "mainstream" of the group to provide a firm standard for comparison. One of the best examples among recent studies is Abbott's booby (*Sula abbotti*), a treetop-nesting species that Nelson (1971) has compared with the other ground- and bush-nesting sulids. Associated with its jungle nesting habitat, where a fall to the ground is fatal for these long-winged oceanic birds, overt hostility at the nest is avoided, and the display repertoire has evidently been modified to minimize the danger of being dislodged during interactions between mates and neighbors.

Comparative reviews of ecology–behavior relationships paralleling that by Crook on weaverbirds are still scarce and only a few groups can yet be considered fairly well worked. In pursuing the implications of the basic three-step conceptual model (ecology–social system–communication methods) many variations are being revealed on the interactions between levels in the hierarchy of selection pressures. As Crook (1972, p. 368) cautions "each type of social system requires an individual analysis before any broader generalisations can be made," and he notes that the building of oversimplified models could lead to premature closure of interest in this area of research. In view of the complexity of the field, it seems especially important to heed this warning.

I will single out three generalizations that are emerging from these studies. First, in concentrating attention on details of social behavior comparative ethologists have frequently neglected the role of ecological factors (especially seasonal and spatial distribution of food and nest sites, vulnerability to predators, and habitat characteristics) in shaping species-characteristic social behavior. It is already clear that specific patterns of social behavior cannot be interpreted properly until key factors in the feeding, breeding, and antipredator strategies of each species have been identified and placed in demographic perspective. Second, the concept of the "social system" has helped to integrate and direct research at a level that had been neglected. In particular, by extending interest in displays and signaling, threat and appeasement, pairing, and territory defense to the broader levels of mating systems and spacing patterns, it has become easier to view behavior as a part of specific coadapted systems. Third, by deliberately concentrating on the interests of individuals, as opposed to thinking about species, colonies, flocks, or pairs, as though the interests of such groups are promoted by natural selection, many problems can now be faced more directly. The extent to which these viewpoints guide research in behavioral biology still varies enormously, but their importance is rapidly being recognized. Their application to studies of waterfowl behavior illustrate this trend.

For many years, ecological and ethological research on ducks tended to proceed in quite different directions. Because of the economic importance of these birds as game, a tremendous amount of ecological information has been collected, much of it relevant to their conservation and management. Hundreds of waterfowl biologists (especially in North America) have gathered information on breeding biology and migration patterns, and a few of these field workers have been interested also in behavior. Much of this interest has centered on the breeding grounds, where the topics of home ranges, territoriality, and aerial pursuit flights have attracted much attention (e.g., Hochbaum, 1944; Sowls, 1955; Dzubin, 1955; Lebret, 1961), but some studies have also been made on wintering duck populations (Bezzel, 1959; Tamisier, 1970).

Ethological literature on ducks has been far removed in orientation from these ecological field studies. By focusing on such topics as displays as fixed-action patterns useful in taxonomy (Lorenz, 1941, 1953; Johnsgard, 1965), ethogram studies of single species with motivational interpretations (Weidmann, 1956; Lind, 1959; McKinney, 1961), experimental studies of imprinting (Weidmann, 1958; Schutz, 1965), behavior development in the egg (Gottlieb, 1971), analyses of the stereotypy of displays (Dane *et al.,* 1959), analyses of social courtship sequences (Weidmann and Darley, 1971), and comparative studies on the origins of displays and their ritualization (McKinney, 1965) we made little impact on waterfowl ecologists. In recent years, however, interest in behavior–ecology relationships and species adaptations has provided much common ground for waterfowl ecologists and ethologists and the comparative study of social systems is beginning to provide a vital link. Much attention is now being given to specific differences in ecology and, even in such apparently homogeneous groups as the dabbling ducks, much diversity is being revealed in habitat and food preferences. In the northern hemisphere many species of dabbling duck can be observed using the same ponds, but, in spite of the radical changes produced by man in many of these habitats, it is now recognized that each species has somewhat different feeding methods (Lack, 1974, p. 63) and new, more efficient methods of determining foods are revealing differences in diet (Swanson *et al.,* 1974; Krapu, 1974; Serie and Swanson, 1976). Attempts to correlate seasonal and spatial distribution of food with specific differences in mobility (e.g., breeding home range sizes), energetic costs of reproductive activities for males and females, and the presence or absence of territorial defense behavior are now in progress (e.g., Dwyer, 1975; Seymour, 1974; Derrickson, in press).

Correlations between ecological factors and social systems are beginning to emerge in dabbling ducks (McKinney, 1973, 1975). Some species have strong seasonal pair bonds lasting late into the period when females are incubating and males tend to be strictly monogamous and territorial (e.g., *Anas clypeata*). In other species, pair bonds are weaker, and males spend much of their time pursuing females other than the mate and attempting to rape them. This type of balance between pair bonding and promiscuity is associated with reduction or absence of territorial defense. In *A. platyrhynchos,* for example, males are territorial for a brief period only; in *A. crecca* and *A. acuta* males show no territorial defense at all.

Additional variations in dabbling duck social systems are found in southern hemisphere species. In some (e.g., *A. capensis, A. sibilatrix, A. flavirostris*) males accompany the female and brood (in contrast to the pattern in the northern hemisphere species, where the female alone leads the brood). In at least one species, the African *A. sparsa*, a highly territorial river specialist, pair bonds persist through several years (see below).

Only about one-quarter of the 36 living species of dabbling ducks have been studied in enough depth to form tentative hypotheses about the factors that have promoted these variations in mating systems. At this point, however, it appears that males have had more "options" open to them than have females during the adaptive radiation of the group. By trying to determine the adaptive value of pair bonding versus promiscuity, short-term versus long-term bonds, territoriality versus nonterritoriality, and the ways in which different compromises have been arrived at by each species, it should be possible to reveal the major trends.

Correlations between the characteristics of social systems and the displays used by each duck species are also beginning to emerge, but this step depends on understanding what individuals are "trying to achieve" in various social situations. Our ideas on what is really going on in complex situations such as social courtship, aerial pursuits, and rape attempts in dabbling ducks were hopelessly confused for many years, and no sense could be made of the displays until we began to develop hypotheses on their functions. By postulating short-term and long-term objectives toward which individuals appear to be directed, it is possible to pose questions in profitable ways.

Once it was recognized that males of some species defend territories (e.g., *A. clypeata*) it became obvious why they have conspicuous long-distance threat displays ("hostile pumping"). A more subtle possibility is that the presence of displays derived from the dabbling movements used in feeding, in species specializing in filter feeding (*A. clypeata* and its relatives), might be accounted for by the opportunity that this offers for signaling at the same time as ingesting food. If, as we suspect, filter feeding is a time-consuming feeding method, this may have provided enough selective advantage to individuals to promote ritualization of these movements.

More subtle still is the possibility that the evolution of highly specifically directional displays such as the grunt–whistle (which involves directing a jet of water droplets by a flick of the bill toward the female) might have been favored in situations where males needed to switch the orientation of their displays quickly from one female to another. This is exactly what happens in situations where males are courting females other than their mates; when the mate approaches, their displays are suddenly reoriented to her. We are still uncertain as to what males are gaining by such extra-pair-bond courtship—perhaps an advantage in situations where re-pairing is necessary or perhaps an advantage in stealing copulations. In any event, it seems better to postulate some such advantage, and to search for it, than to attribute the performance of such displays to motivational

misfiring or the ''infectiousness'' of courtship in progress as we might once have
been tempted to do.

The African black duck (*A. sparsa*) has provided an enlightening example of
the value of this line of research. Like the kittiwake among the gulls, this species
is a habitat specialist, showing a strong preference for rivers (Siegfried, 1968).
Recent studies (Ball *et al.,* 1977; McKinney *et al.,* in press) have confirmed
the pattern of territorial pair spacing noted in Siegfried's earlier observations, and
paralleling the picture in the other three river-dwelling duck species (*A.
waigiuensis, Hymenolaimus malacorhynchos,* and *Merganetta armata*) (Kear,
1972, 1975; Johnsgard, 1966). Although many peculiar aspects of its behavior
had led to the view that *A. sparsa* is close to the ancestral type for all dabbling
ducks (Johnsgard, 1965; Mayr, 1969), the presence of many mallardlike characteristics suggests that it has diverged from mallard stock. Most of the unexpected
behavioral features can be explained in relation to specialization for river life; in
particular, the whole social system appears to be dominated by the need for pairs
to hold territories at all costs since only territory holders are able to breed. Unlike
typical dabbling ducks, females as well as males engage in defense, both sexes
have wing spurs that they use in exhausting and damaging fighting, pair bonds
tend to be long lasting but competition for mates as well as territories is severe,
and promiscuous stolen matings have not been recorded. In association with this
system, social courtship is almost nonexistent (although the characteristic mallardlike displays are still performed on rare occasions) and ''mutual greeting''
displays by mates (convergently similar to those of geese) are used apparently to
reaffirm bonds.

In summary, even in groups such as the dabbling ducks where striking variations in feeding ecology and social systems were not previously recognized, a
deliberate search with specific variations in mind is proving fruitful and instructive. As in studies of several other bird groups, the objective of trying to understand how species differences have evolved does not now seem hopelessly intan-
gible. Progress is being made in identifying key sources of selection not previously recognized as such and gradually the problems of distinguishing between
''adaptations'' and ''effects'' (Williams, 1966) are being resolved. Learning to
pose questions in terms of the interests of individuals has been fundamental to
much of this progress, and we may still be giving insufficient attention to this
aspect of social behavior.

VIII. THE INTERESTS OF INDIVIDUALS

The controversy over interpretations of avian social behavior in terms of group
selection as proposed by Wynne-Edwards (1962) has had extremely important
consequences. The vigorous critiques by Crook (1965), Lack (1966), Wiens
(1966), Williams (1966), and others stimulated a flood of research into the

implications of selection at the individual level and set the stage for current thinking on mechanisms of behavior evolution. For example, in his recent stimulating review, Alexander (1974) argues that animals "live to reproduce" and that behavior promoting reproduction is of paramount importance; that individuals are genetically programmed to behave in basically selfish ways; that seemingly "altruistic" behavior may be expected to confer advantages to the performer and/or to its genetically close relatives (especially offspring); that competition between individuals for genetic representation in the gene pool is the primary mechanism of natural selection.

Based on the theoretical application of genetic principles to social behavior (Hamilton, 1964), a fusion of the concepts of life-history strategies (Cole, 1954) and optimal use of time and energy (Orians, 1961; Rosen, 1967), and comparative reexamination of social systems, attempts are now being made to interpret species differences in social behavior in terms of evolutionary "strategies" and economics. Especially crucial for research on birds has been the development of the concepts of "kin selection" (Hamilton, 1964; Maynard Smith, 1964), "parental investment" (Trivers, 1972), "evolutionarily stable strategies" (Maynard Smith and Price, 1973), and "parent–offspring conflict" (Trivers, 1974). Williams (1975, p. ix) concludes: "Much of courtship and family life is interpretable as resulting from partly conflicting male and female strategies."

The main thrust of this approach comes from the consideration that in sexually reproducing organisms the contributions of each sex to the production of progeny are seldom if ever equal. In turn, this is likely to entail different degrees of "interest," "commitment," and "investment" to eggs and young on the part of males and females. At each stage in the breeding cycle, natural selection may be expected to favor behavior on the part of males and females which contributes most effectively on average to individual fitness. However, it will be progeny produced over an individual's lifetime that counts, and the most effective "breeding strategy" for males and females may be quite different among species. Factors affecting "inclusive fitness" vary greatly, for example, between long-lived and short-lived species.

These ideas were first explored in relation to the matings systems of birds by Orians (1969), and his predictive model for the evolution of polygyny has been a major stimulus to current attempts to extend and fully integrate evolutionary theory into studies of social behavior (e.g., Graul et al., 1977). Investigations of the possible role of kin selection in explaining apparently altruistic behavior in birds (e.g., cooperative breeding, alarm calls) provide another focus for research at the moment (see Brown, 1975). I will concentrate here on the relevance of the concept of conflicting interests in interpreting specific differences in intersexual behavior—"the battle of the sexes" as Dawkins (1976) calls it.

Apart from the use of the word "strategy," which is now very familiar in its evolutionary context, many other terms are now being adopted from human social behavior to refer to evolved patterns or mechanisms in animals. Many of these terms are conveniently brief and graphic (cuckoldry, rape, deceit, divorce), but they have the disadvantage that the uninitiated reader may take them to imply foresight or reasoning. In this respect, the ideas on "manipulation" (e.g., of offspring by parents) and "exploitation" (e.g., of one sex by another) are basic to much current discussion.

The conflicting interests of males and females are impossible to ignore in the "raping" activities of male dabbling ducks (McKinney, 1975). Many observers had noted that "sexual assaults" are common in city park mallards, and it was often assumed that these are associated with artificial crowding and domestication. However, similar attempts by males to overpower females and copulate with them have been observed in a number of *Anas* species under natural conditions, and the adaptive significance of such behavior "for the species" was long a puzzle. Since pair bonding is the usual pattern in these birds, it was difficult to imagine how severe harassment of females could profit the population. If this behavior is viewed as part of the reproductive strategy of paired males, however, it becomes necessary to regard females as sexual "victims" of the social system. We would then predict that males must have evolved mate-guarding behavior to offset their chances of being cuckolded, while females may be expected to have antiharassment behavior to minimize damage that they might suffer.

We are now pursuing this hypothesis in studies of a number of duck species and all evidence points to the conclusion that the term "rape" is justified in these birds (females resist and are apparently overpowered). We can begin to see that males face difficult problems in balancing the time they spend guarding their own mates against time spent pursuing other females. The amount of time and energy involved in rape attempts can be considerable, and it is likely that males have developed tactics for maximizing their chances of locating females that are in the laying phase and in competing with rivals for inseminations. The implications for gaining new insight into the significance of aerial pursuits and the postures, display movements, and calls occurring during interactions between breeding ducks are great. We can now look for ways in which females might be giving "misinformation" about their reproductive status, and if they cannot avoid betraying their status, we can investigate why this is so.

The literature on bird behavior is sprinkled with references to "stolen matings," and occasionally the word "rape" is used in describing "sexual chases." The details of exactly what happens on these occasions are seldom reported, however. These are difficult aspects of behavior to document; stealth and secretiveness are to be expected and, if insemination by rape is really the objective, they might well be rare events. Their importance, for the rapist, however, could be great. If even a single egg can be fertilized in this way each season, the advantages could be sufficient to promote selection for skill in raping among males.

Sperm competition has been little studied in birds, but its importance in insects has been pointed out by Parker (1970). The importance of behavior relating to maintaining pair bonds is widely studied in birds, but the element of "mate guarding" has perhaps been neglected, and Parker's (1974a) discussion is likely to stimulate more focus on this aspect. There may yet be unexpected discoveries to be made by intensive work on species that we consider to be strictly monogamous.

IX. Breadth versus Depth in Comparative Studies

No limits can be set to the information required to "fully understand" the evolution of a single species or group. Each study can contribute a piece to the puzzle, but new possibilities and problems are constantly being revealed and it is impossible to anticipate what new lines of inquiry will open up in the future. This difficulty is particularly acute for researchers using the comparative approach, where the method entails switching attention from species to species. Decisions have to be made on how intensively to study each species and how many species to include. In part, decisions may be influenced by which lines of research are being pursued by other investigators, and, for each taxon under study, each worker inevitably becomes one member of a team.

The roles that comparative workers can play in these combined attacks on specific animal groups can vary considerably. In the case of families with many species, broad comprehensive coverage can become a full-time occupation, precluding intensive study of any one species and requiring strong will power to avoid being distracted by tempting problems. Researchers with strong taxonomic interests are particularly suited to this approach, and their work is of fundamental importance in providing descriptive inventories, refining taxonomic relationships, revealing evolutionary trends, and providing ideas on factors that have been important during the evolution of the group. Many examples of studies of this broad type have already been noted, and the recent work of Newton (1972) on British finches and Short (e.g., 1971a, b, 1972) on woodpeckers (Picidae) should also be mentioned.

At the other end of the scale, intensive long-term studies of single species are necessary to work out the fine details of social systems, to test ideas on the adaptive value of behavior, and to relate behavior to demography and population dynamics. Examples of some of the most important programs of this kind are those on red grouse (*Lagopus l. scoticus*) (Watson and Moss, 1970, 1972), black grouse (*Lyrurus tetrix*) (Kruijt and Hogan, 1967; Kruijt *et al.*, 1972), kittiwake (Coulson, 1966, 1972), black-headed gull (*Larus ridibundus*) (Tinbergen, 1967), scrub jay (*Aphelocoma coerulescens*) (Woolfenden, 1974, 1975), and Mexican jay (*Aphelocoma ultramarina*) (Brown, 1963, 1970, 1972).

Especially important in testing ideas on factors influencing the characteristics of social systems are studies on intraspecific variations. It is already apparent that the extent to which males are polygynous can vary between populations, between individuals, and within the same individual from year to year. Well-documented variations are known for long-billed marsh wren (*Telmatodytes palustris*) (Verner, 1964; Kale, 1965) and spotted sandpiper (*Actitis macularia*) (Hays, 1972; Oring and Knudson, 1972), and there are indications that plasticity in avian mating systems is greater than previously imagined. This poses special problems for comparative workers who frequently study only a single population of each species and generalizations must be made cautiously. At the same time, it will become increasingly important to undertake intrapopulation comparisons in attempting to separate effects of such factors as habitat quality and availability of food and mates on social systems. The need for further intraspecific comparisons is beautifully illustrated by the intriguing questions raised by the detailed study of social organization in acorn woodpeckers (*Melanerpes formicivorus*) in central California by MacRoberts and MacRoberts (1976).

There are still only a few groups of birds for which both extensive and intensive studies of these kinds are available, but even here the extent to which ecology, social systems, behavior, and taxonomy have been integrated varies considerably. In addition to the gulls, sulids, grouse, and weaverbirds, which have been noted earlier, current information has been reviewed for the Icteridae (Orians, 1972), Meropidae (Fry, 1972), jays (Brown, 1974) and calidridine sandpipers (Pitelka *et al.*, 1974), and several other groups are likely to be discussed in this way by specialists in the near future.

There are particular advantages in aiming toward a "middle ground" in combining extensive with intensive research on families, subfamilies or genera, as the above studies show. At either extreme, the approach is one-sided. Wide-ranging but necessarily superficial coverage of a group can provide an overview but without intensive work on some species it is impossible to understand how the social systems are working.

In the early stages of a comparative program, information from extensive taxonomic review of the group combined with intensive descriptive studies on the social behavior and ecology of one or a few species begin to provide a framework for building working hypotheses. Clues to the extent of the radiation in respect to habitats, feeding niches, breeding strategies, social systems and communication methods emerge and some probable key factors in the evolution of the group suggest themselves. Once the commonest patterns emerge, the "specialists" become obvious. By using the ecology–social systems–communication methods model, specializations can be sought at each level on the theory that there are likely to be causal links of some kind.

In the case of the dabbling ducks, for example, most living species use freshwater habitats (lakes, ponds, lagoons, marshes) and they feed in shallow water by swimming on the surface. Of special interest then are the few species that live primarily on rivers (*Anas sparsa, A. waiguiensis*), and those using diving as a regular feeding technique (e.g., *A. capensis*). Island forms that have adopted largely terrestrial ways of life (e.g., *A. laysanensis*) or live largely on marine shorelines and estuaries (the races of *A. aucklandica* on islands near New Zealand: Weller, 1974, 1975) provide interesting opportunities to compare with mainland relatives. Note that in such cases we can be reasonably sure that these types are secondary specialists, and so the direction of evolutionary changes in behavior can be deduced with confidence.

Alternatively, we can seek instances where species are known to have peculiarities in their social systems or in their signal repertoires suggesting that these are specializations associated with unknown ecological factors. For example, the invariable presence of both parents with broods in such species as *A. capensis* (Siegfried, 1974), a rare pattern in *Anas,* calls for explanation. Why are mutual displays between mates so frequent and noisy in the three species of wigeon (*A. penelope, A. americana, A. sibilatrix*)?

In these ways, comparative studies can mature from a haphazard procedure involving looking at one species after another to the development of predictions based on emerging patterns. Species can be selected for study to test ideas, and intensive work on certain species can be directed at problems that require solution.

X.   THE INFORMATION NEEDED ON EACH SPECIES

Even in the preliminary phase of a comparative program, where the main task is to compile ethograms on a number of species, it is simply not possible to achieve the ideal of "unprejudiced observation" without being influenced by "preconceived ideas" as Lorenz (1950) advocated. We have to make use of the existing literature, and inevitably the way observations are collected, arranged, and presented will be influenced by current conventions and concepts. If taxonomic questions are prominent we will tend to look for homologies, if we are thinking in motivational terms this will influence the way the data are arranged and interpreted, and the methods and rationale will be different again if the main interest is in tactical aspects of social systems or in signal functions of displays.

If recent developments in ecoethology and behavior evolution theory are to be used as a basis for comparative research on social behavior in birds, there are important implications for methodology. The older approach of listing the displays observed in males and females, and analyzing the situations in which they occur is no longer enough. In order to relate social behavior to the inclusive fitness of individuals, it is necessary to investigate short- and long-term goals of the behavior in the light of costs and benefits to individuals.

This task of identifying the goals or achievements toward which individuals are proceeding can be extremely difficult, especially since some kinds of behavior may well be serving several functions simultaneously. By posing questions more pointedly in terms of individual selection, however, it is becoming easier to tackle these problems directly. As Brown (1964b) argued in regard to the functions of territory, the answers are likely to come from identifying which requisites are in short supply and how it is economical for certain ones to be defended. The optimal balance between strong and weak aggressiveness in individuals (which tends to be the norm for the species) will depend on the balance between the advantages and disadvantages.

By measuring benefits of behavior, ultimately in terms of progeny, and costs in terms of time, energy, opportunities and risk, the possibility is open for analyses of species-characteristic behavior in terms of population biology (Wilson, 1975). The implications for ethology are far-reaching, and already theoretical developments are well ahead of empirical knowledge.

In view of the difficulty of carrying out cost–benefit analyses of social behavior, it can be argued that the greatest need is for long-term studies on single species. As in the past, however, comparisons between closely related species can continue to complement intensive studies, and, to be most useful, they need to be made with relevant theoretical concepts in mind.

Again I can illustrate the needs by pointing to some of the most glaring gaps in current knowledge about breeding behavior in ducks. Although the early studies of home range and territorial behavior have been followed up by a number of field projects entailing observations on individually marked birds, the progress in applying a modern functional approach to social behavior has been relatively slow. In particular, there is still much uncertainty about the benefits to males of engaging in aerial pursuits. I believe that the only way to unravel these puzzles is through intensive observations on a few marked birds. The clues to the "achievements" involved emerge slowly; some are subtle (as with mate guarding), some are rarely observed (as with rape attempts). While the compiling of time budgets is relatively easy in some species (e.g., Dwyer, 1975), the difficulties may be great in species in which the birds are highly mobile and prone to hide in vegetation.

Unfortunately, the intensive following of a small number of marked individuals throughout a breeding season is a most unpopular research method. The demands on time and patience are great, a team of observers is needed, special marking methods may be essential (e.g., radio tracking), and the resulting sample sizes (in terms of individual birds) are inevitably low. Nevertheless, there is now a new need for such studies if we are to test current ideas on the adaptive significance of social behavior. Even more demanding is the need for long-term studies on birds of known parentage, notably in work on cooperative breeding, and it is not surprising that little is known about relationships between related individuals in birds. Perhaps the greatest practical difficulty (for example in working out the functional significance of rape in ducks) will be to determine paternity of offspring with certainty.

If selection is operating primarily at the level of individuals, we are unlikely to understand how the process works without deliberately focussing on individuals as the objects of study. A strong focus of attention on the problems, needs and achievements of individuals seems particularly important to include in comparative studies where attention tends to be given automatically to behavior as a species characteristic.

XI. Conclusions

I have tried to show that the traditional comparative approach developed by Lorenz and Tinbergen continues to play a fundamental role in research on social behavior. It is the method whereby interspecies diversity in behavior is revealed. It is the main source of clues to explain similarities and differences in species-characteristic behavior in closely related species. But the concepts guiding comparisons have changed, questions can now be posed more precisely, and earlier studies need to be extended and developed using new ideas.

The concept of homology can be applied confidently to certain bird displays and the procedure can be important not only in establishing taxonomic relationships but in revealing evolutionary problems. At least in studies of closely related species of birds such as the waterfowl, behavioral homologies are especially valuable in attempts to reconstruct ancestral display repertoires.

The method of ecological correlation, developed through comparative field studies, has been especially important in focusing attention on social systems and thereby linking research on ecological factors to studies of social interactions and communication. Focus on selection at the individual level has helped to develop new ideas on short-term and long-term goals of behavior. By inquiring into the relative importance of different ways of behaving in contributing to fitness, more attention is being directed to "tactical" aspects of the behavior of individuals.

If selection favors individuals which make optimal use of time and energy, minimize the risks they take, and make the most of the opportunities available to them, predictions can be made which help greatly in determining the goals of behavior. Time and energy spent in different activities can be measured and risks and opportunities can be assessed. However, cost–benefit analyses of social behavior are premature if the goals toward which individuals are working are uncertain.

Although pair bonding is recognized to be the predominant mating system in birds (Lack, 1968) the details of relationships between mates, between neighboring pairs, and between paired and unpaired birds have been examined carefully in very few species. The need for such studies is well illustrated by the many subtle variations already revealed in sandpiper mating systems (Pitelka *et al.*, 1974). More attention needs to be given to conflicts of interest between mates and their implications. As McLaren (1972) has suggested, possibilities for polygynous matings may be more important in interpreting breeding territoriality in birds than has usually been thought. The possible significance of rare stolen matings needs careful study.

Comparative studies of displays, with interpretations in terms of signal functions and conflicting motivation, are unlikely to be very productive in the future unless they are made on individually marked birds. If individuals cannot be identified, many interactions cannot be interpreted meaningfully, changes in relationships over time are missed, and the social system can remain obscure. Furthermore, presumed functions of displays are likely to be confused with "effects" (Otte, 1974), multiple functions may not be detected (Beer, 1975), and the interests of males and females are unlikely to be assessed properly.

Many years of field work are required to yield the information needed to formulate tentative hypotheses on the evolution of social systems within a group. Current knowledge is inadequate to permit profitable generalizations for most bird groups, but recent syntheses on such well-worked groups as the jays, sulids, and sandpipers are enlightening. The need for further detailed comparative work on birds is obvious and the fruitfulness of focusing on closely related species has been thoroughly established.

Acknowledgments

I am very grateful to Michael G. Anderson, Colin Beer, Scott Derrickson, Hans Kruuk, Douglas Mock and Bryan Nelson for helpful critical comments on the manuscript. My research has been supported by National Science Foundation Grants GB-36651X and BMS76-02233 and by the Graduate School, University of Minnesota.

References

Alcock, J. 1975. "Animal Behavior, an Evolutionary Approach." Sinauer, Sunderland, Mass.

Alexander, R. D. 1969. Comparative animal behavior and systematics. *In* "Systematic Biology." Publ. 1692, Nat. Acad. Sci., Washington D.C.

Alexander, R. D. 1974. The evolution of social behavior. *Annu. Rev. Ecol. Syst.* **5**, 325–383.

Andrew, R. J. 1972. The information potentially available in mammal displays. *In* "Non-verbal Communication" (R. A. Hinde, ed.), pp. 179–206. Cambridge Univ. Press, London and New York.

Atz, J. W. 1970. The application of the idea of homology to behavior. *In* "Development and Evolution of Behavior" (L. R. Aronson, E. Tobach, D. S. Lehrman and J. S. Rosenblatt, eds.), pp. 53–74. Freeman, San Francisco.

Baerends, G. P. 1958. Comparative methods and the concept of homology in the study of behavior. *Arch. Neerl. Zool. Suppl.* **13**, 401–417.

Baerends, G. P. 1975. An evaluation of the conflict hypothesis as an explanatory principle for the evolution of displays. *In* "Function and Evolution in Behaviour" (G. Baerends, C. Beer, and A. Manning, eds.), pp. 187–227. Oxford Univ. Press (Clarendon), New York and London.

Baerends, G. P., and Baerends-van Roon, J. M. 1950. An introduction to the study of the ethology of cichlid fishes. *Behaviour Suppl.* **1**, 1–242.

Ball, I. J., Frost, P. P. G., Siegfried, W. R., and McKinney, F. 1977. Territories and local movements of African black ducks. In preparation.

Bastock, M., Morris, D., and Moynihan, M. 1953. Some comments on conflict and thwarting in animals. *Behaviour* **6**, 66–84.

Beer, C. G. 1973. Species-typical behavior and ethology. In "Comparative Psychology: A Modern Survey" (D. A. Dewsbury and D. A. Rethlingshafer, eds.), pp. 21–77. McGraw-Hill, New York.

Beer, C. G. 1975. Multiple functions and gull displays. In "Function and Evolution in Behaviour" (G. Baerends, C. Beer, and A. Manning, eds.), pp. 16–54. Oxford Univ. Press (Clarendon), London and New York.

Bezzel, E. 1959. Beiträge zur Biologie der Geschlechter bei Entenvögeln. *Anz. Ornithol. Ges. Bayern* **5**, 269–355.

Blest, A. D. 1961. The concept of ritualization. In "Current Problems in Animal Behaviour" (W. H. Thorpe and O. Zangwill, eds.), pp. 102–124. Cambridge Univ. Press, London and New York.

Brown, J. L. 1963. Social organization and behavior of the Mexican jay. *Condor* **65**, 126–153.

Brown, J. L. 1964a. The integration of agonistic behavior in the Steller's jay *Cyanocitta stelleri* (Gmelin). *Univ. Calif. Publ. Zool.* **60**, 223–328.

Brown, J. L. 1964b. The evolution of diversity in avian territorial systems. *Wilson Bull.* **76**, 160–169.

Brown, J. L. 1970. Cooperative breeding and altruistic behaviour in the Mexican jay, *Aphelocoma ultramarina*. *Anim. Behav.* **18**, 366–378.

Brown, J. L. 1972. Communal feeding of nestlings in the Mexican jay (*Aphelocoma ultramarina*): Interflock comparisons. *Anim. Behav.* **20**, 394–402.

Brown, J. L. 1974. Alternate routes to sociality in jays—with a theory for the evolution of altruism and communal breeding. *Am. Zool.* **14**(1), 63–80.

Brown, J. L. 1975. "The Evolution of Behavior." Norton, New York.

Campbell, C. B. G., and Hodos, W. 1970. The concept of homology and the evolution of the nervous system. *Brain, Behav. Evol.* **3**, 353–367.

Clark, A. 1971. The behaviour of the hottentot teal. *Ostrich* **42**, 131–136.

Clutton-Brock, T. H. 1974. Primate social organization and ecology. *Nature (London)* **250**, 539–542.

Cole, L. C. 1954. The population consequences of life history phenomena. *Q. Rev. Biol.* **29**, 103–137.

Collias, N. E., and Collias, E. C. 1964. The evolution of nest-building in weaverbirds (*Ploceidae*). *Univ. Calif. Publ. Zool.* **73**, 1–239.

Collias, N. E., and Collias, E. C. 1967. A quantitative analysis of breeding behavior in the African village weaverbird. *Auk* **84**, 396–411.

Collias, N. E., Victoria, J. K., and Shallenberger, R. J. 1971a. Social facilitation in weaverbirds: importance of colony size. *Ecology* **52**(5), 823–828.

Collias, N. E., Brandman, M., Victoria, J. K., Kiff, L. F., and Rischer, C. E. 1971b. Social facilitation in weaverbirds: effects of varying the sex ratio. *Ecology* **52**(5), 829–836.

Coulson, J. C. 1966. The influence of the pair-bond on the breeding biology of the kittiwake gull, *Rissa tridactyla*. *J. Anim. Ecol.* **35**, 269–279.

Coulson, J. C. 1972. The significance of the pair-bond in the kittiwake. *Proc. Int. Ornithol. Congr.* **15**, 424–433.

Cracraft, J. 1972. The relationships of the higher taxa of birds: Problems in phylogenetic reasoning. *Condor* **74**, 379–392.

Crook, J. H. 1964. The evolution of social organization and visual communication in the weaver birds (Ploceinae). *Behaviour Suppl.* **10**, 1–178.

Crook, J. H. 1965. The adaptive significance of avian social organizations. *Symp. Zool. Soc. London* **14**, 181–218.

Crook, J. H. 1970a. Social organization and the environment, aspects of contemporary social ethology. *Anim. Behav.* **18**, 197–209.

Crook, J. H. 1970b. The socio-ecology of primates. *In* "Social Behaviour in Birds and Mammals" (J. H. Crook, ed.), pp. 103–166. Academic Press, New York.

Crook, J. H. 1972. Evolution of pairing behaviour in birds. *Proc. Int. Ornithol. Congr.* **15**, 365–370.

Crook, J. H. and Gartlan, J. S. 1966. Evolution of primate societies. *Nature, (London)* **210**, 1200–1203.

Crook, J. H. and Goss-Custard, J. D. 1972. Social ethology. *Annu. Rev. Ecol. Syst.* **3**, 277–312.

Cullen, E. 1957. Adaptations in the kittiwake to cliff-nesting. *Ibis* **99**, 275–302.

Cullen, J. M. 1959. Behaviour as a help in taxonomy. *Syst. Assoc. Publ.* **3**, 131–140.

Cullen, J. M. 1972. Some principles of animal communication. *In* "Non-Verbal Communication" (R. A. Hinde, ed.), pp. 101–122. Cambridge Univ. Press, London and New York.

Daanje, A. 1951. On locomotory movements in birds and the intention movements derived from them. *Behaviour* **3**, 48–98.

Dane, B., Walcott, C., and Drury, W. H. 1959. The form and duration of the display actions of the goldeneye (*Bucephala clangula*). *Behaviour* **14**, 265–281.

Dawkins, R. 1976. "The Selfish Gene." Oxford Univ. Press, London and New York.

Delacour, J., and Mayr, E. 1945. The family Anatidae. *Wilson Bull.* **57**, 3–55.

Derrickson, S. R. (in press). Mobility of breeding pintails. *Auk.*

Dewsbury, D. A. 1973. Comparative psychologists and their quest for uniformity. *Ann. N.Y. Acad. Sci.* **223**, 147–167.

Dewsbury, D. A. 1975. Diversity and adaptation in rodent copulatory behavior. *Science* **190**, 947–954.

Dewsbury, D. A., and Rethlingshafer, D. A. 1973. "Comparative Psychology: A Modern Survey." McGraw-Hill, New York.

Dwyer, T. J. 1975. Time budget of breeding gadwalls. *Wilson Bull.* **87**(3), 335–343.

Dzubin, A. 1955. Some evidences of home range in waterfowl. *Trans. N. Am. Wildlife Conf.* **20**, 278–298.

Eisenberg, J. F., Muckenhirn, N. A., and Rudran, R. 1972. The relation between ecology and social structure in primates. *Science* **176**, 863–874.

Emlen, J. M. 1973. "Ecology: An Evolutionary Approach." Addison-Wesley, Reading, Mass.

Fry, C. H. 1972. The social organization of bee-eaters (Meropidae) and co-operative breeding in hot-climate birds. *Ibis* **114**, 1–14.

Geist, V. 1971. "Mountain Sheep: A Study in Behavior and Evolution." Univ. of Chicago Press, Chicago.

Gill, F. B. 1973. Intra-island variation in the Mascarene white-eye *Zosterops borbonica*. *Ornithol. Monogr.* **12**, 66 pp.

Gottlieb, G. 1971. "Development of Species Identification in Birds: An Inquiry into the Prenatal Determinants of Perception." Univ. of Chicago Press, Chicago.

Graul, W. D., Derrickson, S. R., and Mock, D. W. 1977. The evolution of avian polyandry. *Am. Nat.* **111**, 812–816.

Hailman, J. P. 1976a. Uses of the comparative study of behavior. *In* "Evolution, Brain, and Behavior: Persistent Problems" (R. B. Masterton, W. Hodos, and H. Jerison, eds.), pp. 13–22. Erlbaum Assoc., Hillsdale, N.J.

Hailman, J. P. 1976b. Homology: Logic, information and efficiency. *In* "Evolution, Brain, and Behavior: Persistent Problems" (R. B. Masterton, W. Hodos, and H. Jerison, eds.), pp. 181–198, Erlbaum, Hillsdale, N.J.

Hamilton, W. D. 1964. The genetical theory of social behaviour, I, II. *J. Theoret. Biol.* **7**(1), 1–16, 17–52.

Hays, H. 1972. Polyandry in the spotted sandpiper. *Living Bird* **11**, 43–57.

Heinroth, O. 1911. Beiträge zur Biologie, namentlich Ethologie und Psychologie der Anatiden. *Int. Orn. Kong. Verh.* **5**, 589–702.

Hinde, R. A. 1959. Behaviour and speciation in birds and lower vertebrates. *Biol. Rev.* **34**, 85–128.

Hinde, R. A. 1970. "Animal Behaviour," 2nd ed. McGraw-Hill, New York.

Hinde, R. A., and Tinbergen, N. 1958. The comparative study of species-specific behavior. *In* "Behavior and Evolution" (A. Roe and G. G. Simpson, eds.), pp. 251–268. Yale Univ. Press, New Haven, Conn.

Hjorth, I. 1970. Reproductive behaviour in Tetraonidae with special reference to males. *Viltrevy* **7**(4), 183–596.

Hochbaum, H. A. 1944. "The Canvasback on a Prairie Marsh." American Wildlife Inst., Washington, D.C.

Hodos, W. and Campbell, C. B. G. 1969. *Scala Naturae*: Why there is no theory in comparative psychology. *Psychol. Rev.* **76**(4), 337–350.

Hogan-Warburg, A. J. 1966. Social behavior of the ruff *Philomachus pugnax* (L.) *Ardea* **54**, 109–229.

Jarman, P. J. 1974. The social organization of antelope in relation to their ecology. *Behaviour* **58**(3,4), 215–267.

Johnsgard, P. A. 1961. The systematic position of the marbled teal. *Bull. Brit. Ornithol. Club* **81**, 37–43.

Johnsgard, P. A. 1963. Behavioral isolating mechanisms in the family Anatidae. *Proc. Int. Ornithol. Congr.* **13**, 531–543.

Johnsgard, P. A. 1965. "Handbook of Waterfowl Behavior." Cornell Univ. Press, Ithaca, N.Y.

Johnsgard, P. A. 1966. The biology and relationships of the torrent duck. *Wildfowl Trust Annu. Rep.* **17**, 66–74.

Johnsgard, P. A. 1967. Observations on the behaviour and relationships of the white-backed duck and the stiff-tailed ducks. *Wildfowl Trust Annu. Rep.* **18**, 98–107.

Kahl, M. P. 1966. Comparative ethology of the Ciconiidae. Part 1. The marabou stork, *Leptoptilos crumeniferus* (Lesson). *Behaviour* **27**, 76–106.

Kahl, M. P. 1972a. Comparative ethology of the Ciconiidae. Part 2. The adjutant storks, *Leptoptilos dubius* (Gmelin) and *L. javanicus* (Horsfield). *Ardea* **60**, 97–111.

Kahl, M. P. 1972b. Comparative ethology of the Ciconiidae. The woodstorks (genera *Mycteria* and *Ibis*). *Ibis* **114**, 15–29.

Kahl, M. P. 1972c. Comparative ethology of the Ciconiidae, Part 4. The "typical" storks (genera *Ciconia, Sphenorhynchus, Dissoura,* and *Euxenura*). *Z. Tierpsychol.* **30**, 225–252.

Kahl, M. P. 1972d. Comparative ethology of the Ciconiidae. Part 5. The openbill storks (genus *Anastomus*). *J. Ornithol.* **113**, 121–137.

Kahl, M. P. 1973. Comparative ethology of the Ciconiidae. Part 6. The blacknecked, saddlebill, and jabiru storks (genera *Xenorhynchus, Ephippiorynchus,* and *Jabiru*). *Condor* **75**, 17–27.

Kahl, M. P. 1975. Ritualized displays. *In* "Flamingos" (J. Kear and N. Duplaix-Hall, eds.), pp. 142–149. T. & A. D. Poyser, Berkhamsted, Hertfordshire, England.

Kale, H. W., II. 1965. Ecology and bioenergetics of the long-billed marsh wren *Telmatodytes palustris griseus* (Brewster) in Georgia salt marshes. *Publ. Nuttall Ornithol. Club* **5**, 1–142.

Kaufmann, J. H. 1974. The ecology and evolution of social organization in the kangaroo family (Macropodidae). *Am. Zool.* **14**, 51–62.

Kear, J. 1972. The blue duck of New Zealand. *Living Bird* **11**, 175–192.

Kear, J. 1975. Salvadori's duck of New Guinea. *Wildfowl Trust Annu. Rep.* **26**, 104–111.

Keast, A. 1972. Faunal elements and evolutionary patterns: Some comparisons between the continental avifaunas of Africa, South America, and Australia. *Proc. Int. Ornithol. Congr.* **15**, 594–622.

Kleiman, D. G., and Eisenberg, J. H. 1973. Comparisons of canid and felid social systems from an evolutionary perspective. *Anim. Behav.* **21**(4), 637–659.

Klopfer, P. H. 1973. Does behavior evolve? *Ann. N.Y. Acad. Sci.* **223**, 113–119.

Krapu, G. L. 1974. Foods of breeding pintails in North Dakota. *J. Wildlife Mgmt.* **38**, 408–417.

Kruijt, J. P. and Hogan, J. A. 1967. Social behaviour on the lek in black grouse *Lyrurus tetrix tetrix* (L). *Ardea* **55**, 203–240.

Kruijt, J. P., de Vos, G. J., and Bossema, I. 1972. The arena system of black grouse. *Proc. Int. Ornithol. Congr.* **15**, 399–423.

Kruuk, H. 1972. "The Spotted Hyena: A Study of Predation and Social Behavior." University of Chicago Press, Chicago.

Lack, D. 1947. "Darwin's finches." Cambridge Univ. Press, London and New York.

Lack, D. 1966. "Population studies of birds." Oxford Univ. Press (Clarendon), London and New York.

Lack, D. 1968. "Ecological Adaptations for Breeding in Birds." Methuen, London.

Lack, D. 1974. "Evolution Illustrated by Waterfowl." Blackwells, Oxford.

Lanyon, W. E. 1969. Vocal characters and avian systematics. *In* "Bird Vocalizations" (R. A. Hinde, ed.), pp. 291–310. Cambridge Univ. Press, London and New York.

Laurie-Ahlberg, C. C., and McKinney, F. In press. The nod-swim display of male green-winged teal (*Anas crecca*). *Anim. Behav.*

Lebret, T. 1961. The pair formation in the annual cycle of the mallard, *Anas platyrhynchos* L. *Ardea,* **49**, 97–158.

Lind, H. 1959. Studies on the courtship and copulatory behaviour in the goldeneye (*Bucephala clangula* (L.)) *Dan. Ornithol. Foren. Tidsskr.* **53**, 177–219.

Lockard, R. B. 1971. Reflections on the fall of comparative psychology: Is there a message for us all? *Am. Psychol.* **26**, 168–179.

Lorenz, K. 1935. Der Kumpan in der Umwelt des Vögels. *J. Ornithol.* **88**, 137–213, 289–413.

Lorenz, K. 1941. Vergleichende Bewegungsstudien an Anatinen. *J. Ornithol.* **89**, Erg, Bd. 3, 194–294.

Lorenz, K. 1950. The comparative method in studying innate behaviour patterns. *Sym. Soc. Exp. Biol.* **4**, 221–268.

Lorenz, K. 1952. "King Solomon's Ring." Methuen, London.

Lorenz, K. 1953. Comparative studies on the behaviour of the Anatinae. Reprinted from *Avicult. Mag.* **57**, 157–182; **58**, 8–17, 61–72, 86–94, 172–184; **59**, 24–34, 80–91.

McKinney, F. 1961. An analysis of the displays of the European eider *Somateria mollissima millissima* (Linnaeus) and the Pacific eider *Somateria mollissima* v. *nigra* Bonaparte. *Behaviour Suppl.* **7**, 124 pp.

McKinney, F. 1965. The comfort movements of Anatidae. *Behaviour* **25**, 120–220.

McKinney, F. 1967. Breeding behaviour of captive shovelers. *Wildfowl Trust Annu. Rep.* **18**, 108–121.

McKinney, F. 1970. Displays of four species of blue-winged ducks. *Living Bird,* **9**, 29–64.

McKinney, F. 1973. Ecoethological aspects of reproduction. *In* "Breeding Biology of Birds" (D. S. Farner, ed.), pp. 6–21. Nat. Acad. Sci., Washington, D.C.

McKinney, F. 1975. The evolution of duck displays. *In* "Function and Evolution in Behaviour" (G. Baerends, C. Beer, and A. Manning, eds.), pp. 331–357. Oxford Univ. Press (Clarendon), London and New York.

McKinney, F., Siegfried, W. R., Ball, I. J., and Frost, P. P. G. (in press). Behavioral adaptations for river life in the African black duck. *Z. Tierpsychol.*

McLaren, I. A. 1972. Polygyny as the adaptive function of breeding territory in birds. *Trans. Conn. Acad. Arts Sci.* **44**, 189–210.

MacLean, G. L. 1972. Problems of display postures in the Charadrii (Aves: Charadriiformes). *Zool. Afri.* **7**, 57–74.

MacRoberts, M. H., and MacRoberts, B. R. 1976. Social organization and behavior of the acorn woodpecker in central coastal California. *Ornithol. Monogr.* **21.**

Marler, P. 1961. The evolution of visual communication. *In* "Vertebrate Speciation" (W. F. Blair, ed.), pp. 96–121. Univ. cf Texas Press, Austin.

Maynard Smith, J. 1964. Group selection and kin selection. *Nature (London)* **201**, 1145–1147.

Maynard Smith, J. 1976. Evolution and the theory of games. *Am. Sci.* **64**, 41–45.

Maynard Smith, J., and Price, G. R. 1973. The logic of animal conflicts. *Nature (London)* **246**, 15–18.

Mayr, E. 1969. "Principles of Systematic Zoology." McGraw-Hill, New York.

Mayr, E. 1972. Geography and ecology as faunal determinants. *Proc. Int. Ornithol. Congr.* **15**, 551–561.

Mengel, R. M. 1964. The probable history of species formation in some northern wood warblers (Parulidae). *Living Bird* **3**, 9–43.

Meyerriecks, A. J. 1960. Comparative breeding behavior of four species of North American herons. *Publ. Nuttall Ornithol. Club* No. 2.

Mock, D. W. 1976. Pair-formation displays of the great blue heron. *Wilson Bull.* **88**(2), 185–230.

Morris, D. 1956. The function and causation of courtship ceremonies. *In* "Symposium Fondation Singer-Polignac: L'instinct dans le comportement des animaux et de l'homme" (M. Autori, ed.), pp. 261–286. Masson, Paris.

Morris, D. 1957. "Typical intensity" and its relation to the problem of ritualization. *Behaviour* **11**, 1–22.

Moynihan, M. 1955a. Some aspects of reproductive behavior in the black-headed gull (*Larus ridibundus* L.) and related species. *Behaviour Suppl.* **4**.

Moynihan, M. 1955b. Remarks on the original sources of displays. *Auk* **72**, 240–246.

Moynihan, M. 1958a. Notes on the behavior of some North American gulls. II: Non-aerial hostile behavior of adults. *Behaviour* **12**, 95–182.

Moynihan, M. 1958b. Notes on the behavior of some North American gulls. III. Pairing behavior. *Behaviour* **13**, 112–130.

Moynihan, M. 1962. Hostile and sexual behavior patterns of South American and Pacific Laridae. *Behaviour Suppl.* **8**.

Nelson, J. B. 1970. The relationship between behaviour and ecology in the Sulidae with reference to other sea birds. *Oceanogr. Mar. Biol. Annu. Rev.* **8**, 501–574.

Nelson, J. B. 1971. The biology of Abbott's booby *Sula abbotti*. *Ibis* **113**(4), 429–467.

Nelson, J. B. 1972. Evolution of the pair bond in the Sulidae. *Proc. Int. Ornithol. Congr.* **15**, 371–388.

Nelson, J. B. 1975. Functional aspects of behaviour in the Sulidae. *In* "Function and Evolution in Behaviour" (G. Baerends, C. Beer, and A. Manning, eds.), pp. 313–330. Oxford Univ. Press (Clarendon), London and New York.

Newton, I. 1972. "Finches." Collins, London.

Norton-Griffiths, M. N. 1969. The organisation, control and development of parental feeding in the oystercatcher (*Haematopus ostralegus*). *Behaviour* **34**, 55–114.

Orians, G. H. 1961. The ecology of blackbird (*Agelaius*) social systems. *Ecol. Monogr.* **31**, 285–312.

Orians, G. H. 1969. On the evolution of mating systems in birds and mammals. *Am. Nat.* **103**, 589–603.

Orians, G. H. 1971. Ecological aspects of behavior. *In* "Avian Biology" (D. S. Farner, J. R. King and K. C. Parkes, eds.), Vol. 1, pp. 513–546. Academic Press, New York.

Orians, G. H. 1972. The adaptive significance of mating systems in the Icteridae. *Proc. Int. Ornithol. Congr.* **15**, 389–398.

Oring, L. W., and Knudson, M. L. 1972. Monogamy and polyandry in the spotted sandpiper. *Living Bird* **11**, 59–73.

Otte, D. 1974. Effects and functions in the evolution of signaling systems. *Annu. Rev. Ecol. Syst.* **5**, 385–417.

Parker, G. A. 1970. Sperm competition and its evolutionary consequences in the insects. *Biol. Rev.* **45**, 525–567.

Parker, G. A. 1974a. Courtship persistence and female-guarding as male time investment strategies. *Behaviour* **48**, 157–184.

Parker, G. A. 1974b. Assessment strategy and the evolution of fighting behaviour. *J. Theoret. Biol.* **47**, 223–243.

Pitelka, F. A., Holmes, R. T., and MacLean, S. A., Jr. 1974. Ecology and evolution of social organization in arctic sandpipers. *Am. Zool.* **14**, 185–204.

Ricklefs, R. E. 1973. "Ecology." Chiron Press, Newton, Massachusetts.

Rosen, R. 1967. "Optimality Principles in Biology." Plenum, New York.

Schaller, G. B. 1972. "The Serengeti Lion: A Study of Predator–Prey Relations." Univ. of Chicago Press, Chicago.

Schutz, F. 1965. Sexuelle Prägung bei Anatiden. *Z. Tierpsychol.* **22**, 50–103.

Sebeok, T. A. (Ed.) 1968. "Animal Communication." Indiana Univ. Press, Bloomington.

Selander, R. K. 1972. Sexual selection and dimorphism in birds. *In* "Sexual Selection and the Descent of Man 1871–1971" (B. Campbell, ed.). Aldine, Chicago.

Serie, J. R., and Swanson, G. A. 1976. Feeding ecology of breeding gadwalls on saline wetlands. *J. Wildlife Mgmt.* **40**, 69–81.

Seymour, N. R. 1974. Territorial behavior of wild shovelers at Delta, Manitoba. *Wildfowl* **25**, 49–55.

Short, L. L. 1971a. The evolution of terrestrial woodpeckers. *Am. Mus. Nov.* **2467**, 12, 1–23.

Short, L. L. 1971b. Systematics and behavior of some North American woodpeckers, Genus *Picoides* (Aves). *Bull. Am. Mus. Nat. Hist.* **145**, 1–118.

Short, L. L. 1972. Systematics and behavior of South American flickers (Aves, *Colaptes*). *Bull. Am. Mus. Nat. Hist.* **149**, 1–109.

Sibley, C. G. 1957. The evolutionary and taxonomic significance of sexual dimorphism and hybridization in birds. *Condor* **59**, 166–191.

Siegfried, W. R. 1968. The black duck in the south-western Cape. *Ostrich* **39**(2), 61–75.

Siegfried, W. R. 1974. Brood care, pair bonds and plumage in southern African Anatini. *Wildfowl* **25**, 33–40.

Simmons, K. E. L., and Weidmann, U. 1973. Directional bias as a component of social behaviour with special reference to the mallard *Anas platyrhynchos*. *J. Zool. London* **170**, 49–62.

Smith, W. J. 1965. Message, meaning, and context in ethology. *Am. Nat.* **99**, 405–409.

Smith, W. J. 1966. Communication and relationships in the genus *Tyrannus*. *Publ. Nuttall Ornithol. Club* **6**, 250 pp.

Smith, W. J. 1968. Message-meaning analyses. *In* "Animal Communication" (T. A. Sebeok, ed.), pp. 44–60. Indiana Univ. Press, Bloomington.

Smith, W. J. 1977. "The Behavior of Communicating." Harvard Univ. Press, Cambridge, Mass.

Snow, B. K. 1974. The plumbeous heron of the Galapagos. *Living Bird* **13**, 51–72.

Sowls, L. K. 1955. "Prairie Ducks." Wildlife Management Inst., Washington, D.C.

Storer, R. W. 1969. The behavior of the horned grebe in spring. *Condor* **71**(2), 180–205.

Studer-Thiersch, A. 1974. Die Balz der Flamingogattung *Phoenicopterus*, unter besonderer Berücksichtingung von *Ph. ruber roseus*. *Z. Tierpsychol.* **36**, 212–266.

Studer-Thiersch, A. 1975. Group display in *Phoenicopterus*. *In* "Flamingos" (J. Kear and N. Duplaix-Hall, eds.), pp. 150–158. T. & A. D. Poyser, Berkhamsted, Hertfordshire, England.

Swanson, G. A., Meyer, M. I., and Serie, J. R. 1974. Feeding ecology of breeding blue-winged teals. *J. Wildlife Mgmt.* **38**, 396–407.

Tamisier, A. 1970. Signification du gregarisme diurne et de l'alimentation nocturne des sarcelles d'hiver *Anas crecca crecca* L. *Terre Vie* **4**, 511–562.

Thielcke, G. 1964. Lautäusserungen der Vögel in ihrer Bedeutung für die Taxonomie. *J. Ornithol.* **105**, 78–84.

Thorpe, W. H. 1961. "Bird Song. The Biology of Vocal Communication and Expression in Birds."
Cambridge Univ. Press: Cambridge Monogr. Exp. Biol., No. 12.

Tinbergen, N. 1952. Derived activities: Their causation, biological significance, origin and emancipation during evolution. Q. Rev. Biol. 27, 1–32.

Tinbergen, N. 1953. "The Herring Gull's World." Collins, London.

Tinbergen, N. 1954. The origin and evolution of courtship and threat display. In "Evolution as a Process" (J. Huxley, A. C. Hardy, & E. B. Ford, eds.), pp. 233–250. Allen & Unwin, London.

Tinbergen, N. 1959. Comparative studies of the behaviour of gulls (Laridae): A progress report. Behaviour 15, 1–70.

Tinbergen, N. 1962. The evolution of animal communication—a critical examination of methods. Symp. Zool. Soc. London 8, 1–8.

Tinbergen, N. 1963. On aims and methods of ethology. Z. Tierpsychol. 20, 410–433.

Tinbergen, N. 1967. Adaptive features of the black-headed gull Larus ridibundus L. Proc. Int. Ornithol. Congr., 14th, pp. 43–59.

Tinbergen, N. 1972. Functional ethology and the human sciences. The Croonian Lecture, 1972. Proc. R. Soc. London B182, 385–410.

Tobach, E., Adler, H. E., and Adler, L. L. 1973. Comparative psychology at issue. Ann. N.Y. Acad. Sci. 223.

Trivers, R. L. 1972. Parental investment and sexual selection. In "Sexual Selection and the Descent of Man, 1871–1971" (B. Campbell, ed.), pp. 136–179. Aldine, Chicago.

Trivers, R. L. 1974. Parent-offspring conflict. Am. Zool. 14(1), 249–264.

van Tets, G. F. 1965. A comparative study of some social communication patterns in the Pelecaniformes. Ornithol. Monogr. 2.

Verner, J. 1964. Evolution of polygyny in the long-billed marsh wren. Evolution 18, 252–261.

Vuilleumier, F. 1975. Zoogeography. In "Avian Biology" (D. S. Farner and J. R. King, eds.), Vol. 5, pp. 421–496. Academic Press, New York.

Watson, A., and Moss, R. 1970. Dominance, spacing behaviour and aggression in relation to population limitation in vertebrates. In "Animal Populations in Relation to Their Food Resources" (A. Watson, ed.), pp. 167–220. Blackwell, Oxford.

Watson, A., and Moss, R. 1972. A current model of population dynamics in red grouse. Proc. Int. Ornithol. Congr. 15, 134–149.

Weidmann, U. 1956. Verhaltensstudien an der Stockente (Anas platyrhynchos L.). I. Das Aktionssystem. Z. Tierpsychol. 13, 208–271.

Weidmann, U. 1958. Verhaltensstudien an der Stockente (Anas platyrhynchos L.) II. Z. Tierpsychol. 15, 277–300.

Weidmann, U., and Darley, J. 1971. The role of the female in the social display of mallards. Anim. Behav. 19, 287–298.

Weller, M. W. 1974. Habitat selection and feeding patterns of brown teal (Anas castanea chlorotis) on Great Barrier Island. Notornis 21, 25–35.

Weller, M. W. 1975. Ecological studies of the Auckland Islands flightless teal. Auk 92, 280–297.

Whitman, C. O. 1919. The behavior of pigeons. Publ. Carnegie Inst. 257, 1–161.

Wickler, W. 1961a. Okologie und Stammesgeschichte von Verhaltensweisen. Fortschr. Zool. 13, 303–365.

Wickler, W. 1961b. Über die Stammesgeschichte und den taxonomischen Wert einiger Verhaltensweisen der Vögel. Z. Tierpsychol. 18, 320–342.

Wickler, W. 1967. Vergleichende Verhaltensforschung und Phylogenetik. In "Die Evolution der Organismen" (G. Heberer, ed.), Vol. 1, pp. 420–508. Fischer, Stuttgart.

Wiens, J. A. 1966. On group selection and Wynne-Edwards' hypothesis. Am. Sci. 54, 273–287.

Wiley, R. H. 1974. Evolution of social organization and life-history patterns among grouse. Q. Rev. Biol. 49, 201–227.

Williams, G. C. 1966. "Adaptation and natural selection." Princeton Univ. Press, Princeton, N.J.

Williams, G. C. 1975. Sex and evolution. *Monogr. Population Biol.* **8**, Princeton Univ. Press, Princeton, N.J.

Willis, E. O. 1972. The behavior of spotted antbirds. *Ornithol. Monogr.* **10**.

Wilson, E. O. 1975. "Sociobiology: The new synthesis." Belknap Press, Cambridge, Mass.

Woolfenden, G. E. 1961. Postcranial osteology of the waterfowl. *Bull. Florida State Mus. Biol. Sci.* **6**, 1–129.

Woolfenden, G. E. 1974. Nesting and survival in a population of Florida scrub jays. *Living Bird* **12**, 25–49.

Woolfenden, G. E. 1975. Florida scrub jay helpers at the nest. *Auk* **92**(1), 1–15.

Wynne-Edwards, V. C. 1962. "Animal Dispersion in Relation to Social Behaviour." Oliver & Boyd, Edinburgh.

Zusi, R. L. 1971. Functional anatomy in systematics. *Taxon* **20**(1), 75–84.

The Influence of Daylength and Male Vocalizations on the Estrogen-Dependent Behavior of Female Canaries and Budgerigars, with Discussion of Data from Other Species

ROBERT A. HINDE AND ELIZABETH STEEL

M.R.C. UNIT ON THE DEVELOPMENT AND INTEGRATION OF BEHAVIOUR
UNIVERSITY SUB-DEPARTMENT OF ANIMAL BEHAVIOUR
MADINGLEY, CAMBRIDGE, ENGLAND

I. Introduction

That changes in the activity of the gonads control changes in avian reproductive behavior is well established (Lehrman, 1961; Lofts and Murton, 1973). Gonadal activity is one aspect of the hypothalamus–pituitary–gonad system, which is synchronized with the natural season by the influences of specific environmental factors (Assenmacher, 1973; Immelmann, 1973). During reproduction the species-characteristic sequence, involving activities such as pair formation, nest building, egg laying, incubation, and feeding the young, is determined by complex interactions between the external stimuli to which the birds are exposed, the internal endocrine state, morphological changes, and behavior. These interactions have been studied in a number of species, particularly the ring dove, *Streptopelia risoria* (Lehrman, 1965) and the domesticated canary, *Serinus canarius* (Hinde, 1965; Hinde & Steel, 1966), although in none are they yet completely understood.

One small segment of the web of interactions involved in the reproductive behavior of female canaries serves to illustrate their complexity. Under the influence of long photoperiods female canaries begin to come into reproductive condition. Their reproductive development is accelerated by various other external factors, including stimuli from the male. As a result of changes in the hypothalamus–pituitary–gonad system, estrogen is secreted and induces the female to show nest-building behavior. Secretion of estrogen and other hormones results also in the development of a brood patch on the ventral surface, involving increased sensitivity to tactile stimulation in that region. The nest-building behavior leads to the construction of a nest, and thus to a change in the stimulation the female receives through the increasingly sensitive broodpatch region. This stimulation leads, in turn, to a change in the nature of the nest material selected, to a decrease in the total amount of nest building shown, and to an acceleration of other aspects of reproductive development (reviewed by Hinde, 1965; Hinde & Steel, 1966).

In this chapter, we are concerned with an aspect of this interaction omitted from the above account—namely, the influence of external factors on the effectiveness of a given level of gonadal hormone in producing a change in behavior. The literature contains a number of indications that there may be such an influence (Section III): in our own research it arose as a possibility when we found that exogenous estrogen, although able to induce nest building outside the normal breeding season, did so only at nonphysiological dose levels. Our first hypothesis, that the estrogen normally acts synergistically with another hormone, could not be confirmed, although the evidence on this issue is not yet conclusive (see Section II.D.3c and d). Evidence on the second (and not necessarily incompatible) hypothesis, that external factors influence the effectiveness of estrogen, is brought together here.

In the first part of this chapter we review experiments on two species with marked differences in breeding biology, the domesticated canary, *Serinus canarius*, and the budgerigar or shell parakeet, *Melopsittacus undulatus*. Data on these species demonstrate that two types of external factors (photoperiod and male vocalizations) affect reproductive behavior not only by influencing hormone secretion by the hypothalamus–pituitary–gonad system but also by other as yet undefined mechanisms, involving influences on the effectiveness of given steroid levels. In the second part of the chapter the possible generality of this finding is considered in the light of evidence from other species.

II. Experiments with Canaries and Budgerigars

A. Aspects of Natural History

Wild-living canaries occur between latitudes 27°N and 40°N (Vaurie, 1959) where breeding occurs in spring. Pairs are formed early in the reproductive season, and the female builds a cup-shaped nest in a bush or tree. The outside of the nest is typically made of grass, and the cup lined with feathers. Aspects of nest-building behavior provide the dependent variables for the experiments reviewed here.

In contrast budgerigars breed in tropical and subtropical latitudes. They are predominantly opportunistic breeders, nesting after the irregular rains (Immelmann, 1963; Rothwell and Amadon, 1964). Eggs are laid in natural holes, in which the female may perform a limited amount of excavation, but no nest is built. Entry or occupation of the nest cavity by the female was assessed in these experiments.

These two species have markedly different life histories: they also belong to distantly related phyletic groups. Findings common to the two species are therefore likely to have some generality.

B. Material and Methods

Full procedural details have been reported in the papers cited, and will be repeated only briefly here. Birds of both species came from domesticated stock; how far reproductive behavior has been modified by the selective pressures of domestication is unknown. During experiments all birds were kept in individual cages. Canaries were provided with a felt-lined plastic nest cup and a dispenser of 10-cm lengths of pliable string with which to build. Budgerigars had access to nest boxes with a circular entrance hole and a concave wooden floor.

For canaries we recorded daily the number of strings removed from the dispenser (gathering score) and the number of strings placed in the nest pan (placing score). Latency to placing was taken as the first of two consecutive days on which placing occurred. A record of the first time a budgerigar entered the nest box was obtained by placing a piece of smoked paper on the nest floor. Records of time spent in the nest box were obtained during daily watches.

All injections were made three times weekly. Canaries (mean body weight 20 gm) received 50 μg of estradiol benzoate per injection and budgerigars (mean body weight 43 gm) 100 μg of estradiol benzoate, either alone or in combination with 50 or 100 IU of prolactin.

Left ovaries were removed under Nembutal and ether anesthesia as far as possible by suction and the site cauterized: canary testes were removed intact by suction. We have never found growth of the rudimentary right ovary after sinistral ovariectomy in canaries. All birds with remaining ovarian tissue weighing more than 0.1% body weight or with a follicle over 1 mm in diameter after the experiment were excluded from the analysis (Section II.D.3.a). Castrated male canaries were used in a few experiments as total gonadectomy was much easier than with females; estrogen-injected males built nests indistinguishable from females.

C. Background Data on the Effects of Photoperiod and Male Vocalizations Mediated by the Hypothalamus–Pituitary–Gonad System

In this section earlier evidence that the two categories of external factors do influence the reproductive development of intact birds, and that such effects are mediated at least in part by pituitary and gonadal hormones, is reviewed. This is intended solely as a background against which evidence on the influence of external factors on the behavioral effectiveness of gonadal steroids can be considered (Section II.D): discussion of data not relevant to that issue, and most data on other species, are therefore omitted in the interests of brevity.

1. Influences of Photoperiod on Reproductive Development of Intact Females

a. Canary. In the laboratory, intact females built nests and laid eggs under artificially increased photoperiods in winter. The effect on brood patch development varied slightly with the season, but nest building occurred in all of three groups exposed to long days, starting at intervals between October and January (Steel and Hinde, 1966a). The nest building of birds kept previously under natural day lengths and exposed to artificial photoperiods for four weeks from mid-January, was not increased with 8 hr light and 16 hr darkness (8L:16D) or with 10L:14D, but was increased with 12L:12D or 14L:10D schedules (Follett *et al.*, 1973). The influence of these photoperiods on various aspects of reproductive development is shown in Fig. 1.

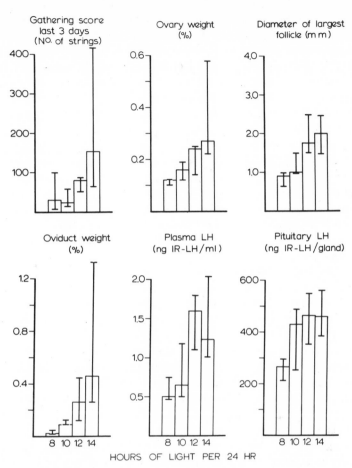

FIG. 1. Median values and interquartile ranges (vertical lines) for six parameters of reproductive development from female canaries kept on one of four different daylengths for 4 weeks starting in mid-January. Ovary and oviduct weights are expressed as a percentage of body weight. LH = luteinizing hormone; IR–LH = immunoreactive luteinizing hormone. (Adapted from Follett *et al.*, 1973.)

These data show that the photoperiod affects various aspects of the pituitary–gonad system; since a long photoperiod has little effect on nest building in ovariectomized females (Steel and Hinde, 1972a), and since exogenous estrogen induces nest building (Section II.D.2), it is a reasonable assumption that the effects of a long photoperiod on behavior are mediated at least in part through that system.

Birds measure the length of the day by means of a circadian rhythm of photosensitivity, being least sensitive in the hours following dawn and most photosensitive later in the 24 hr. This hypothesis was first proposed by Bünning (1936) and extended by Pittendrigh and Minis (1964). Light itself has two functions: it entrains the circadian rhythm of photosensitivity and acts as an inducer on the pituitary–gonad system during the photosensitive (or photoinducible) phase of that rhythm. These two functions have different thresholds of light intensity in *Passer domesticus* (Menaker and Eskin, 1967).

The technique used to assess the photosensitive phase is that of night interruption or skeleton days. Birds are entrained to a short photoperiod which does not induce gonadal growth. If a brief period of light is given during the dark part of the cycle it can mimic a long day in terms of subsequent gonadal growth. Thus 8L:5D:1L:10D has a similar effect to 14L:10D, but 8L:1D:1L:14D does not. The position of the photosensitive phase in the 24-hr light–darkness cycle has been defined for a number of species (for a review see Follett, 1973). Intact female canaries can be induced to nest build in response to endogenous estrogen production on a 14-hr skeleton photoperiod (7L:6D:1L:10D) (Steel and Hinde, 1975, unpublished observations).

b. Budgerigar. Despite their near tropical habitat (Section II.A) the egg laying of budgerigars in the laboratory is affected by the light regime. Females provided with a nest box and exposed to male vocalizations laid more rapidly under a 14L:10D photoregime than under regimes of shorter light periods (Putman and Hinde, 1973).

In the previous experiment there was little difference in the number of birds laying between groups kept on 6L:18D, 2L:22D, or 0L:24D schedules: earlier data on breeding in total darkness has been presented by Vaugien (1951), Brockway (1962), and Van Tienhoven et al. (1966). Two different effects appear to be involved here. Possession of a nest hole accelerates egg laying, and darkness is an important characteristic of a nest hole. Thus, in addition to the positive effect of a long photoperiod, periods of darkness also have a stimulating effect; in the absence of a nest box females laid more rapidly in continuous darkness than on 14L:10D; and intermittent periods of darkness imposed on the light period of a 14L:10D regime slightly accelerated egg laying (Hinde & Putman, 1973).

We may now ask whether long photoperiods produce these effects as a result of circadian changes in photosensitivity, as in temperate zone species. In four experiments (Shellswell et al., 1975) groups of females were placed on a variety of photoregimes. The females were in individual cages all within sound of four group-caged males. In all experiments each group received an initial 6 hr of light, and a total of 8L each day, but the groups differed in the interval between the initial 6L of light and the 2L given subsequently (Section II.C.1.a). In each experiment egg laying occurred with the shortest latency in the group given 6L:6D:2L:10D (Fig. 2a).

This result could indicate one of the following:

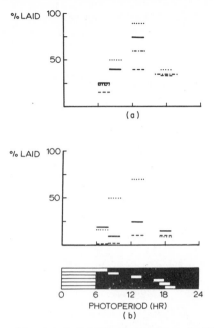

FIG. 2. The percentage of female budgerigars that had laid eggs after 30-day exposure to various skeleton photoperiods: (A) males housed in a separate cage in the same room as the females; (B) females exposed to taped male vocalizations during the light periods only. Each horizontal line represents one group of between 10 and 12 individuals: within each graph groups with identical symbols were tested simultaneously. (Adapted from Shellswell *et al.*, 1975.)

1.   Light is more effective on a 6L:6D:2L:10D regime than on any of the others used.

2.   Male song has more effect on the female if she experiences it 12–14 hr after dawn that at other times of day.

3.   Males sing more when on this regime.

The third possibility was eliminated by standardizing the amount of male song that the females heard. Females exposed to tape-recorded male song during the light periods (Fig. 2B) still laid more rapidly on a 14-hr skeleton photoperiod than on the other light regimes (Shellswell *et al.*, 1975).

The second possibility was tested in part by keeping female budgerigars on a 14L:10D regime and playing male vocalizations during either the first 7 hr or the second 7 hr of the light period. Reproductive development was more rapid, in each of two experiments, if song was played in the first half of the 14-hr photoperiod than in the second half. Thus, with the most effective skeleton photoperiod (6L:6D:2L:10D) the second light period falls within that part of the day when the female is least responsive to male song. The effectiveness of this photoregime is therefore unlikely to be mediated solely by male song (Gosney and Hinde, 1976). It thus seems that budgerigars, like temperate zone birds, show a circadian rhythm in photosensitivity.

2. Influence of Stimulation from the Male on Reproductive Development of Intact Females

a. Canary. The female's reproductive development is accelerated by stimulation from the male. Although isolated females may lay eventually, they lay earlier if caged with males. The effect is exerted primarily during a limited part of the breeding season: in one experiment the presence of a male appeared to have little influence on the start of defeathering of the brood patch, but marked effects on its completion and on the start and completion of nest building (Warren & Hinde, 1961).

Tape-recorded male song played to intact females transferred to 11L:13D in November accelerated reproductive development more than the 11-hr photoperiod alone. After 56 days more song-exposed birds had ovarian follicles over 1 mm in diameter, and significantly more had placed material in the nest. Peak plasma luteinizing hormone (LH) levels (from 6 samples taken up to Day 28) were also significantly higher. Females transferred at the same time to 14L:10D showed a rapid effect of day length on reproductive development: this was not enhanced by exposure to song, presumably because it was near maximal already (Steel and Hinde, unpublished observations).

b. Budgerigar. The role of vocal behavior in accelerating and synchronizing reproductive development is relatively more important in the budgerigar than in any other avian species so far studied: interactions between vocalizations and hormonal state play an essential role. Isolated bisexual pairs of budgerigars rarely breed. In the wild, budgerigars breed in large colonies where the mutual- and self-stimulatory effect of male song facilitates rapid sexual development in this opportunistic breeder. In the laboratory, male budgerigars are stimulated to warble by hearing others. The performance and/or hearing of warbling increases gonadotrophic secretion and testicular development, and the resulting testosterone output further increases the likelihood of warbling. Male vocalization also promotes gonadotrophic secretion and consequent ovarian activity in females, which in time leads to nest-box occupation and solicitation for copulation (for a review see Brockway, 1969). Only one (the soft warble) of the many types of male vocalization stimulated female ovarian development (Brockway, 1965).

3. Effects of Gonadotrophins

a. Canary. Intact females injected with pregnant mare serum gonadotropin (PMSG) during the winter months showed considerable reproductive development, and in some cases egg laying. However the effect on nest-building behavior varied with the season: nest-building occurred in September–October, was slight in groups tested in November–December and January–February, but occurred again in a group tested in February–March (Steel and Hinde, 1966b) (see also Section II.D.1).

b. Budgerigar. In males both PMSG and testosterone caused intact birds to warble. The PMSG was ineffective in castrates, confirming that it acts on song only by promoting gonadal secretion (Brockway, 1968). No studies on gonadotrophin-injected females have been made.

4. Effects of Gonadal Steroids

a. Canary. Exogenous estradiol benzoate induced nest building in intact female canaries, but only at supraphysiological dose levels (0.5 mg three times weekly). These experiments were carried out under natural winter day lengths (Warren and Hinde, 1959).

Other hormones act synergistically with estrogen in inducing development of the brood patch (Steel and Hinde, 1963; Hutchison *et al.,* 1967) and oviduct (Hutchison *et al.,* 1968; Hinde *et al.,* 1971), changes that occur at about the same time as nest building (White and Hinde, 1968). However, we have not been able to establish any such synergistic effect with nest building. Progesterone (0.125 or 0.25 mg three times weekly) produced no clear effects. Testosterone propionate (2.0 mg three times weekly) alone or in combination with estradiol benzoate (0.05 mg three times weekly) tended to suppress gathering by birds kept on normal winter day lengths, although there was some suggestion that it augmented gathering on a 20-hr day (Warren and Hinde, 1959; Steel and Hinde, 1972a).

b. Budgerigar. Brockway (1969) found that loud warbling could be induced in intact female budgerigars by either exogenous estrogen or testosterone. The soft warble (by which the male stimulates female ovarian growth) was not induced by testosterone but was by estrogen; it was further increased by estrogen in combination with progesterone.

Naturally breeding females first enter the nest box 8 or 9 days before the first egg is laid and thereafter tend to spend increasingly greater amounts of time in the nest hole until the eggs are laid and incubation established. Hutchison (1975a) found that naive, ovariectomized females did not enter the nest box. However, after injection of estradiol benzoate most birds entered, and estrogen (100 μg) in combination with prolactin caused all females to enter and to spend more time in the nest box, especially sitting in the nest hollow. They also adopted the incubation posture and did not expel eggs provided by the experimenter (Hutchison, 1971, 1975b).

As with canaries, estrogen with other gonadal hormones and prolactin can influence brood patch and oviduct development (Hutchison, 1971).

D. Influence of Photoperiod on the Effect of Exogenous Hormones on Canary Nest Building

1. Influence of Photoperiod on the Effect of Exogenous Gonadotrophin

It was mentioned above (Section II.C.3.a) that exogenous PMSG induced some nest-building behavior in intact females kept on natural day lengths and tested in September–October and also in February–March; less building was elicited from groups similarly tested in the intervening months when the day lengths were shorter. These birds had been tested under natural day lengths in the belief that the photoperiod affected gonadotrophin production, but would be of no importance if exogenous gonadotrophins were provided. Three explanations of the above result are possible:

1. pregnant mare serum gonadotrophin caused less ovarian estrogen production on shorter day lengths; or

2. the estrogen produced in response to a given dose of PMSG was less effective in inducing nest building on shorter day lengths; or

3. short day lengths themselves imposed some constraint on the amount of nest building shown.

Further evidence for the differential effect of PMSG on nest building on long and short days was obtained from the following experiment.

Intact female canaries were treated with PMSG and kept on either 20L:4D or 9½L:13½D photoperiods from March 1 (Steel and Hinde, 1972b). Sixty-five percent of the birds laid within about 10 days, whereas untreated controls kept on

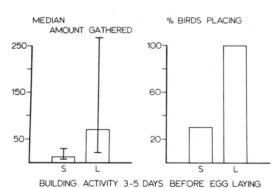

FIG. 3. The nest-building response of intact female canaries on two photoperiods to endogenous estrogen produced in response to injected pregnant mare serum gonadotrophin (PMSG). All birds laid eggs with a latency of 9–10 days after the start of PMSG treatment. The vertical lines enclose the interquartile range; S = 9.5L:13.5D, L = 20L:4D. (Adapted from Hinde and Steel, 1975.)

natural day lengths (about 11½ hr) did not lay until about a month later. Of the PMSG-treated birds that produced eggs, those kept on long photoperiods nest built much more 5 to 2 days before egg laying than did those on short photo-periods. The median amount gathered was five times greater in the long-day birds than in the short-day ones (Fig. 3), although the day length was only twice as long. Furthermore, a higher proportion of long-day birds placed nest material. The difference in building was therefore unlikely to be due solely to the greater time available for building (see Section II.D.3).

Photoperiod did not influence the speed of PMSG-induced ovarian develop-ment to the point of ovulation presumably because the high dose used (75 IU three times weekly) swamped any differences in endogenous levels. Since the nest-building analysis utilized only data from birds 5 to 2 days before laying their first egg, it seemed probable that hormonal differences between short- and long-day birds were not crucial and that the photoperiod was affecting the expression of estrogen-induced nest building. However a more direct role of gonadotrophins on nest building cannot be entirely dismissed (see also Section II.D.3.c).

2. Influence of Photoperiod on the Effect of Exogenous Estrogen

The next step was to see if, in fact, photoperiod could affect the behavioral response to a given amount of exogenous estrogen. In a number of experiments we have established that overiectomized females (and castrated males) treated with a standard dose (0.05 mg three times weekly) of estradiol benzoate build more if kept on long days than if kept on short days.

a. Normal Winter Day Length (8–10 hr Light) versus a 20-hr Photo-period. When exogenous estrogen was given to ovariectomized birds on nor-mal midwinter day lengths they showed only a slight increase in gathering behavior; birds similarly treated on an extreme 20-hr day showed a rapid increase in both gathering and placing up to a level approaching that shown by intact birds kept for five weeks on a similar photoperiod (Steel and Hinde, 1972a).

b. Intermediate Day Lengths. On a range of day lengths between 6 and 18 hr of light per day, estrogen-treated, ovariectomized birds built more when exposed to the longer photoperiods. Some data are shown in Fig. 4. The var-iability of responsiveness to 12L:12D suggests that this day length is around threshold for the effect to occur. This agrees with data for the pituitary–gonad response of intact birds.

c. Photorefractory Birds. Comparable results were obtained with ovariec-tomized and intact females during the postbreeding refractory period when the pituitary–gonad axis is unresponsive to long days. The females were kept on either a 8L:16D or 16L:8D schedule. Ovariectomized and intact birds differed little in their building behavior, but estrogen-treated birds on the longer photo-period showed significantly more nest-building behavior than those on short

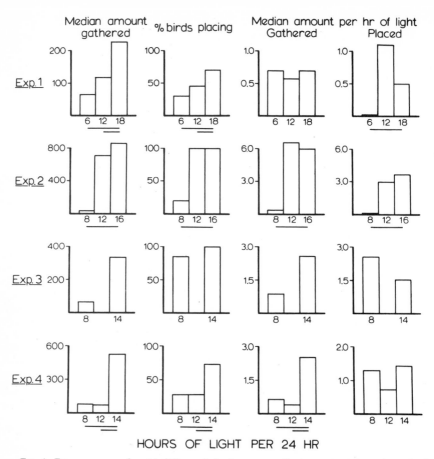

FIG. 4. Four measures of nest-building activity for groups of estrogen-treated ovariectomized canaries kept on a range of photoperiods from 6 to 18 hr of light per day. Lines below the histograms indicate significant differences ($p < 0.05$, one tailed) between the group medians as assessed by the Mann–Whitney U test or by the χ^2 test in the case of proportion of birds placing. (Partly from Hinde and Steel, 1976, by permission of the Zoological Society of London.)

photoperiods. That the birds were indeed refractory was shown by the absence of ovarian or oviducal development under the influence of the long photoperiods (Section II.D.3.a) (Hinde *et al.*, 1974).

d.   *Castrated Males.*   Finally comparable results were also obtained with castrated males: these were used because complete gonadectomy is much easier to achieve in males (see Section II.B) (Hinde and Steel, 1975). Estrogen-treated males kept on 16L:8D built more vigorously than those on 8L:16D. The typical time course of the response over the first two weeks of treatment is shown in Fig. 5.

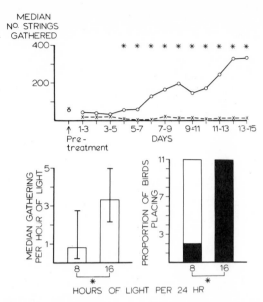

FIG. 5. Nest-building response of estrogen-injected, castrated male canaries kept on either long or short days. Building scores were measured on three days before the first estrogen injection and for 15 days thereafter. The graph shows the course of gathering over the experimental period for birds on 8L:16D (×) and 16L:8D (○); the gathering scores are expressed as medians of 3-day running totals. The left-hand histogram shows the amount gathered per hour of light over the 15-day period. Vertical lines enclose interquartile ranges. In the right hand histogram the numbers of birds placing (black) are plotted as a proportion of the total group, $N = 11$ in each case. The asterisk indicates that the difference between groups is significant, $p < 0.01$, one tailed. Statistical tests are as in Fig. 4. (Adapted from Steel and Hinde, 1976.)

e. Skeleton Photoperiods.   Two experiments using skeleton photoperiods have been carried out (Steel and Hinde, 1976). In the first, castrated male birds on a 14-hr skeleton day involving 9 hr of light (8L:5D:1L:10D, 7L:5D:2L:10D, or 6L:5D:3L:10D) were compared with birds on a continuous light 9-hr day. The occurrence of placing had previously distinguished short from long-day birds: the 9-hr and 14-hr skeleton birds also differed on this measure. Significantly more skeleton long-day birds reached the placing criterion, and with a shorter latency. Significant differences in the numbers of birds placing were apparent by the fifth day after the start of treatment. There was, however, some constraint on the total amount of material used by the 14-hr skeleton birds compared with similarly treated birds on a full 14-hr day. A similar experiment using intact photorefractory females reinforced those results. Control groups on either an 8- or a 14-hr day were compared with birds on a 14-hr skeleton photoperiod with 8 hr of light (6 + 2 hr). Both long-day groups were almost identical, and significantly higher than the short-day birds, on the measures of total and of peak gathering scores and the proportion of birds placing material. Therefore, building activity can differ widely between groups with only 8 hr of light per day according to its temporal distribution within the 24 hr.

These two experiments support the hypothesis that the daylength-dependent effect of estrogen on nest building is mediated by a circadian change in photosensitivity comparable with that involved in the effect of longer photoperiods on gonadal growth.

3. Possible Mechanisms for the Greater Effectiveness of Exogenous Estrogen on Long Day Lengths

The experiments just cited clearly demonstrate that gonadectomized canaries given physiological dose levels of exogenous estrogen show more nest building on long days than on short days. We may now consider some possible mechanisms for this effect.

a. Inadequate Ovariectomy. Complete ovariectomy is difficult to achieve. It was decided to set an upper weight and follicle size limit for remaining ovarian fragments found at autopsy after each experiment (see Section II.B); no birds with larger fragments were used in the behavioral analysis. These criteria were chosen as characteristic of reproductive development before the start of nest building in the natural breeding season (Hinde, 1967). A further check was made by comparing, within each group, the building scores of those birds with remaining ovarian tissue (meeting the criteria cited above) with those that were completely ovariectomized. In no case were there any significant differences, and in some experiments enough completely ovariectomized birds were available for statistical evaluation by themselves. No correlations were found between building activity and amount of remaining ovarian tissue.

In later experiments stronger evidence, against the view that inadequate ovariectomy could explain the observed effects, was obtained by using castrated males (Section II.D.2.d). Gonadectomy was complete in all cases and the possibility of endogenous estrogen negligible.

Photorefractory females also showed a daylength-related response to estrogen (Section II.D.2.c). The intact birds had no larger ovaries after several weeks exposure to 16L:8D than birds on 8L:16D and the oviducts were completely regressed indicating very low levels of endogenous gonadal steroids. The ovary and oviduct development of these birds is contrasted with those of photosensitive birds on similar photoperiods in Fig. 6.

b. More Time Available for Building. Short days could impose a real constraint upon the birds in terms of actual time available for fitting in all essential activities in addition to the time-consuming activity of nest building. Four types of evidence indicate that this is not an important issue.

First, birds on long photoperiods not only built more over the whole experimental period, but also usually showed higher hourly rates of building. Some

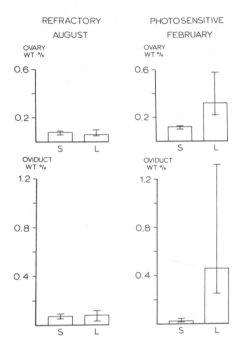

FIG. 6. A comparison of the median response of ovaries and oviducts of photorefractory and photosensitive female canaries to short (S = 8L:16D) and long (L = 16L:8D or 14L:10D) photoperiods. Vertical lines enclose the interquartile ranges. (From Hinde and Steel, 1976, by permission of the Zoological Society of London.)

examples are shown in Fig. 4; in three out of four experiments the amount gathered per hour or the amount placed per hour, or both, was significantly greater on long day lengths than on short. Similar data were obtained in other experiments (e.g., Fig. 5). It must be noted however that there are considerable difficulties in comparing the time budgets of birds on different photoperiods. Not only do energy requirements alter with the photoperiod, but the efficiency of essential activities change; feeding, for example, becomes more dilatory in that the time spent feeding increases disproportionately to food intake on long photoperiods (Croft, 1975).

Second, the response of long day birds differed from that of short-day birds not only in the median scores of gathering and placing. More long-day birds placed material in the nest and they did so with a shorter latency. These differences were unlikely to be affected by the amount of time available.

Third, there are indications that even 8-hr photoperiods do not necessarily constrain nest building. In all short-day groups studied a few individuals responded to estrogen by building at rates approaching those of long-day birds, and it is shown in Section II.F that the building activity of short-day birds can be raised further by playing them male song. In a detailed study of canaries, Croft (1975) found that the distribution of maintenance activities throughout the day varied with photoperiod and that long-day birds spent more time in rest and in locomotion than short-day birds. In reproductively active birds on 12- or 14-hr photoperiods nest building replaced these two activities. His data indicated that, for at least some individuals, even on an 8-hr day enough time was available for building to take place.

Finally, estrogen-treated birds kept on long or short skeleton photoperiods showed different amounts of nest building (Section II.D.2.e). Here the daily number of light hours was the same for each group, only the timing of the second light pulse varied. This provides strong evidence that short hours of light do not necessarily constrain nest building.

c. Direct Effect of Gonadotrophins. In at least some avian species negative feedback operates between the gonad and the hypothalamic–hypophyseal axis. Long days elevate plasma LH levels, and subsequent castration results in an even further rise; plasma LH in these castrates can be reduced by exogenous testosterone (male Japanese quail, Follett *et al.*, 1972). There can be a fourteenfold difference in plasma LH between long-day intact and ovariectomized female quail (Gibson *et al.*, 1975). Negative feedback also operates on short days; estrogen injection decreased both pituitary and plasma LH in intact canaries on 8L:16D (Follett *et al.*, 1973). Ovariectomy of such canaries increased plasma LH and injected estrogen reduced LH to a low level (Hinde *et al.*, 1974). In *Spizella arborea* castrated males had significantly increased LH levels on a short day compared with intact males (Wilson and Follett, 1974). The difference in gonadotrophin levels between ovariectomized canaries on long and short days is thus likely to be marked. It is therefore possible that gonadotrophins, alone or in synergy with estrogen, may have a direct effect on nest building and could account for our results.

Ovariectomized untreated canaries on 20L:4D showed a small but significant rise in building activity over a five-week period while short-day controls did not. This rise was suppressed by Methallibure, a putative gonadotrophin inhibitor (Steel and Hinde, 1972a). However, Methallibure did not reduce estrogen-induced nest building in ovariectomized females (Steel and Hinde, 1972a), suggesting that there is no estrogen–gonadotrophin synergism.

Attempts to show that gonadotrophins have a direct effect on nest building have failed. Intact females given large amounts of PMSG, sufficient to induce egg laying, built more on long days than on short days (Section II.D.1). The dose used was high and would have swamped any intergroup difference in endogenous gonadotrophins.

Both mammalian and avian LH have been injected in combination with estrogen into short-day, ovariectomized females. Neither caused an increase in gathering activity over that produced by the estrogen alone (Hinde *et al.*, 1974). Thus replacement of LH in estrogen-treated short-day birds does not restore building to long-day levels.

In the two experiments where plasma LH was measured at the end of treatment no positive correlations were found between LH levels and any measures of building activity (Hinde *et al.*, 1974).

The strongest evidence against involvement of gonadotrophins comes from work with photorefractory birds. In *Spizella arborea* plasma LH levels fall as the gonads regress (Wilson and Follett, 1974) and remain low although the days are still long. In the canary, photorefractory birds on short and long days have similar, low ovary weights (Section II.D.3.a and Fig. 6). In spite of this evidence of low gonadotrophin levels, estrogen treatment produces far more building activity on long days than on short days.

d. Effect of Gonadotrophin-Releasing Factors. There are two reports of an apparent potentiating effect of luteinizing hormone–releasing hormone (LH–RH) on the effectiveness of estrogen in producing behavioral ostrus in the female rat (Moss and McCann, 1973; Pfaff, 1973). Given this possibility of a synergism between a hypothalamic hormone and estrogen in affecting behavior, we tested whether it could account for daylength-dependent differences in the behavior of canaries.

A dose of 1 μg LH–RH, known to raise canary plasma LH within 10 min (T. J. Nicholls and C. Storey, 1975, personal communication) was used. On 8L:16D estrogen plus saline-injected controls were compared with estrogen plus LH–RH-treated ovariectomized females. In three separate experiments injections were given at different times of day including the dark period. Follett and Sharp (1969) had found in the quail a rapid depletion of hypothalamic gonadotrophin-releasing activity 14–16 hr after dawn on a long day. Injection during the dark period was designed to mimic the time of maximum LH–RH activity in a long-day bird. Injection of LH–RH was ineffective 1, 7, and 14 hr after dawn. However, Cheng (1977) has subsequently found a synergistic effect of LH–RH and estrogen on female sexual behavior in the ring dove, so the matter should be regarded as still open.

e. Differential Central Uptake of Estrogen. Zigmond and Steel (unpublished observations) failed to demonstrate a difference in the amount of tritiated estradiol bound in the hypothalamic areas of canaries preexposed to short or long photoperiods. The brain areas mediating nest building have not been identified in the canary, but by analogy with sex-related behavior of other species it may be expected to lie within the preoptic anterior hypothalamic area (Zigmond, 1975a, b; see also Erickson and Hutchison, 1977). However, as the negative feedback effect of estrogen on gonadotrophins functions with both day lengths it is likely that, even on short days, some areas of the hypothalamus are taking up estrogen. A much finer dissection of the areas controlling behavior may be necessary to demonstrate differences in estrogen retention.

f. Possible Involvement of the Pineal. We have not investigated the possible role of the pineal in mediating the effects of day length on responsiveness to estrogen. Pineal involvement in the seasonal breeding cycles of some mammals is well established (Reiter, 1975), but its role in birds is equivocal as the brain itself is a photoreceptor and the pineal is not necessarily a transducer of photoperiodic information (Menaker *et al.*, 1970). Removal of the pineal does not interfere with the gonadal response to increased day length (Hamner and Barfield, 1970; Menaker *et al.*, 1970), nor does it prevent the onset of refractoriness (Donham and Wilson, 1970). Pinealectomy, however, does abolish the free-running locomotor rhythm in constant darkness (Gaston and Menaker, 1968).

4. Summary

The evidence cited in this section rules out some of the more obvious explanations of the effect of photoperiod on the response to estrogen in gonadectomized canaries. However, it does not elucidate the mechanism involved: in particular, the roles of gonadotrophin-releasing hormones and of pineal factors remain open.

E.   INFLUENCE OF PHOTOPERIOD ON THE EFFECT OF EXOGENOUS HORMONES ON BUDGERIGAR NEST-BOX OCCUPATION

We have seen that budgerigar reproductive development is affected by the photoperiod, and that nest-box entry by the female is accelerated by estrogen. The question thus arises: Is the effectiveness of estrogen in inducing nest-box behavior photoperiod dependent in the budgerigar as is nest building in the canary?

In each of four experiments ovariectomized female budgerigars were injected with 0.1 mg estradiol benzoate three times weekly. One group was kept under 8L:16D and the other under 14L:10D. In each experiment a higher proportion of the birds kept on long photoperiods entered nest boxes, and did so with a shorter latency, than birds on short photoperiods. In two of the experiments the latency difference was significant. Furthermore, those birds on the longer photoperiods that entered spent a larger proportion of the light period in the box than did those on short photoperiods. Autopsy results ruled out an explanation in terms of residual ovarian fragments (Gosney and Hinde, 1975).

Results similar in direction, but failing to reach statistical significance, were obtained in two experiments involving skeleton photoperiods (8L:16D versus 6L:2D:2L:14D versus 6L:6D:2L:10D in each case) (Gosney and Hinde, 1975).

This renders an explanation in terms of time available unlikely, and indicates that the influence of photoperiod on the effectiveness of estrogen, like that on egg laying, depends on circadian changes in photosensitivity.

F. INFLUENCE OF MALE SONG ON THE EFFECT
   OF EXOGENOUS ESTROGEN ON CANARY NEST BUILDING

Experiments reviewed in the preceding sections show that the photoperiod affects aspects of reproductive behavior in two ways: first, via the hypothalamus–pituitary–gonad route, leading to the production of endogenous hormones that affect behavior; and second, by influencing the effectiveness of those hormones in producing behavioral change. The light regime is not the only source of external stimulation that affects reproductive development, however: male courtship and song also play a role. This raises the question of whether stimuli from the male influence the effectiveness of estrogen in inducing nest building.

Ovariectomized canaries treated with estrogen were exposed to three photoperiods: 8L:16D, 12L:12D, and 14L:10D, tape-recorded canary song being played for alternate hours through the light period. Control groups, with no song, were run simultaneously (Fig. 7). The effect of male song was detectable on all photoperiods. On an 8-hr day no more birds were stimulated to build by hearing song than were stimulated by the photoperiod alone. Once stimulated by the photoperiod, however, individual birds in the upper quartile were induced to increase their amount of building by playing them male song. On a 12-hr day song seemed to summate with the photoperiod to stimulate the group as a whole to show an increase in gathering. No more birds placed than with the photoperiodic stimulus alone but the latency to placing was shortened. On a 14-hr day gathering was at a high level, but, even so, song increased the amount gathered on peak days. Nearly all birds placed in both 14-hr day groups but those hearing song had a decreased latency; they also placed more on peak placing days. This suggests that light is the primary factor in allowing or preventing nest building to occur in response to estrogen. Once a bird is building or is about to build, however, hearing male song can accelerate the response and increase the amount of building shown (Hinde and Steel, 1976).

These data do not show in themselves that the effect is specific to canary song, as any auditory stimulation might have produced the same effect. In a further experiment using a 12L:12D regime estrogen-treated, ovariectomized female canaries exposed to budgerigar song showed little difference in building behavior from controls not exposed to song, while canaries exposed to canary song built vigorously (Fig. 8).

No test of whether the birds were more likely to build when the song was actually playing was made; any tendency to do so would have to interact with the

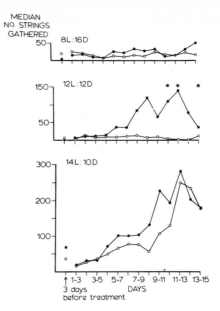

FIG. 7. The median numbers of strings gathered by estrogen-treated, ovariectomized female canaries kept on three different photoperiods and (●) exposed (song) or (○) not exposed (control) to tape-recorded male song. Gathering was measured on 3 days before the first estrogen injection and for 15 days thereafter. The data are given as 3-day running totals. The asterisk indicates that the difference between groups is significant, $p < 0.05$. (From Hinde and Steel, 1976.)

underlying diurnal variation in building activity that occurs in naturally breeding birds (Croft, 1975). Earlier observations indicated that the male of a pair of canaries was less likely to sing when the female was engaged in nest building than when she was not (Hinde, 1965). Song thus could help to initiate building activity in the female.

These data indicate that, just as long photoperiods appear to affect canary nest building by two routes, affecting both steroid production and the behavioral effectiveness of the steroids produced, so also does the song of the male. The next step is to ask whether there are circadian changes in sensitivity to song comparable with those in sensitivity to light.

Estrogen-treated, ovariectomized canaries were kept on 12L:12D: half were exposed to male song for the first 6 hr of the light period and half during the last 6 hr. The summary presented here is based on a combination of data from two replications of the experiment which gave closely similar results (Steel and Hinde, unpublished observations). On every measure (total and peak gathering and placing, proportion of birds placing and latency to placing) the early-song group had higher median scores, but the differences did not reach the 5% level of probability. The proportion of building performed in each half of the 12-hr day

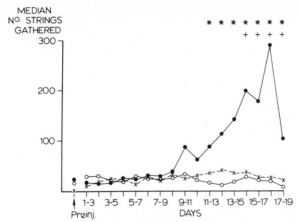

Fig. 8. The median numbers of strings gathered by estrogen-treated, ovariectomized female canaries kept on 12L:12D day and exposed to (●) tape-recorded male canary song (song); (×) budgerigar song (control–song); (○) to no song (control). Gathering was measured on three days before the first estrogen injection and for 19 days thereafter. The data are given as running 3-day totals. The asterisk indicates that the difference between control and song groups is significant, $p <$ 0.05. The plus indicates that the difference between control and control–song groups is significant, p < 0.05, Mann–Whitney U tests, one tailed. (From Hinde and Steel, 1976.)

was similar in both groups. Such differences as there were thus consisted of a higher level of building throughout the day in the early song group, and not of either an immediate effect of the song or a carryover of the effect of song into the quiet part of the day. Further experiments testing the response to song played at hours 0–3 or 6–9 after dawn failed to give consistent results; 3 hr of song per day may be too little to be stimulatory. Thus, if a diurnal effect of song is present, it appears to be weak. This is in contrast with the effect in the budgerigar (Section II.G) and may reflect the relative importance of day length and song in the reproductive cycles of the two ecologically distinct species.

G. Influence of Male Vocalizations on the Effect of Exogenous Hormones on Budgerigar Nest-Box Occupation

We have seen that male vocalizations are normally essential for reproductive development in female budgerigars. The question considered here is whether, as in canaries, male vocalizations act also to enhance the effectiveness of exogenous estrogen.

Using ovariectomized females kept on 14L:10D and treated with a combination of estrogen and prolactin to induce nest-box entry, Steel, Gosney, and Hinde (1977) assessed the effect of taped male vocalizations on the time spent in the nest box by the female. During 2-hr daily watches females spent more time in the nest box if exposed to male song than if exposed to no song. A comparison of two groups receiving either canary or budgerigar song showed that the females were clearly responding to the song of their own species; this induced them to spend significantly more time in the nest box.

Finally, the effect of budgerigar song played early or late in the day was assessed; the tape was played either during the first or the last 7 hr of the 14-hr day. All birds were watched daily both under the song-on and song-off conditions. There was no consistent tendency to spend more time in the nest early or late in the day and consequently no tendency to spend more time in the nest while the recording of male song was actually playing. Over all watches the early-song group spent a highly significantly greater amount of time in the nest box than the late-song group.

Thus, under closely controlled conditions, both species showed a marked effect of male song on their behavioral responsiveness to estrogen. Diurnal variation in the effectiveness of song was most noticeable in the budgerigar.

H.   INHIBITORY EFFECT OF STIMULI FROM THE NEST ON ESTROGEN-INDUCED NEST BUILDING IN THE CANARY

Feedback via tactile stimulation received from the nest is instrumental in bringing building to an end in the natural breeding season. In the laboratory active building can be reduced by substitution of an artificial nest of small internal diameter and grassy texture for the standard plastic canary pan (Hinde, 1958). Conversely, if the material placed daily in the nest by the female is constantly removed, a high rate of nest building is sustained for long periods (Hinde, 1965). In the intact female tactile stimulation could reduce nest building by lowering estrogen production or by altering the responsiveness of central mechanisms to continuing high estrogen levels. It was noticed that nest building can decline in the presence of high levels of exogenous estrogen and may even be replaced by a new behavior pattern, that of incubation (Hinde et al., 1974), suggesting that a modification in responsiveness to estrogen was the most likely of these alternatives.

This was tested by allowing two groups of ovariectomized estrogen-treated birds to build nests: one group had all material removed from the nest daily while the other was allowed to build undisturbed. Over a 26-day period the nest-removed birds carried over twice as much material to the nest as their controls. The general pattern of building differed between the two groups; typically the controls built actively on one or two days and subsequently added or removed only a few strings to or from the nest, while the nest-removed birds placed actively on a large number of days with wide daily fluctuations. The nest-removed groups had at least 4 days when the median amount placed was over

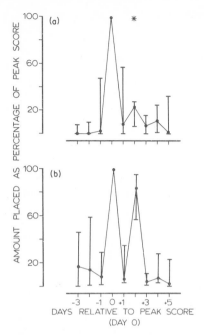

FIG. 9. Medians and interquartile ranges: (A) birds allowed to build undisturbed; (B) all nest material removed from nest pan daily. Peak placing scores (expressed as 100%) attained during a 26-day period for each bird are superimposed on Day 0. Placing scores of Days −3 to +5 are expressed as percentages of the Day 0 placing score. The asterisk indicates that the difference between A and B on Day +2 is significant, $p < 0.01$, Mann–Whitney U test, one tailed. (From Steel and Hinde, 1977.)

50% of their peak score, whereas the control group never attained 50% of their peak score. The peak day of placing was followed by a day of reduced placing in both groups. This was followed by a recovery to near peak value by the birds whose nests were removed but by a sustained suppression of placing by the control birds (Fig. 9). Three out of seven controls established incubation (Steel and Hinde, 1977).

These data show that high levels of estrogen are not incompatible with a decline in nest building or with incubation behavior. It is therefore possible that, in intact birds, stimuli from the nest exert an inhibitory effect on nest building not (or not only) by reducing ovarian estrogen output but by interfering with the effectiveness of the steroid in inducing the behavior. If the nest material is removed, this inhibitory effect is largely dissipated over 24 hr, but the continued presence of the nest and/or contact of the bird with it prolongs the inhibition of building behavior.

III. Discussion and Review

A. Summary of Findings with Canaries and Budgerigars

In our experiments the influence of day length and song on the behavioral effects of estrogen are unlikely to have been mediated by an increased output of gonadal estrogen. All experiments involved gonadectomized or refractory birds; although ovariectomy was sometimes incomplete, a variety of lines of evidence indicates that the presence of remaining ovarian fragments was not crucial. In the case of photostimulation, an increase in the amount of time available for building appears to be highly improbable as an explanation of the data: the problem, of course, does not arise in the experiments involving song. No evidence for the view that nest building resulted from a synergistic effect of estrogen and pituitary gonadotrophins could be found.

The data given above show clearly that two classes of external stimuli affect behavior in two avian species not only by influencing the production of gonadal steroids, but also by influencing the effectiveness of these steroids. Although ovarian hormones are necessary for nest-oriented behavior to be shown, the amount of behavior is increased by longer photoperiods and by vocal stimuli from the male. In the canary yet a third external factor has been found to modify the consequences of constant steroid levels on behavior; stimuli from the nest reduce nest building even when estrogen levels remain high.

B. The Hormonal–External Stimulus Interaction

These results are in harmony with the view, obtained from studies of a number of species, that the role of gonadal steroids on sexual behavior can be regarded as normally necessary rather than as primary and sufficient; a complex interplay of developmental and experiential processes, morphological changes, and external stimuli determines the final expression of the behavior. We have tended (because of the historical development of the study of sexual behavior) to emphasize that external factors enhance the behavioral effect of hormones, but it would be equally justifiable to say that hormones enhance the effect of external factors on behavior. For example, in the female rat the sensory field of the pudendal nerve is enlarged under the influence of estrogen, making her more sensitive to male stimulation during estrus (Komisaruk et al., 1972; Kow and Pfaff, 1973); in the canary the brood-patch sensitivity to tactile stimulation increases during the breeding season under gonadal control, making stimuli received from the nest more effective in influencing building behavior (Hinde et al., 1963). Until the mechanisms involved in behavior have been worked out in detail, it would be wiser to consider the control of behavior as a network of interactions rather than to assume that the hormones are primary. In contrast, the nonbehavioral effects of hormones appear not to be influenced by these external factors: we found no effect of current external stimuli on the response of oviducts to estrogen. Rosenblatt (1965) made a similar point with regard to the effects of experience, suggesting that one could equally well say either that experience increases the effectiveness of hormones in activating the sexual behavior of male cats, or that hormones increase the effectiveness of experience (see also Beach, 1944, 1951).

C. Can Photoperiod and Male Song Be Regarded as Eliciting Stimuli?

It has been shown for a number of hormone-dependent responses (e.g., Baerends *et al.*, 1955; Beach, 1942; Komisaruk, 1971) that low hormone levels can be compensated for by increasing the strength of the eliciting stimuli, and vice versa. It is possible that male song has an eliciting effect on female nest-oriented behavior, and it could therefore be that the song experiments alone do not demand the postulation of any other mechanism. It does not seem reasonable, however, to describe the effect of photoperiod on nest building as one of elicitation, especially as, in some circumstances at least, building can occur under very low light levels (Steel, unpublished observations, 1974). In the final analysis any absolute distinction between the eliciting effects of stimuli, the effects of stimuli on "mood" [defined as a state of responsiveness to (other) external stimuli], and hormone-mediated effects of stimuli on reproductive condition, may, of course, prove elusive. In the meantime, however, we incline to the view that the influence of photoperiod on the nest-oriented behavior of these birds, and perhaps also that of song, are neither mediated by the hypothalamus–pituitary–gonad system nor can be described in terms of these traditional paradigms of hormone-stimulus interactions.

D. Are the Mechanisms by which External Factors Affect the Hypothalamus–Pituitary–Gonad Axis the Same as Those by which They Influence the Effectiveness of Steroids?

Since neither the mechanisms by which either photostimulation or male vocalizations affect the hypothalamus–pituitary–gonad axis, nor those by which they influence the behavioral effects of hormones, are fully known, we can say little about how much they have in common. However, a few points are worth making.

1. Male and Photoperiod Can Act Synergistically

Evidence from other species indicates that the effects of stimulation from the mate can be masked if photostimulation is producing near maximal reproductive development. Thus, in unilaterally castrated male doves Cheng (1976) found a greater compensatory growth of the left testis in birds exposed to a female than in isolated males. However, this occurred only when the birds were kept on short days; the long days were in themselves adequate for testis growth, and the presence of the female produced no additional effect. Similarly, Schwab and Lott (1969) found that the presence of females delayed testes involution and photorefractoriness at the end of the breeding season on a 12-hr day but that this effect was not seen on a 14-hr day. These reports suggest that long photoperiods may mask the effect of other stimuli. However, none of these studies throws light on the exact pathways by which these stimuli have their effect.

The current experiments indicate that male song and photoperiod can also compensate for each other in their influence on the behavioral effectiveness of steroids. For instance, the effect of male song on the nest building of intact female canaries was slight on a 14-hr day, where light alone induced near maximal behavior (Section II.C.2.a), but was evident in females kept on an 11-hr day (see also Fig. 7).

2. Stimulation from Male and Photoperiod Normally Act at Different Stages of the Reproductive Cycle

Although photostimulation and stimuli from the male can compensate for each other, they normally act at different stages in the breeding cycle. In the canary, changes in daylength alone can initiate reproductive development. Thus, the start of defeathering was unaffected by the presence of a mate, but the completion of defeathering and the occurrence of nest building were. The few isolated females that laid eggs also built nests and completed reproductive development at the same time as paired females. It therefore seems likely that the male accelerates the development initiated by the photoperiod, and later on stimuli from the nest integrate later stages of reproductive development (Warren and Hinde, 1961; Hinde and Steel, 1965).

The effectiveness of the courtship of male ring doves also varies with the stage of the cycle. Cheng (1974) paired doves at different stages of ovarian development with intact or castrated male birds to evaluate different levels of courtship on ovulation. When the females' ovarian development was already advanced, castrated males were effective in stimulating further ovarian development to egg laying. However, the courtship activity of intact males was necessary for stimulating the early stages of follicular growth.

3. Diurnal Changes in Effectiveness

These experiments indicate that the diurnal rhythm of responsiveness is similar for both effects of each type of external stimulus, but differs between the stimuli. In both canary and budgerigar the influence of light both on the hypothalamus–pituitary–gonad axis and on the effectiveness of steroids involves a diurnal rhythm with peak sensitivity late in the day. In the budgerigar both effects of male vocalization were more effective early in the day, and a similar tendency is found in the canary (Sections II.F and G).

Short-term changes in tissue responsivity, usually with a marked diurnal rhythm, are well known and are being used increasingly in chemotherapy (Simpson, 1974). The diurnal changes in responsiveness of pigeon crop sac tissue to prolactin has been studied by Meier *et al.* (1971); fat deposition and mobilization, also controlled by prolactin, show similar daily fluctuations (Meier, 1972). Similar diurnal changes in the effects of hormones on behavior have been found, although the level at which the changes in responsiveness lie remains to be discovered. Thus, male ring doves with chronic hypothalamic implants of androgen, which induce nest building, show the behavior only at certain times of day (Erickson and Hutchison, 1977). Steel and Hinde (unpublished observations) found that estrogen-injected refractory female canaries showed both nest-building and incubation behavior, but with nest building confined mainly to the first half of a 16-hr day and incubation mainly to the latter half.

E. SEASONAL CHANGES IN THE BEHAVIORAL EFFECTIVENESS
    OF STEROIDS IN OTHER SPECIES

The influence of steroids on reproductive behavior has been shown to vary in some other seasonally breeding species. Typically the behavioral refractoriness to steroids occurs outside the normal breeding season.

In the red deer stag (*Cervus elaphus*) both sexual and social–aggressive behavior are androgen dependent, but sexual (rutting) behavior is limited to two months in the autumn. Studies involving castration and the implantation of long-acting testosterone pellets into castrated or intact free-living animals have revealed a differential effect of testosterone on social and sexual behavior (Lincoln *et al.*, 1972). Briefly, castration abolished both aggressive and sexual behavior. Testosterone can restore aggressiveness at any time of year, although the mode of fighting and its outcome are affected by a seasonal effect of the hormones on antler growth. Implanted animals showed rutting behavior only at the appropriate time of year, although testosterone levels were high both before and after this brief period. Breeding in this species is dependent on daylength; reproductive development occurs in response to declining daylength. The specific effect of testosterone on sexual behavior only during the autumn suggests an effect of daylength on the behavioral effectiveness of testosterone, but this has not been tested experimentally.

There is clear evidence that the responsiveness of the ewe to ovarian hormones varies throughout the year. Sheep, like the red deer, breed in response to declining photoperiods, and show repeated 16-day ovarian cycles during a restricted period of a few months. In spayed ewes estrus may be induced by priming with progesterone followed by a single injection of estrogen; in intact ewes a 17-day period of progesterone treatment is followed by a rise in ovarian estrogen and by behavioral heat. The following results are based on the use of these two techniques.

Raeside and McDonald (1959) found a clear seasonal pattern over 2½ years in the proportions of spayed ewes coming into estrus after a standard hormone treatment. The highest percentage of response corresponded with declining day lengths and to the period when normal untreated ewes would be cycling (Reardon and Robinson, 1961). These studies are open to criticism, however, in that behavioral estrus can only be measured by the ewes' response to the ram; there was no control over possible seasonal changes in the ram's stimulus quality. Fletcher and Lindsay (1971) found that, as the breeding season approached, intact ewes showed a decrease in the interval between the last progesterone injection and the start of estrus; furthermore, the estrous period was lengthened. Groups of spayed ewes treated either during decreasing daylengths (autumn) or increasing daylengths (spring) showed highly significant seasonal differences. The latency to estrus was longer and its duration shorter in spring. Estrogen dosage is positively related to incidence of estrus and to its duration and negatively related to its onset. Such seasonal differences could depend on a changing threshold of responsiveness to estrogen or to changes in estrogen uptake (Fletcher and Lindsay, 1971; Scaramuzzi et al., 1971).

Many rodent species are seasonal breeders (Sadleir, 1969), but so far the hamster has been investigated in the greatest detail. This species responds to day length through a circadian rhythm of photosensitivity (Section II.C.1.a), the males breed only on daylengths exceeding 12.5 hr (Elliott et al., 1972). An attempt to show behavioral refractoriness to steroids in short-day hamsters has been made by Morin et al. (1977). Ovariectomized, hormone-injected females on both long and short days responded with lordosis to an active male; unfortunately the latency and duration of estrus, which would be more likely to show a difference, were not assessed. The mating response of males, castrated and kept on long or short days for 12 weeks and then implanted with testosterone for 4 weeks, varied with the day length. A smaller proportion of animals showed intromission and ejaculation on short days than on long days.

In the ring dove Hutchison (1974a) found a slight effect of photoperiod on the restoration of behavior in long-term castrates by means of intrahypothalamic implants of testosterone. One behavioral component of courtship failed to reappear on a short day but did so on a long day.

The stickleback (Gasterosteus aculeatus) is a seasonally breeding fish with a marked photoperiodic response (Baggerman, 1972). Hoar (1962) gives data on the nest-building response of castrated males given testosterone on long and short days. Statistical evaluation of his data by the present authors revealed highly significant differences; fewer fishes kept on an 8-hr day built nests, and did so with a much longer latency (median intergroup differences 20 days), than fishes kept on a 16-hr day. This finding is remarkably similar to that found with canaries.

Thus, a number of species show what appear to be daylength-dependent differences in responsiveness to steroids. Of course, it must be emphasized that there is no evidence so far of any common mechanism underlying these phenomena.

F. OTHER STUDIES SHOWING CHANGES IN THE BEHAVIORAL EFFECTIVENESS OF STEROIDS

A number of other studies have demonstrated changes in the behavioral effectiveness of steroids. These changes, which can occur throughout life, are often mediated by the steroids themselves.

The organizing effects of perinatal hormones may involve permanent changes in sensitivity as the central nervous system develops into a "male" or a "female" pattern (Gorski, 1971). In the rat androgens acting perinatally allow both central and peripheral tissues, which mediate reproduction, to be appropriately activated by testosterone in the adult male. During this critical period, androgens may cause anatomical differentiation of the brain and/or change the sensitivity of central neurons to steroids. For example, they may increase the responsivity of certain tissues (e.g., spinal cord) to testosterone and decrease the responsiveness of brain areas controlling adult sexual behavior to estrogen and progesterone. Estrogen given perinatally to female rats can decrease the number of estrogen receptors in the adult brain (for a review see Feder and Wade, 1971).

Around the time of puberty in the rat increasing levels of testosterone further sensitize the tissues mediating mating behavior to androgens. As the sensitivity of the target tissue is increased a change from a pubertal to an adult pattern of sexual behavior occurs (Larrson, 1967).

In adults of both sexes several examples of a post-castration decline in responsiveness to gonadal steroids have been found. In the male ring dove (*Streptopelia risoria*) Hutchison (1969, 1974b) found that the hormonal thresholds for restoration of reproductive behavior with intrahypothalamic implants rose with the interval between castration and hormone replacement. The three behavioral components that he measured also had their own individual levels of hormone sensitivity and declined at different rates after castration. Latency to reappearance of the behaviors after treatment was again dependent on the castration–treatment interval, suggesting that testosterone first needed to resensitize the hypothalamus before it could have an activating effect. Similar effects with systemic hormones have been found in male rats (Davison, 1972) and hamsters (Morin *et al.*, 1977), in which continuous low dosage with testosterone maintained the behavioral mechanism in a state of immediate responsiveness to an activating dose of the hormone. The estrogenic control of female sexual behavior in the rat appears to function similarly (Damassa and Davidson, 1973; Beach and Orndoff, 1974).

One direct effect of light on estrogen uptake has been found (Illei-Donhoffer *et al.*, 1974). After exposure to constant light a reduction in estrogen-binding receptor proteins was found in the hypothalami of female rats. Such rats do not ovulate spontaneously. Reduced sensitivity to circulating estrogen has been postulated to account for the absence of positive estrogen feedback in causing the normal preovulatory surge of LH. Reduction in estrogen-binding capacity could explain this deficiency.

G. CONCLUSIONS

Considerable progress in dissecting apart the interacting effects of internal and external, behavioral, and physiological changes in sexual and parental behavior has come not only in the studies of birds cited earlier, but also in studies of mammals (e.g., rat sexual behavior, Adler, 1978; rodent maternal behavior, Rosenblatt and Lehrman, 1963; cat maternal behavior, Rosenblatt and Schneirla, 1962). We believe that the data reviewed here for two avian species demonstrate that external factors may affect not only the production of steroid hormones but also their effectiveness in influencing behavior.

Of the two factors in question, the photoperiod at least is not a direct elicitor of the nest-oriented behavior we studied: it must influence the probability of that behavior both by affecting steroid output and by another mechanism that we have not yet elucidated. We would suggest that a further search for such effects in mammals would be likely to be profitable, although, of course, the mechanisms underlying any such effects might well be different.

Acknowledgments

This work was supported by the Medical Research Council and the Royal Society. We are grateful to the National Institutes of Health, Bethesda, for supplying (ovine) prolactin. We would also like to thank R. Putman, G. B. Shellswell, and Susan Gosney, who assisted with some of the experiments, and L. Bardon who prepared the figures.

References

Adler, N. T. 1978. On the mechanisms of sexual behaviour and their evolutionary constraints. *In* "Biological Determinants of Sexual Behaviour" (J. B. Hutchison, ed.). Wiley, New York.
Assenmacher, I. 1973. Reproductive endocrinology: the hypothalamo–hypophyseal axis. *In* "Breeding Biology of Birds" (D. S. Farner, ed.), pp. 158–191. Nat. Acad. Sci., Washington, D.C.

Baerends, G. P., Brouwer, R., and Waterbolk, H. Tj. 1955. Ethological studies on *Lebistes reticulatus*. I. An analysis of the male courtship pattern. *Behaviour* **8**, 249–335.

Baggerman, B. 1972. Photoperiodic responses in the stickleback and their control by a daily rhythm of sensitivity. *Gen. Comp. Endocrinol. Suppl.* **3**, 466–476.

Beach, F. A. 1942. Importance of progesterone to induction of sexual receptivity in spayed female rats. *Proc. Soc. Exp. Biol. Med.* **50**, 369–371.

Beach, F. A. 1944. Relative effects of androgen upon the mating behavior of male rats subjected to forebrain injury or castration. *J. Exp. Zool.* **97**, 249–295.

Beach, F.A. 1951. Effects of forebrain injury upon mating behavior in male pigeons. *Behaviour* **4**, 36–59.

Beach, F. A., & Orndoff, R. K. 1974. Variation in responsiveness of female rats to ovarian hormones as a function of preceding hormonal deprivation. *Horm. Behav.* **5**, 201–205.

Brockway, B. F. 1962. The effects of nest-entrance positions and male vocalizations on reproduction in budgerigars. *Living Bird* **1**, 93–101.

Brockway, B. F. 1965. Stimulation of ovarian development and egg laying by male courtship vocalization in budgerigars (*Melopsittacus undulatus*). *Anim. Behav.* **13**, 575–578.

Brockway, B. F. 1968. Influences of sex hormones on the loud and soft warbles of male budgerigars. *Anim. Behav.* **16**, 5–12.

Brockway, B. F. 1969. Roles of budgerigar vocalization in the integration of breeding behaviour. *In* "Bird Vocalizations" (R. A. Hinde, ed.), pp. 131–158. Cambridge Univ. Press, London and New York.

Bünning, E. 1936. Die endogene Tagesrhythmik als Grundlage der photoperiodischen Reaction. *Ber. Dtsch. Bot. Ges.* **54**, 590–607.

Cheng, M-F. 1974. Ovarian development in the female ring dove in response to stimulation by intact and castrated male ring doves. *J. Endocrinol.* **63**, 43–53.

Cheng, M-F. 1976. Interaction of lighting and other environmental variables on the activity of hypothalamo-hypophyseal–gonadal system. *Nature* **263**, 148–149.

Cheng, M-F. 1977. Role of gonadotrophin-releasing hormones in the reproductive behaviour of female ring doves (*Streptopelia risoria*). *J. Endocrinol.* **74**, 37–45.

Croft, D. B. 1975. The effect of photoperiod length on the diurnal activity of canaries. Ph.D. thesis, Cambridge University.

Damassa, D., and Davidson, J. M. 1973. Effects of ovariectomy and constant light on responsiveness to estrogen in the rat. *Horm. Behav.* **4**, 269–279.

Davidson, J. M. 1972. Hormones and reproductive behaviour. *In* "Reproductive Biology" (H. Balin and S. Glasser, eds.), pp. 877–918. Excerpta Medica, Amsterdam.

Donham, R. S., and Wilson, F. E. 1970. Photorefractoriness in pinealectomized Harris' Sparrows. *Condor* **72**, 101–102.

Elliott, J. A., Stetson, M. H., and Menaker, M. 1972. Regulation of testis function in goldem hamsters: A circadian clock measures photoperiodic time. *Science* **178**, 771–773.

Erickson, C. J., and Hutchison, J. B. 1977. Induction of nesting behaviour in male barbary doves by intracerebral androgen. *J. Reprod. Fertil.* **50**, 9–16.

Feder, H. H., and Wade, G. N. 1974. Integrative actions of perinatal hormones on neural tissues mediating adult sexual behavior. *In* "Third Neurosciences Study Program" (F. O. Schmitt and R. G. Worden, eds.), pp. 583–586. M.I.T. Press, Cambridge, Mass.

Fletcher, I. C., and Lindsay, D. R. 1971. Effect of oestrogen on oestrous behaviour and its variation with season in the ewe. *J. Endocrinol.* **50**, 685–696.

Follett, B. K. 1973. Circadian rhythms and photoperiodic time measurement in birds. *J. Reprod. Fertil. Suppl.* **19**, 5–18.

Follet, B. K., and Sharp, P. J. 1969. Circadian rhythmicity in photoperiodically induced gonadotropin release and gonadal growth in the quail. *Nature* **223**, 968–971.

Follett, B. K., Scanes, C. G., and Cunningham, F. J. 1972. A radioimmunoassay for avian luteinizing hormone. *J. Endocrinol.* **52**, 359–378.

Follett, B. K., Hinde, R. A., Steel, E., and Nicholls, T. J. 1973. The influence of photoperiod on nest-building, ovarian development and LH secretion in canaries (*Serinus canarius*). *J. Endocrinol.* **59**, 151–162.

Gaston, S., and Menaker, M. 1968. Pineal function: The biological clock in the sparrow. *Science* **160**, 1125–1127.

Gibson, W. R., Follett, B. K., and Gledhill, B. 1975. Plasma levels of luteinizing hormone in gonadectomized Japanese Quail exposed to short or to long daylengths. *J. Endocrinol.* **64**, 87–101.

Gorski, R. A. 1971. Gonadal hormones and the perinatal development of neuroendocrine function. *In* "Frontiers of Neuroendocrinology" (L. Martini and W. F. Ganong, eds.), pp. 237–290. Oxford Univ. Press, London and New York.

Gosney, S., and Hinde, R. A. 1975. An oestrogen-mediated effect of photoperiod on the reproductive behavior of the budgerigar. *J. Reprod. Fertil.* **45**, 547–548.

Gosney, S., and Hinde, R. A. 1976. Changes in the sensitivity of female budgerigars to male vocalizations. *J. Zool. (London)* **179**, 407–410.

Hamner, W. M., and Barfield, R. J. 1970. Ineffectiveness of pineal lesions on the testis cycle of a finch. *Condor* **72**, 99–101.

Hinde, R. A. 1958. The nest-building behaviour of domesticated canaries. *Proc. Zool. Soc. London* **131**, 1–48.

Hinde, R. A. 1965. Interaction of internal and external factors in integration of canary reproduction. *In* "Sex and Behavior" (F. A. Beach, ed.), pp. 381–415. Wiley, New York.

Hinde, R. A. 1967. Aspects of the control of avian reproductive development within the breeding season. *Proc. Int. Ornithol. Congr.* **14**, 135–153.

Hinde, R. A., and Putman, R. J. 1973. Why budgerigars breed in continuous darkness. *J. Zool. London* **170**, 475–491.

Hinde, R. A., and Steel, E. 1966. Integration of the reproductive behaviour of female canaries. *Symp. Soc. Exp. Biol.* **20**, 401–426.

Hinde, R. A., and Steel, E. 1975. The dual role of daylength in controlling canary reproduction. *Symp. Zool. Soc. London* **35**, 245–259.

Hinde, R. A., and Steel, E. 1976. The effect of male song on an estrogen-dependent behavior pattern in the female canary (*Serinus canarius*). *Horm. Behav.* **7**, 293–304.

Hinde, R. A., Bell, R. Q., and Steel, E. 1963. Changes in sensitivity of the canary brood patch during the natural breeding season. *Anim. Behav.* **11**, 553–560.

Hinde, R. A., Steel, E., and Hutchison, R. E. 1971. Control of oviduct development in ovariectomized canaries by exogenous hormones. *J. Zool. London* **163**, 265–276.

Hinde, R. A., Steel, E., and Follett, B. K. 1974. Effect of photoperiod on oestrogen-induced nest-building in ovariectomized or refractory female canaries (*Serinus canarius*). *J. Reprod. Fertil.* **40**, 383–399.

Hoar, W. S. 1962. Reproductive behaviour in fish. *Gen. Comp. Endocrinol. Suppl.* **1**, 206–216.

Hutchison, J. B. 1969. Changes in hypothalamic responsiveness to testosterone in male Barbary doves. (*Streptopelia risoria*). *Nature (London)* **222**, 176–177.

Hutchison, J. B. 1974a. Effect of photoperiod on the decline in behavioural responsiveness to intra-hypothalamic androgen in doves (*Streptopelia risoria*). *J. Endocrinol.* **63**, 583–584.

Hutchison, J. B. 1974b. Post-castration decline in behavioural responsiveness to intrahypothalamic androgen in doves. *Brain Res.* **81**, 169–181.

Hutchison, R. E. 1971. The integration of reproductive behaviour in female budgerigars. Ph.D. thesis, Cambridge University.

Hutchison, R. E. 1975a. Influence of oestrogen on the initiation of nesting behaviour in female budgerigars. *J. Endocrinol.* **64**, 417–428.

Hutchison, R. E. 1975b. Effects of ovarian steroids and prolactin on the sequential development of nesting behaviour in female budgerigars. *J. Endocrinol.* **67**, 29–39.

Hutchison, R. E., Hinde, R. A., and Steel, E. 1967. Effects of oestrogen, progesterone and prolactin on brood patch formation in ovariectomized canaries. *J. Endocrinol.* **39**, 379–385.

Hutchison, R. E., Hinde, R. A., and Bendon, B. 1968. Oviduct development and its relation to other aspects of reproduction in domesticated canaries. *J. Zool. (London)* **155**, 87–102.

Illei-Donhoffer, A., Flerko, B., and Mess, B. 1974. Reduction of estradiol-binding capacity of neural target tissues in light-sterilized rats. *Neuroendocrinology*, **14**, 187–194.

Immelmann, K. 1963. Drought adaptations in Australian desert birds. *Proc. Int. Ornithol. Congr.* **13**, 649–657.

Immelmann, K. 1973. Role of the environment in reproduction as source of "predictive" information. *In* "Breeding Biology of Birds" (D. S. Farner, ed.), pp. 121–147.   Nat. Acad. Sci., Washington, D.C.

Komisaruk, B. R. 1971. Induction of lordosis in ovariectomized rats by stimulation of the vaginal cervix: Hormonal and neural interrelationships. *In* "Steroid Hormones and Brain Function" (C. H. Sawyer and R. A. Gorski, eds.), pp. 127–135. Univ. of California Press, Berkeley.

Komisaruk, B. R., Adler, W. T., and Hutchison, J. 1972. Genital sensory field: Enlargement by estrogen treatment in female rats. *Science* **178**, 1295–1298.

Kow, L. M., and Pfaff, D. W. 1973. Effects of estrogen treatment on the size of receptive field and response threshold of pudendal nerve in the female rat. *Neuroendocrinology* **13**, 299–313.

Larrson, K. 1967. Testicular hormone and developmental changes in mating behavior in the male rat. *J. Comp. Physiol. Psychol.* **63**, 233–230.

Lehrman, D. S. 1961. Gonadal hormones and parental behaviour in birds and infrahuman mammals. *In* "Sex and Internal Secretions" (W. C. Young, ed.), pp. 1268–1382. Williams & Wilkins, Baltimore.

Lehrman, D. S. 1965. Interaction between internal and external environments in the regulation of the reproductive cycle of the ring dove. *In* "Sex and Behavior" (F. A. Beach, ed.), pp. 355–380. Wiley, New York.

Lincoln, G. A., Guiness, F., and Short, R. V. 1972. The way in which testosterone controls the social and sexual behaviour of the red deer stag (*Cervus elaphus*). *Horm. Behav.* **3**, 373–396.

Lofts, B., and Murton, R. K. 1973. Reproduction in Birds. *In* "Avian Biology (D. S. Farner and J. R. King, eds.), Vol. III, pp. 1–107. Academic Press, New York.

Meier, A. H. 1972. Temporal synergism of prolactin and adrenal steroids. *Gen. Comp. Endocrinol. Suppl.* **3**, 499–508.

Meier, A. H., Burns, J. T., Davis, K. B., and John, T. M. 1971. Circadian variations in sensitivity of the Pigeon cropsac to prolactin. *J. Interdiscipl. Cycle Res.* **2**, 161–171.

Menaker, M., and Eskin, A. 1967. Circadian clock in photoperiodic time measurement: A test of the Bünning hypothesis. *Science* **157**, 1182–1184.

Menaker, M., Roberts, R., Elliott, J., and Underwood, H. 1970. Extraretinal light perception in the sparrow, Ill. The eyes do not participate in photoperiodic photoreception. *Proc. Natl. Acad. Sci. U.S.A.* **67**, 320–325.

Morin, L. P., Fitzgerald, K. M., Rusak, B., and Zucker, I. 1977. Circadian organization and neural mediation of hamster reproductive rhythms. *Psychoneuroendocrinology* **2**, 73–98.

Moss, R. L., and McCann, S. M. 1973. Induction of mating behaviour in rats by luteinizing hormone-releasing factor. *Science* **181**, 177.

Pfaff, D. W. 1973. Luteinizing hormone-releasing factor potentiates lordosis behaviour in hypophysectomized ovariectomized female rats. *Science* **182**, 1148–1149.

Pittendrigh, C. S., and Minis, D. H. 1964. The entrainment of circadian oscillations by light and their role as photoperiodic clocks. *Am. Nat.* **98**, 261–294.

Putman, R. J., and Hinde, R. A. 1973. Effects of the light regime and breeding experience on budgerigar reproduction. *J. Zool. (London)* **170**, 475–484.

Raeside, J. I., and McDonald, M. F. 1959. Seasonal changes in the oestrous response by the ovariectomized ewe to progesterone and oestrogen. *Nature (London)* **184**, 458–459.

Reardon, T. F., and Robinson, T. J. 1961. Seasonal variations in the reactivity to oestrogen of the ovariectomized ewe. *Aust. J. Agric. Res.* **12**, 320–326.

Reiter, R. J. 1975. Endocrine rhythms associated with pineal gland function. *In* "Biological rhythms and endocrine function" (L. W. Hedlund, J. M. Franz, and A. D. Kenny, eds.) (*Adv. in Exp. Med. Biol., Vol. 54*), pp. 43–73. Plenum, New York.

Rosenblatt, J. S. 1965. Effects of experience on sexual behavior in male cats. *In* "Sex and Behavior" (F. A. Beach, ed.), pp. 416–439. Wiley, New York.

Rosenblatt, J. S., and Lehrman, D. S. 1963. Maternal behavior of the laboratory rat. *In* "Maternal behavior in mammals" (H. L. Rheingold, ed.), pp. 8–57. Wiley, New York.

Rosenblatt, J. S., and Schneirla, T. C. 1962. The behaviour of cats. *In* "The behaviour of domestic animals" (E. S. E. Hafez, ed.), pp. 453–388. Baillière Tindall and Cox, London.

Rothwell, R., and Amadon, D. 1964. Ecology of the budgerigar. *Auk* **81**, 82.

Sadleir, R. M. F. S. 1969. "The ecology of reproduction in wild and domestic mammals." Methuen, London.

Scaramuzzi, R. J., Lindsay, D. R., and Shelton, J. N. 1971. The effect of oestradiol benzoate on the duration of oestrous behaviour in the ovariectomized ewe. *J. Endocrinol.* **50**, 345–346.

Schwab, R. G., and Lott, D. F. 1969. Testis growth and regression in starlings (*Sturnus vulgaris*) as a function of the presence of females. *J. Exp. Zool.* **171**, 39–42.

Shellswell, G. B., Gosney, S., and Hinde, R. A. 1975. Photoperiodic control of budgerigar reproduction: Circadian changes in sensitivity. *J. Zool. London* **175**, 53–60.

Simpson, H. W. 1974. Medical chronobiology: Past, present and future. *Chronobiologia* **1**, 131–136.

Steel, E., and Hinde, R. A. 1963. Hormonal control of brood patch and oviduct development in domesticated canaries. *J. Endocrinol.* **26**, 11–24.

Hinde, R. A., and Steel, E. 1965. Integration of reproductive behaviour in female canaries. *Symp. Soc. Exp. Biol.* **20**, 401–426.

Steel, E., and Hinde, R. A. 1966a. Effect of artificially increased day length in winter on female domesticated canaries. *J. Zool. (London)* **149**, 1–11.

Steel, E., and Hinde, R. A. 1966b. Effect of exogenous serum gonadotrophin (PMS) on aspects of reproductive development in female domesticated canaries. *J. Zool. (London)* **149**, 12–30.

Steel, E., and Hinde, R. A. 1972a. Influence of photoperiod on oestrogenic induction of nest-building in canaries. *J. Endocrinol.* **55**, 265–278.

Steel, E., and Hinde, R. A. 1972b. Influence of photoperiod on PMSG-induced nest-building in canaries. *J. Reprod. Fertil.* **31**, 425–431.

Steel, E., and Hinde, R. A. 1976. Effect of a skeleton photoperiod on the daylength dependent response to oestrogen in canaries (*Serinus canarius*). *J. Endocrinol.* **70**, 247–254.

Steel, E., and Hinde, R. A. 1977. Inhibition of oestrogen-induced nest-building in the canary (*Serinus canarius*) by stimuli from the nest. *J. Reprod. Fertil.* **49**, 151–153.

Steel, E., Gosney, S., and Hinde, R. A. 1977. Effect of male vocalizations on the nest-occupation response of female budgerigars to oestrogen and prolactin. *J. Reprod. Fertil.* **49**, 123–125.

Van Tienhoven, A., Sutherland, C., and Saatman, R. R. 1966. The effects of exposure to darkness on the reproductive and hypothalamo–hypophyseal system of budgerigars (*Melopsittacus undulatus*). *Gen. Comp. Endocrinol.* **6**, 420–427.

Vaugien, L. 1951. Ponte induite chez la Perruche ondulée maintenue a l'obscurité dans l'ambiance des volières. *C. R. Hebd. Seances Acad. Sci. Paris*, **232**, 1706–1708.

Vaurie, C. 1959. "The birds of the palearctic fauna." Witherby Ltd., London.

Warren, R. P., and Hinde, R. A. 1959. The effect of oestrogen and progesterone on the nest-building of domesticated canaries. *Anim. Behav.* **7**, 209–213.

Warren, R. P., and Hinde, R. A. 1961. Roles of the male and the nest-cup in controlling the reproduction of female canaries. *Anim. Behav.* **9**, 64–67.

White, S. J. and Hinde, R. A. 1968. Temporal relations of brood patch development, nest-building and egg-laying in domesticated canaries. *J. Zool. London* **155**, 145–155.

Wilson, F. E. and Follett, B. K. 1974. Plasma and pituitary luteinizing hormone in intact and castrated tree sparrows (*Spizella arborea*) during a photo-induced gonadal cycle. *Gen. Comp. Endocrinol.* **23**, 82–93.

Zigmond, R. E. 1975a. Target cells for gonadal steroids in the brain: studies of hormone binding and metabolism. *In* "Neural and Endocrine Aspects of Behaviour in Birds" (P. Wright, P. G. Caryl, and D. M. Vowles, eds.), pp. 111–121. Elsevier, Amsterdam.

Zigmond, R. E. 1975b. Binding, metabolism and action of steroid hormones in the central nervous system. *In* "Handbook of Psychopharmacology" (L. L. Iversen, S. D. Iversen, and S. H. Snyder, eds.), pp. 239–328. Plenum, New York.

Ethological Aspects of Chemical Communication in Ants

BERT HÖLLDOBLER

DEPARTMENT OF BIOLOGY
HARVARD UNIVERSITY
MUSEUM OF COMPARATIVE ZOOLOGY LABORATORIES
CAMBRIDGE, MASSACHUSETTS

I. INTRODUCTION

The complex organization of an ant society depends on the efficiency of many different forms of communication, involving a diversity of mechanical and chemical cues. The functional division into reproductive and sterile castes, the cooperation in rearing the young, in gathering food, defending the nest, exploring new foraging grounds, and establishing territorial borders are regulated by the precise transmission of these signals in time and space. Probably the best studied communication behavior in ants is chemical communication. Chemical releasers, or *pheromones* as they are commonly called, are produced in a variety of exocrine glands. When these communicative secretions are discharged to the outside, they usually release a specific behavioral response in members of the same species. In recent years considerable progress has been made in chemically identifying many of these pheromones. In this report, however, I will not emphasize the natural product chemistry of ant pheromones (for review see Wilson 1971; Law and Regnier 1971; Blum 1974), so much as concentrate on the ethological aspects of chemical communication in ants.

II. Communication between Sexual Stages

Males and females of social insects, no less than those of solitary insects, must communicate in order to find each other. Although female sex attractants have been demonstrated in many insect orders, the experimental evidence for sexual communication in ants is still scarce. The reason for this might be that most ant species have a short nuptial flight period, which occurs only once a year. Consequently, in only a few species can the reproductive behavior be studied in the laboratory. Nevertheless, more recent data demonstrate that in ants sexual behavior is regulated by chemical signals at least in part.

In the carpenter ant (*Camponotus herculeanus*) it has been demonstrated that the mass takeoff during the nuptial flight of both sexes is synchronized by a strongly smelling secretion released from the mandibular glands of the males. The males release this synchronizing pheromone during the peak of the swarming activity, at which time the females are stimulated to take off also (Hölldobler and Maschwitz, 1965). Although several compounds from the male mandibular glands are now chemically identified (Brand *et al.*, 1973; Falke, 1968), the effective component seems still to remain unknown. The mechanisms by which the females are attracted to one another after they have left the nest, as well as those controlling copulatory behavior, were only recently uncovered in a few species.

In the ponerine species *Rhytidoponera metallica* alate females are either absent or rare and apparently do not play a role in colony reproduction. Instead a portion of workers, externally morphologically indistinguishable from their fellows, possess functional spermatheca, are inseminated by males, and serve as reproductives in the colony (Whelden, 1960; Haskins and Whelden 1965). Since none of these worker reproductives or "ergatoids" has wings by which they can conduct nuptial flights, they have to employ other means to advertise their "readiness" for mating and attract flying males. We have now succeeded in analyzing the female sexual calling behavior in *Rhytidoponera metallica* (Hölldobler and Haskins, 1977). Ergatoid *R. metallica* emerge from the nest and group quietly near their nest entrance, with the head and thorax lowered to the ground, the gaster raised and arched, and the intersegmental membrane between the last two segments dorsally extended (Fig. 1). Males flying out from other nests are attracted by these "calling" females. On drawing close to a female the male first touches her with his antennae, then grasps the female's thorax with the mandibles. While riding on her back, he extends his copulatory apparatus in search of the female's genitalia. If she is ready to mate, she turns her abdomen slightly to the side, so that the male is able to couple. Then the male releases his mandibular grip on the female's thorax. With the pair in this position the copulation can last from a few seconds to several minutes (Fig. 1). During calling the female exposes a large, hitherto unrecognized gland, which opens dorsally between the last two abdomi-

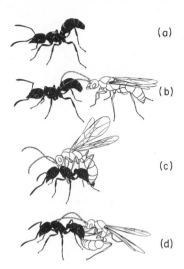

(a)

(b)

(c)

(d)

FIG. 1. Mating in *Rhytidoponera metallica*. From above: (a) Ergatoid female (black) in calling posture, during which the dorsal intersegmental membrane between the last two segments is extended. (b) A male (white) approaches a calling female, touching her with his antennae. (c) The male grasps the female at the thorax and mounts her. Simultaneously he extends his copulatory organ in a search for the female's genitals. (d) Copulation: the male has released his mandibular grip on the female's thorax. The drawings are based on photographs and observations. (From Hölldobler and Haskins, 1977.)

nal tergites (Fig. 2). We called this organ the *tergal gland* and were able to demonstrate that its secretions release agitated locomotion and attraction in *R. metallica* males. When several males were exposed to tergal gland secretions, some of them attempted to mount one another. When a worker was made available, some males tried to mate with it, even though it was not "calling." These results strongly suggest that some *Rhytidoponera metallica* workers discharge a sex attractant from the tergal gland during sexual calling. A similar calling behavior has been described in the myrmicine ant *Harpagoxenus sublaevis*, the calling females of which release a sex pheromone from the poison gland (Buschinger, 1968, 1972). Similarly we could demonstrate that another myrmicine species, *Xenomyrmex floridanus*, produces a sex pheromone in the poison gland, while a third, pharaoh's ant (*Monomorium pharaonis*), manufactures it in the Dufour's gland (Hölldobler, 1971a; Hölldobler and Wüst, 1973).

This leads us to another very little investigated aspect of reproductive behavior in ants, namely, the behavioral mechanisms of reproductive isolation in closely related sympatrically living species. In some areas of the southwestern United States several·species of the harvester ant (*Pogonomyrmex*) do coexist in the same habitat. Our recent investigations demonstrated that the sympatric species

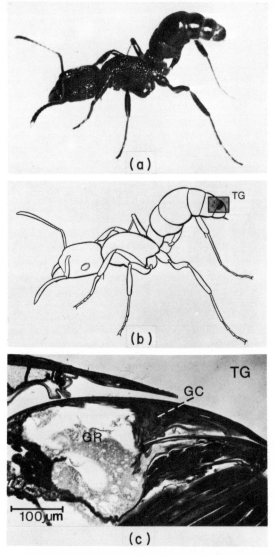

FIG. 2. *Rhytidoponera metallica* female in calling posture (a). Note the expanded intersegmental membrane between the last two tergites, the location where the tergal gland (TG) opens to the outside (b). (c) Longitudinal section through the gaster of a *R metallica* female, showing the tergal gland (TG) with its glandular cells (GC) and reservoir (GR). (From Hölldobler and Haskins, 1977.)

Pogonomyrmex maricopa, P. desertorum, P. barbatus, and *P. rugosus* are reproductively isolated in part by their distinct daily nuptial flight rhythms (Hölldobler, 1977a). *Pogonomyrmex maricopa* swarms in the morning between the hours of 10:00 and 11:30, followed by *P. desertorum* (11:00–13:00), while the remaining two species conduct their nuptial flights in the afternoon (*P. barbatus* 15:30–17:00; *P. rugosus* 16:30–18:00). In addition, however, these species are also separated by the use of communal mating sites. For example, an intensive search for the mating aggregations of *P. rugosus* over an area of about 360,000 square meters revealed a single place on the ground to which winged reproductive forms from a wide area converged, primarily by flying upwind. This arena was approximately 60 × 80 m. The first individuals to arrive were males, which alighted and ran about in a frenzied manner. Soon afterward females also began to arrive. As soon as each female alighted, she was surrounded by 3–10 males (Fig. 3). At the height of the activity thousands of such mating clusters literally covered the ground, with as many as 50 mating clusters concentrated in 1 m².

Females often copulated with as many as four males in succession. After mating, the females freed themselves from the surrounding males, climbed on grass leaves, and took off again from the mating arena. Some of them flew long distances (more than 100 m), others only short distances before landing a second time. Then each shed her wings and started to excavate a shallow nest chamber in the soil. General activity in the mating arena lasted about 2 hr, ceasing altogether around 19:00 hr. By this time almost all females had left, and the males were beginning to withdraw into shelters around the aggregation area such as crevices beneath grass clumps or little holes in the soil. There the males remained clustered overnight and through the following day until 15:00–16:00, when they become active again. Then, as on the preceding day, new males arrived in the

FIG. 3. Mating cluster of *Pogonomyrmex rugosus*. A female is surrounded by approximately 10 males. (From Hölldobler, 1976b.)

mating arena, and shortly afterwards new females flew in. These cycles continued for three additional consecutive days.

In the following two years we found mating aggregations of *P. rugosus* in the same arena. Two additional *P. rugosus* arenas were found, one about 1000 m and the other about 900 m distant from the first site. These also appeared again in the same two areas the following year.

Similar observations were made with *P. barbatus*. Of a total of eight mating sites, five were utilized again in the following year. Their areas varied from approximately 10 × 20 m to 40 × 50 m. As in *P. rugosus,* males formed sleeping aggregations and stayed at the places up to seven consecutive days. Somewhat different behavior was displayed by the two remaining species of *Pogonomyrmex*. Unlike *P. barbatus* and *P. rugosus,* which aggregated on the ground, *P. maricopa* and *P. desertorum* selected trees or bushes (approximately 2–4 m high) to gather for mating activities. Although there seems to be greater flexibility in choosing specific trees, we found four particular trees that served repeatedly as mating sites in two consecutive years.

No topographic cues have yet been found that characterize the specific traditional communal mating arenas. In all four species, however, the males discharge a mandibular gland secretion upon landing at the site. The sweet odor of the secretion, which apparently stems from one of its two major components, 4-methyl-3-heptanone or the respective alcohol (McGurk *et al.,* 1966), can sometimes be smelled by observers 10–15 m downwind. Since the males as well as the females approach the site by flying upwind, it seemed likely that they are attracted by this specific pheromone. We plan to test this hypothesis in the near future.

How do the males recognize their reproductive partners, and how is sexual behavior released once the sexuals have assembled at the mating sites? Our experimental results clearly demonstrated that poison gland secretions of *Pogonomyrmex* females stimulate sexual behavior in *Pogonomyrmex* males. In addition, circumstantial evidence strongly indicates that a species-specific surface pheromone is also involved, and that this substance is perceived by the males only when they approach closely enough to make direct antennal contact (Hölldobler, 1977a).

In insects only honeybee drones have been known to assemble every year at the same locations (Zwarlicki and Morse, 1963; Ruttner and Ruttner, 1965, 1972; Strang 1970). Our investigations of the mating strategies of the four sympatric *Pogonomyrmex* species revealed what appears to be the first vertebratelike lek system known in ants. Usually in a vertebrate lek, males occupy small personal territories in which they engage in special displays. Females, which are attracted to the leks, presumably by the communal display, choose one of the males, in some cases after comparing the individual male displays. Although *Pogonomyrmex* males do not occupy personal territories, male competition is extremely high and, as in other leks, females seem to be able to select for especially persistent male partners. Presumably females are more strongly attracted to areas where many males are assembled and where they have a choice, in comparison to single males. In fact it is expected that the female's choice strategy forces male aggregations. On the other hand, as Alexander (1975, p. 71) nas pointed out, "once mating is largely or entirely restricted to male aggregations . . . every male profits from cooperation." It is obvious that large groups of *Pogonomyrmex* males that discharge a lek pheromone collectively attract a larger number of females. It thus appears to us that the courting assemblies of harvester ants resemble in many ways the lek behavior of vertebrates.

III. ALARM COMMUNICATION

Like many solitary insects, social insects use chemicals to repel predators. In social insects, however, defensive responses are closely connected with alarm communication. In many cases the discharge of alarm pheromones and defensive substances is accompanied by characteristic body movements and postures (Fig. 4). The species of *Formica* spray mixtures of formic acid and Dufour's gland

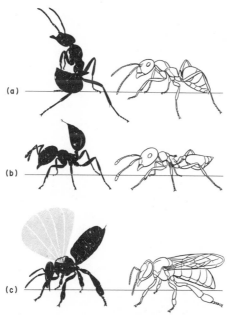

FIG. 4. The alarm-defense behavior (black) is contrasted with the normal posture (white). (a) *Formica polyctena*; (b) *Crematogaster ashmeadi*; (c) *Apis mellifera*. (From Hölldobler, 1970b.)

secretions, both serving simultaneously as defensive substances and alarm pheromones (Maschwitz, 1964). During the emission the ants bend their gasters forward beneath their legs. Species of the myrmicine genus *Crematogaster* lift their abdomen to a characteristic vertical position or even forward over the head while releasing the defensive secretion through the sting and alarm pheromones from the mandibular glands (Blum *et al.*, 1969). The same defensive behavior has been observed in Dolichoderinae, in *Oecophylla,* in *Solenopsis fugax, Monomorium pharaonis,* and in many other myrmicine species. Wilson (1958), and Butenandt *et al.* (1959) carried out the first experimental investigations on alarm pheromones in ants. Butenandt and co-workers worked with the leaf cutter ant *Atta sexdens,* while Wilson studied the harvester ant *Pogonomyrmex badius.* In both species workers discharge a strongly smelling substance out of the mandibular glands (the morphological location of various pheromone glands is illustrated in Fig. 5) if they perceive some kind of threatening stimulus. McGurk *et al.* (1966) identified this alarm pheromone of *Pogonomyrmex* as 4-methyl-3-heptanone. Wilson and Bossert (1963) were able to study precisely the behavioral and physiological parameters of chemical alarm communication. By directly measuring the effects of the pheromone from whole crushed glands they found that workers respond to the threshold concentration averaging 10^{10} molecules per cubic centimeter by moving toward the odor source. The total capacity of the gland reservoir is about 10^{15}–10^{16} molecules. As a consequence the entire content of the mandibular gland substance provides a brief signal. According to the experimental data acquired by Wilson and Bossert, the amount of alarm pheromone of one ant expands in still air to its maximum radius of about 6 cm in 13 sec and fades out in about 35 sec. The lower concentration at the periphery releases attraction behavior; only the inner space of higher concentra-

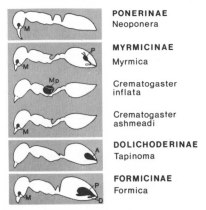

FIG. 5. Alarm pheromone glands in ants: A = anal gland, D = Dufour's gland, M = mandibular gland, Mp = metapleural gland, P = poison gland. (From Hölldobler, 1977b.)

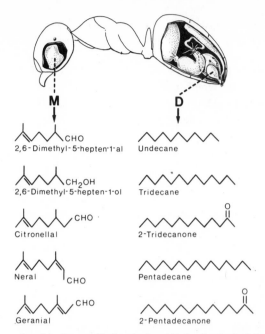

FIG. 6. Substances found in the mandibular gland and Dufour's gland of the ant *Acanthomyops claviger*. Undecane and the mandibular gland substances function both as defensive substances and as alarm substances. D = Dufour's gland, M = mandibular gland. (After Regnier and Wilson, 1968.)

tion, which expands to a radius of 3 cm and fades out in about 8 sec, induces real alarm and aggressive behavior.

These parameters seem very well designed for an economical alarm system. If the danger is local and only short lasting, the signal fades out quickly and only a small group of workers in the immediate vicinity are alerted. If, however, the danger is more persistent, the number of workers discharging the signal increases rapidly, and the signal "travels" through the colony.

The alarm communication system of *Acanthomyops claviger* (Fig. 6) is another well-analyzed example. Regnier and Wilson (1968) found that undecane from the Dufour's gland and a number of terpenes produced in the mandibular glands release alarm response at concentrations of 10^9–10^{12} molecules per cubic centimeter. The quantity of these substances combined in one ant totals about 8 μg. Behavioral experiments have shown that the chemical alarm signal generated by all volatile substances of a single worker releases a response in nestmates up to a distance of about 10 cm. This defensive strategy is well adjusted to the structure of the large *Acanthomyops* colonies, which live widely dispersed through subterranean nests. As in *Pogonomyrmex badius,* the *Acanthomyops* signal fades out rather quickly unless reinforced by other alarming ants.

Bergström and Löfquist (1973) have identified 39 substances from the secretions of the Dufour's gland of *Formica rufa*. Most of these substances were present in traces, and only 11 exceeded amounts of 1% of the total glandular secretions. Recently Löfquist (1976) conducted a detailed behavioral study during which he determined the behavioral responses released by single components and by mixtures of the identified compounds. He confirmed Maschwitz's finding that formic acid from the poison gland releases alarm behavior, and he also found that the combined hydrocarbons of the Dufour's gland function as an alarm signal. Apparently their relative concentrations regulate the intensity and duration of the alarm effect. Löfquist's study again made clear that the alarm defense behavior in ants consists not just of one simple behavioral reaction but of several response steps, such as alert reaction, fast running, attraction, and attack. It is conceivable, as Löfquist pointed out, that several hydrocarbons of a homologous series, due to their different volatility and different response threshold concentrations, regulate these behavioral response steps. In fact, similar considerations were recently suggested by Bradshaw *et al.* (1975), who found that the African weaver ant *Oecophylla longinoda* produces several alarm substances in their mandibular glands. Hexanal has an alerting effect, 1-hexanol functions as an attractant and orientating stimulus, and 3-undecanone and 2-butyl-2-octenal release attack behavior. It is interesting to note that hexanal is the most volatile and 2-butyl-2-octenal the least volatile compound. The first substance alerts nestmates several centimeters away; when the alerted ants have rushed to the source of disturbance, attack and biting behavior is released by the latter substance.

Although alarm signals are not very species specific, the efficiency of an alarm pheromone nevertheless seems to depend on certain structural characteristics. Blum *et al.* (1966) tested a series of 49 ketones on *Iridomyrmex pruinosus* to find out the relationship between chemical structure and alarm-inducing power. The natural alarm pheromone is 2-heptanone. By increasing the number of carbon atoms from 3 to 13 a very low activity was elicited by the first (C_3–C_4) and the last (C_{11}–C_{13}) of the 2-alkanone series. An optimal reaction occurred between C_6 and C_9. Other structural variations, such as a displacement of the carbonyl group, the introduction of a second ketone group or the presence of side-chain methyl groups, usually lowered the response-eliciting efficiency of the substance. Similar results were obtained by Regnier and Wilson (1968) for *Acanthomyops claviger*. They found that alkanes falling between C_{10} and C_{13} usually elicited good response from the workers and showed excellent properties as alarm substances. The main component of the natural alarm substances is undecane, a C_{11} alkane. Riley *et al.* (1974a, b) recently found that workers of *Atta texana* and *A. cephalotes* produce only the (+) isomer of the alarm pheromone 4-methyl-3-heptanone. In behavioral tests it was apparently demonstrated that workers of *A. texana* distinguish the (+) isomer of this ketone from the (−) isomer.

Many alarm pheromones have been chemically identified (see reviews by Gabba and Pavan, 1970; Law and Regnier, 1971; Wilson, 1971; Pain, 1973; Blum 1974). Most of them are ketones, aldehydes, acids, or hydrocarbons. They are produced in a variety of exocrine glands (see Fig. 5). In summarizing the behavioral results one can say that most alarm pheromones in ants are not very specific. This is not surprising because there is little if any selective pressure to develop species specificity of alarm communication. In fact, in many cases it seems even advantageous to be able to understand the alarm signals of a neighboring colony of another species. However, Regnier and Wilson (1971) demonstrated one case in which the lack of specificity can turn to a disadvantage under some circumstances. It is well known that certain ant species conduct "slave raids" on other ants. The raiders bring the pupae of the raided ant colonies into their own nest. When the young workers eclose to adults, they function in the raiders' nest as brood tenders, nest builders, foragers. The raider workers continue to conduct mainly "slave raids." Often the raiders are obviously superior in fighting ability (Fig. 7). *Polyergus,* for example, has specially adapted saber-shaped mandibles. The slave-raiding species *Formica pergandei* and *F. subintegra,* do not carry such armament but instead possess remarkably enlarged Dufour's glands. Regnier and Wilson identified as principal components of the glandular substances decyl acetate, dodecyl acetate, and tetradecyl acetate. One worker of *F. subintegra* contains the relatively enormous amount of 700 μg of these substances. During the slave raids the raider ants discharge these substances upon encountering prey workers and apparently stimulate nestmates to join them in the fighting. In addition, they spray large amounts of the acetates on defending slave ants. It is interesting that these substances not only alarm and stimulate the raider species but they also highly excite the slave ant species. The high concentration of the discharged acetate mixture, however, completely "confuses" the slave ants. They become disoriented, making it easy for the raiders to penetrate the slave ants' nest and to remove the pupae.

The response behavior to an alarm signal varies in time and space, and it varies in different groups and castes of the society. For example, if the signal is discharged close to the nest, it releases aggressive behavior, but at a greater distance from the nest it elicits escape behavior (Maschwitz, 1964). Furthermore, young workers usually retreat into the nest when they smell the alarm signal, while older workers, especially those belonging to the soldier castes, move out and display aggressive behavior (Cammaerts-Tricot, 1975; Wilson 1975).

Cammaerts-Tricot (1974) and Wilson (1975, 1976) have demonstrated that some ant species organize a colony defense by recruiting nestmates with the aid of chemical trails laid down from the vicinity of the intruders back to the nest.

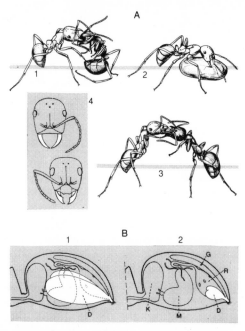

FIG. 7. (A) (1) A worker of the slave raider ant *Polyergus rufescens* (left) attacks a slave ant *Formica fusca* (right); (2) the slave raider carries a pupa of *F. fusca* homeward; (3) a *Polyergus* worker is fed by a *F. fusca* slave ant, which has eclosed from a captured pupa; (4) the saber-shaped mandibles of *Polyergus* are contrasted with the "normal" mandibles of the slave ant species, *Formica fusca*. (B) (1) Gaster of the slave raider ant *Formica subintegra*, showing the enormously developed Dufour's gland (D); (2) gaster of the slave ant *Formica subsericea* with normal Dufour's gland. G = poison gland, R = hindgut, K = crop, M = midgut. (From Hölldobler, 1973a.)

For instance, Wilson discovered that only a few workers of the fire ant *Solenopsis invicta,* introduced into the foraging arena of a *Pheidole dentata* nest invariably release a typical defensive response. Some of the foraging *Pheidole* minor workers

> . . . grapple with the intruders, while others flee momentarily and run in irregular circles
> through the surrounding area. Within several minutes, some of the minor workers run
> back to the nest, dragging the tips of their abdomens over the ground. The trail thus
> deposited attracts both minor and major workers from the nest in the direction of the
> invaders. The trail pheromone comes from the poison gland and is emitted through the
> sting. . . . Upon arriving at the battle scene the major workers become highly excited,
> snapping at the fire ants with their powerful mandibles and soon chopping them to pieces
> (Wilson, 1975, p. 798).

Furthermore Wilson demonstrated that *Pheidole dentata* is able to identify specifically its major enemy ant genus *Solenopsis.* Only one *Solenopsis* worker is enough to release the effective alarm recruitment behavior in *Pheidole dentata*. Indeed, several *Solenopsis* species seem to be specialized to raid and prey on other ant species, and, as a recent study suggests, some of them may employ powerful chemical strategies to invade nests of their prey species (Hölldobler, 1973b). For example, the European thief ant, *Solenopsis (Diplorhoptrum) fugax*, usually lives within the close vicinity of other ant colonies and preys on the brood of its neighbors. Scout workers of *Solenopsis* build an elaborate subterranean tunnel system leading into the neighboring species' brood chambers. As soon as the construction of these tunnels is completed, the scouts lay chemical trails back to their own nest and recruit masses of nestmates in order to invade and to raid the neighboring ant's brood nest. The recruitment pheromones by which the raids are organized originate from the Dufour's gland. While invading the brood chambers and preying on the brood, *Solenopsis* workers also discharge a highly effective and long lasting repellent substance from the poison gland. This secretion prevents the brood tending ants from defending their own larvae and enables *Solenopsis* to rob brood virtually without interference. Laboratory experiments have shown that the secretion of the poison gland releases an intense repellent reaction in workers of 18 different ant species. When a small entrance leading to the brood chamber of a *Lasius flavus* nest was contaminated with the secretion of a single *Solenopsis* poison gland, the entrance was not used by *Lasius* workers for almost 1 hr. These and other experiments have clearly demonstrated that *Solenopsis fugax* workers produce a powerful ant repellent in their poison gland, which enables them to invade the nests of other ant species and to prey on the foreign brood (Hölldobler, 1973b).

IV. RECRUITMENT COMMUNICATION

In order to efficiently exploit newly discovered food sources and nesting sites ant societies require both special communication and orientation signals. The study of recruitment systems in ants has begun to diversify during the past five years. In the 1950s and 1960s the straightforward identification of the glandular source of the trail pheromones was emphasized, with some attention being paid to the details of the trail-laying behavior (see reviews in Wilson, 1971; Blum, 1974; Maschwitz, 1975; Hölldobler, 1973a, 1977b). Now a new emphasis has begun to emerge: the analysis of the organizational levels and the ecological significance of recruitment. The possession of one kind of recruitment system as opposed to another seems to constitute adaptations by individual species to particular conditions in their environment. Indeed, the recruitment strategy appears to make little sense except with reference to the ecology of the species, while, conversely, the ecology of many species cannot be fully understood without a detailed knowledge of their recruitment procedures.

The recruitment techniques employed by different groups of ant species vary considerably. The best studied recruitment behavior is the chemical trail communication. Carthy (1950, 1951) was one of the first to conduct an experimental study on trail laying in *Lasius fuliginosus*. He found strong circumstantial evidence that in this species the trail pheromone originates from the hindgut. This suggestion was later confirmed by Hangartner and Bernstein (1964). Wilson (1959a) working with the fire ant *Solenopsis invicta* (= *S. saevissima*), provided the first bioassay methods to test trail-following behavior even in the absence of a trail-laying ant. He laid artificial trails of different glandular extracts away from the nest entrance and from worker aggregations. By comparing the trail-following response of worker ants, he was able to identify the Dufour's gland as the source of the trail pheromone of the fire ants. This techinque was subsequently used by many investigators, leading to the discovery of a number of trail pheromone glands in different taxonomic groups of ants (Fig. 8).

Wilson's (1962) analyses also revealed for the first time the organization of chemical mass communication in fire ants. It was found that the number of workers leaving the nest along the trail is controlled by the amount of trail substance discharged by workers already on the trail. Using the purified trail pheromone it was demonstrated that the number of ants drawn outside the nest is a linear function of the amount of the substance presented to the colony. This means that under natural conditions the number of workers being recruited can be

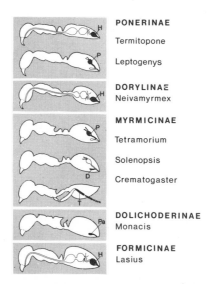

FIG. 8. Trail pheromone glands (black) in several species of five subfamilies of ants. H = hindgut, P = poison gland, D = Dufour's gland, T = tibial gland, Pa = Pavan's gland. (From Hölldobler, 1977b.)

accurately adjusted to the actual needs of recruits at the food source. In other words, the better the food source, the more workers lay an odor trail when they return to the nest. This increases the amount of trail substance discharged and in turn draws more ants to the food source. As the food slowly diminishes, fewer workers lay a trail, with the result that the concentration of the trail substance, which has a relatively high evaporation rate, decreases, and, in turn, a smaller number of workers is stimulated to leave the nest. The phenomenon is called *mass communication* because it entails the transmission of information that is meaningful only with reference to larger groups and cannot be exchanged between mere pairs of individuals. Subsequently, Hangartner (1969b) demonstrated that even individual ants can contribute to the flexibility of this mass communication system. Individual workers of *Solenopsis* are apparently able to adjust the amounts of their own pheromone emissions to the specific food needs of their colony and to the quality of the food source. By inducing the homing foragers to lay their trail on a soot-coated glass plate Hangartner found that the continuity of the sting trail increases with increasing starvation time of the colony, increasing quality of the food source, and decreasing distance between the food and the nest.

This mass communication system is certainly a highly advanced recruitment method. In an attempt to find out from which more primitive forms of recruitment communication this system may have evolved, it is necessary to analyze and compare less sophisticated modes of recruitment communication. The so-called "tandem running behavior" is generally considered to be one of the most primitive recruitment methods. Only one nestmate is recruited at a time, and the follower has to keep close antennal contact with the leader ant. This behavior has been described in a phylogenetically scattered array of species including *Camponotus sericeus* (Hingston, 1929), *Ponera eduardi* (LeMasne, 1952), *Cardiocondyla venestula* and *C. emeryi* (Wilson, 1959b), *Leptothorax acervorum* (Dobrzanski, 1966), and *Bothroponera tesserinoda* (Maschwitz et al., 1974; Hölldobler et al., 1973). Until recently, however, nothing had been learned about the precise nature of the signals involved.

The analyses of the signals by which tandem running is organized in the myrmicine ant *Leptothorax acervorum* have now led to the discovery of a new kind of signal in ant communication, for which we proposed the term "tandem calling" (Möglich et al., 1974b). When a successful scouting forager of *Leptothorax acervorum* returns to the colony, it first regurgitates food to several nestmates. Then it turns around and raises its gaster upward into a slanting position. Simultaneously the sting is exposed and a droplet of a light liquid extruded (Fig. 9). Nestmates are attracted by this calling behavior. When the first ant arrives at the calling ant, it touches it on the hindlegs or gaster with its antennae, and tandem running starts. The recruiting ant leads the nestmate to the newly discovered food source. During tandem running the leader ant lowers the

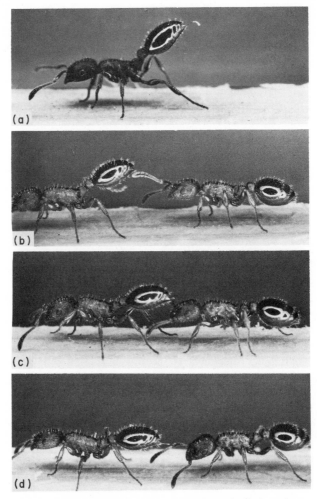

FIG. 9. Behavioral exchange of signals leading to tandem running in *Leptothorax acervorum*: (a) A recruiting worker assumes the calling position; (b and c) a nestmate arrives and touches the gaster (b) and hindlegs (c) of the calling ant with its antennae; (d) the calling ant lowers its gaster and tandem running starts. The sting of the recruiting ant remains extruded, but is not dragged over the surface. (From Möglich *et al.*, 1974b.)

gaster, but the sting remains extruded. It, however, is not dragged over the surface, as it is in the case of those ant species that lay chemical trails from their stings. The follower keeps close antennal contact with the leader, continuously touching its hindlegs and gaster. Whenever this contact is interrupted, for example, when the follower accidentally loses its leader or is removed experimentally, the leader immediately stops and resumes it calling posture. It may remain in this posture for several minutes, continuously discharging the calling pheromone. Under normal circumstances the lost follower rather quickly orients back to the calling leader ant and tandem running continues. We have found similar tandem calling behavior in *Leptothorax muscorum* and *L. nylanderi*.

The analyses of this interesting recruitment behavior has revealed two signal modalities by which tandem running is organized:

1. If a tandem pair has been separated the leader immediately stops and assumes the calling posture. However, when the ant is carefully touched with a hair at the hindlegs or gaster with a frequency of at least two contacts per second, the leader continues running to the target area. This experiment shows that the absence of the tactile signals normally provided by the follower ant is sufficient to release "tandem calling" by a leader ant.

2. The calling pheromone originates from the poison gland. In our studies workers were strongly attracted to dummies that had been contaminated with poison gland secretions but not to secretions of the Dufour's gland. Further experiments revealed that the poison gland substance not only functions as a calling pheromone but plays an important role during tandem running itself by binding the follower ant to the leader. It was found that the leader could easily be replaced by a dummy contaminated with poison gland secretions. Gasters of freshly killed ants from which the sting with its glands had been removed could not replace a leader ant. However, when they were contaminated with secretions of the poison gland, they functioned effectively as leader dummies.

The discovery of a chemical "tandem calling" in *Leptothorax* throws considerable light on the evolution of chemical recruitment techniques in myrmicine ants. It now seems very plausible that the highly sophisticated chemical mass recruitment performed by *Solenopsis* and certain other myrmicine ants was derived from a more primitive chemical tandem calling behavior of the *Leptothorax* mode. With the exception of *Crematogaster,* which produces a trail pheromone in the tibial glands of the hindlegs (Leuthold, 1968b; Fletcher and Brand, 1968), all other myrmicine species generate the trail pheromone from one of the sting glands (see Fig. 8). It is conceivable that a chemical calling behavior, during which an alerting and attracting pheromone is discharged through the sting into the air, was one of the first steps that led to chemical trail laying and mass communication in myrmicine ants.

In addition the tandem calling behavior is also relevant to the evolution of sex pheromones in myrmicine ants. As mentioned above it has been demonstrated that in several myrmicine species the pheromones originate from the sting glands (Hölldobler, 1971a; Buschinger, 1972; Hölldobler and Wüst, 1973). It is interesting to note that in species in which wingless ergatoids attract males for mating, as for example *Harpagoxenus sublaevis* (Buschinger, 1968), the females display sexual calling behavior apparently identical to the tandem calling behavior of *Leptothorax*. This discovery supports the hypothesis that in at least some myrmicine ants sex attractants and recruitment pheromones had the same evolutionary origin. In fact, in some cases the same substances may function in specific situations as sex pheromones and in others as recruitment signals.

In formicine ants the trail pheromones originate from the hindgut (Blum and Wilson, 1964; Hangartner and Bernstein, 1964; Hangartner, 1969a; Hölldobler, 1971c; Hölldobler *et al.*, 1974; Barlin *et al.*, 1976). The analyses of the tandem running technique in the formicine species *Camponotus sericeus* has similarly revealed some of the basic behavioral patterns out of which the more sophisticated methods of "group recruitment" and "mass recruitment" employed by other formicine species may have been evolved (Hölldobler *et al.*, 1974; Möglich *et al.*, 1974a).

In *Camponotus sericeus* the first scouting ant to discover the food source typically fills its crop and returns to the nest. As the worker heads home, it touches its abdominal tip to the ground for short intervals. Tracer experiments have shown that the ant is depositing chemical signposts with material from her hindgut. Inside the nest she performs short-lasting fast runs, which are interrupted by food exchange and grooming behavior. After several regurgitations, the recruiter ant now performs brief food offerings while facing nestmates head on. During one recruitment performance such "rituals" were observed to be repeated 3–16 times. Apparently this behavior functions to keep nestmates in close contact with the successful scout ant. When the scout finally leaves the nest to return to the food source, those ants encountered by the recruiting ant usually try to follow the leader. However, ordinarily only one ant, the one that keeps closest antennal contact with the leader, succeeds in following it. Most of the recruited ants, after feeding at the food source, turn straight back to the nest where many of them start to recruit nestmates on their own. Experiments have shown that the hindgut trail, laid down by homing foragers, has no recruitment effect at all. Only experienced ants follow the trail and use it as an orientation cue. Similarly, during tandem running the presence or absence of the trail pheromone is insignificant. The leader ant and the follower are bound together by a continuous exchange of tactile signals and by a very persistent surface pheromone.

We discovered that *Camponotus sericeus* also employs the tandem running technique for recruitment of nestmates to new nesting sites. Since in this case a whole colony has to be recruited, the behavioral patterns initiating tandem running can be expected to be different from those used during recruitment to food sources. As depicted in Fig. 10, this is indeed the case. When facing the nestmate head on, the recruiter grasps it on the mandibles and pulls it heavily forward. Shortly afterwards it loosens the grip, turns completely around and presents its gaster to the nestmate. If the nestmate responds by touching the recruiting ant's gaster or hindlegs, tandem running starts. This behavioral sequence is very

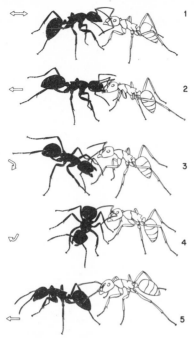

Fig. 10. Invitation behavior to tandem running in *Camponotus sericeus*. (1) the recruiter (black) approaches a nestmate (white) and displays for about 2–3 sec a jerking behavior. (2) The recruiting ant grasps the nestmate at the mandibles and pulls it a distance of about 2–20 cm. (3) The recruiter loosens its grip and (4) turns around 180 degrees. (5) The recruiter presents its gaster to the nestmate. The nestmate contacts the gaster and hindlegs of the leader ant, then tandem running starts. The arrows indicate the direction of the movements. (From Hölldobler *et al.*, 1974.)

stereotyped and is regularly employed when nestmates are invited to follow the signaller to a new nest. We therefore have called this behavior *invitation behavior*.

It is interesting to note that some of the ants that fail to respond to the "invitation signals" are carried to the target area. The first behavioral sequences that initiate carrying behavior are almost identical with that of the "invitation behavior." The main difference is, however, that the recruiting ant keeps the firm grip when turning around. The nestmate is thereby slightly lifted, a movement that apparently causes it to fold its legs tightly to the body and roll its gaster underneath. It is carried to the target area in this posture (Fig. 11). For more details about social carrying behavior and the division of labor during nest movings in ants see Möglich and Hölldobler (1974).

The analyses of the signals by which the tandem running recruitment technique of *Camponotus sericeus* is organized have revealed that mechanical signals and

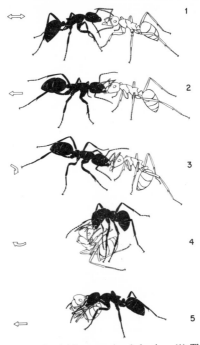

FIG. 11. Behavioral sequences that initiate carrying behavior. (1) The recruiter ant (black) approaches a nestmate (white) and displays a jerking behavior for 2–3 sec. (2) The recruiter grasps the nestmate at the mandibles and pulls it a distance of about 2–20 cm. (3) When the recruiter turns, it holds the nestmate with a firm grip; the nestmate is slightly lifted thereby. (4) The nestmate folds the legs and antennae tightly to the body and rolls the gaster inward. (5) In this posture it is carried to the target area. The arrows indicate the direction of the movements. (From Hölldobler *et al.*, 1974.)

motor patterns play an important role. Although chemical trails with hindgut contents are laid, they function only as orientation cues and do not release any recruitment effect. This brings us to the next higher organization level of recruitment communication in formicine ants, the so-called "group recruitment."

In this case one ant recruits about 5–30 nestmates at a time, and the recruited ants follow closely behind the leader ant to the target area. This behavior has been observed in *Camponotus compressus* (Hingston, 1929), *C. beebei* (Wilson, 1965), and *C. socius* (Hölldobler, 1971c). Working with *Camponotus socius* I found that scouts set chemical "sign posts" around newly discovered food sources and lay a trail with hindgut contents from the food source to the nest. The trail pheromone alone, however, does not release a significant recruitment effect. Inside the nest the recruiting ant performs a "waggle" display when facing nestmates head on (Fig. 12). The vibrations with head and thorax last 0.5–1.5 sec

Fig. 12. Schematical illustration of the "waggle" movements of a recruiting ant (black) which encounters a nestmate. Arrow indicates the to and fro direction of the movement. (From Hölldobler, 1971c.)

with 6–12 strokes in 1 sec. Nestmates are alerted by this behavior and subsequently follow the recruiting ant to the food source. The significance of the motor display inside the nest was demonstrated by closing the gland openings of recruiting ants with wax plugs. In this way it was possible to separate the "waggle" display from the chemical signals, and thus it could be shown that only ants stimulated by the waggle display performed by a recruiting ant would follow an artificial trail drawn with hindgut contents. For a complete recruitment performance, however, the presence of a leader ant was still essential. Freshly recruited ants without a leader would follow a hindgut trail through a distance of only about 100 cm. Essentially similar behavioral patterns are involved during recruitment to new nest sites. The main differences are that the motor display is frequently more a "jerking" movement and in contrast to recruitment to food sources, males respond to the signals and hence are recruited. In *Camponotus socius,* as in *C. sericeus,* the "jerking movement" appears to have been derived from an intention movement which precedes carrying behavior. Indeed, when nestmates do not respond to this signal the jerking display initiates carrying behavior (Hölldobler, 1971c).

The next organizational level within the formicine ants is represented by those species in which the trail pheromone alone also does not elicit a recruitment effect, but in which stimulated ants follow the trail to the food source even in the absence of the recruiting ant. We found this to be the case in *Formica fusca* (Möglich and Hölldobler, 1975). In this species successful scouts lay a hindgut trail from the food source to the nest. The trail pheromone has no primary stimulating effect. However, after the scout has performed a vigorous waggle display inside the nest, frequently interrupted by food exchanges, nestmates rush out and follow the trail to the food source without being guided by the recruiting ant. *Camponotus pennsylvanicus* scouts returning from newly discovered food sources also lay odor trails. These individuals further stimulate nestmates by a waggle motor display. When nestmates are alerted by the display, they follow the previously laid trail; the scout does not usually guide the recruited group to the target area (Traniello, 1977). However, in *C. pennsylvanicus* workers follow an artificial hindgut trail even without being mechanically stimulated by the scout ant. Furthermore, Barlin *et al.* (1976) have chromatographically identified a single peak of the hindgut contents which releases trail following behavior. Nevertheless, motor displays obviously remain an integral part of the recruitment process of *C. pennsylvanicus*; the number of ants responding to an artificial trail consisting of hindgut contents plus poison gland secretion is higher if a scout was allowed to stimulate nestmates by the motor display. These results suggest that recruitment behavior in *C. pennsylvanicus* is of higher organizational level than that of *Formica fusca*. From here it is only a small step to the chemical mass communication, where the trail pheromone alone functions as the recruitment signal and the outflow of foragers is controlled by the amount of pheromone discharged.

The cumulative studies have made clear that motor displays and mechanical signals play an important role during recruitment communication in many ant species (see also Sudd, 1957; Szlep and Jacobi, 1967; Leuthold, 1968a; Szlep-Fessel, 1970). It appears, however, that during the evolutionary process of "designing" more efficient recruitment techniques, these signals became less important with the increasing sophistication of the chemical recruitment system.

There is another important clue from these studies concerning the means by which hindgut material became involved in the recruitment process in formicine ants. Hindgut contents are necessarily frequently discharged by ants. A comparative study has revealed that in many species ants do not defecate randomly but preferably visit specific locations. Besides certain sites inside the nest, other preferred locations include the peripheral nest borders, garbage dumps, and trunk trails leading to permanent food sources or connecting two nest entrances. Thus, these disposal areas seem to be ideally suited to serve as chemical cues in home range orientation, and indeed, this has been documented in a number of species (Hölldobler, 1971c; Hölldobler *et al.*, 1974). These results suggest that in formicine species the trail recruitment communication behavior might have evolved by a gradual ritualization of the defecation process. We can speculate that in the first step hindgut material became an important cue in home range orientation and then was transformed into a more specific orienting and stimulating signal used during recruitment behavior.

The specificity of trail pheromones varies considerably among ant species. Most of our knowledge is based on behavioral investigations, since almost nothing is known about the chemical nature of the trail pheromones. It was only recently that Tumlinson *et al.* (1971, 1972) chemically identified the first such pheromone. The trail substance of leaf-cutting ants (*Atta texana*) is evidently methyl-4-methylpyrrole-2-carboxylate; this substance has been isolated from the poison gland secretions and found to release a strong trail-following behavior in many attine species. Blum *et al.* (1964), working with poison gland extracts had already shown that the trail pheromone of *Atta* releases trail following in many leaf cutting species. A much higher trail pheromone specificity was discovered by Hangartner (1967) in *Lasius fuliginosus*. Although *L. fuliginosus* workers were able to "read" the trail pheromone of many formicine species (with exception of that from *L. flavus*), its own trail could be understood by none of the other species tested. Huwyler *et al.* (1973, 1975) identified as major components in the hindgut contents of *L. fuliginosus* hexanoic acid, heptanoic acid, octanoic acid, nonanoic acid, and decanoic acid. All these acids released trail following behavior in *L. fuliginosus* workers.

Wilson (1962) compared the specificity of trail pheromones in fire ants (*Solenopsis*), which lay trails with secretions from the Dufour's gland. Artificial trails laid with the pheromone of *S. xyloni* released trail-following behavior in *S. invicta* (= *S. saevissima*) and *S. geminata*, but *S. geminata* trails had no effect on the other species. On the other hand, the secretions of *S. invicta* produced no response in *S. xyloni*. Yet, surprisingly, the Dufour's gland secretion of the dacetine ant *Daceton armigerum* invoked strong following in *S. invicta*.

A similar partial specificity of trail pheromones has been reported from other genera, such as *Eciton* (Torgerson and Akre, 1970), *Camponotus* (Barlin *et al.*, 1976), and *Monomorium* (Blum, 1966). According to Blum's investigations the recruitment pheromone of the genus *Monomorium* originates from the poison gland. His specificity tests were therefore carried out with poison gland extracts. However, our own experiments demonstrated that *Monomorium pharaonis* discharges its recruitment pheromone from the Dufour's gland (Hölldobler, 1973b; Möglich, unpublished observations), whereas poison gland secretions release only a very weak trail-following response. These contradictory findings cannot be easily explained.

Recently we analyzed the stimulus modalities responsible for an effective recruitment and group retrieving system which together enable *Novomessor* to transport large prey in a highly coordinated fashion. When a scout ant of *Novomessor* discovers a prey too large to be carried by one ant, it first releases poison gland secretions. *Novomessor* foragers are attracted from as far away as 100 cm by running upwind toward the prey. In case not enough ants can be recruited in this way, one of the foragers runs back to the nest laying a short-lived chemical trail with poison gland secretion. Five to ten additional workers rush out of the nest and, by following the trail, quickly arrive at the prey. In addition, stridulatory signals produced by individual foragers at the prey and transmitted by substrate vibrations to other nestmates modulate the chemical recruitment signals and coordinate the group retrieving of the large prey objects (Hölldobler,

Stanton, and Markl, in prep.). It is interesting to note that *N. albisetosus* also follows artificial trails laid with the poison gland secretion of *N. cockerelli*, but *N. cockerelli* does not follow the poison gland secretion of *N. albisetosus*.

Among different ant species the persistence of chemical trails varies considerably. In those species that use less permanent food sources (insect prey), the recruitment trails are usually short lived, while in other species utilizing long-lasting food sources (especially plants bearing aphids and other honeydew-producing homopteran insects) the trail pheromones are more persistent. Hangartner (1967) studied the physical nature of the relatively high persistence of the chemical trails in *Lasius fuliginosus* and found that in this species the persistence of a trail depends on the volume of substance discharged and on the porosity of the surface. In addition an inactivated trail can be reactivated after days by moistening it with water. Similar results were obtained for the neotropical army ants (*Eciton*), the trails of which can persist for about one week when deposited during the dry season. During the rainy season the same trails are much less persistent (Torgerson and Akre, 1970). In some species, such as *Atta texana,* the trail pheromone contains a short-lived and long-lived component (Moser and Silverstein, 1967).

This leads us to another important function of chemical trails in ants. As already discussed above, some of the formicine trails composed of hindgut material contain relatively long lasting trail substances that serve mainly as chemical cues in home range orientation. These orientation trails, or trunk trails as they are commonly called, can play a major role in regulating territorial behavior and in partitioning of foraging grounds. This has recently been demonstrated for species of the myrmicine harvesting ant genus *Pogonomyrmex*.

V. Communication and Territorial Strategies

Workers of *Pogonomyrmex* lay chemical trails with poison gland secretions to recruit nestmates to new rich seed falls (Hölldobler and Wilson, 1970; Hölldobler, 1976b). These recruitment pheromones are relatively short lived. However, laboratory and field experiments have revealed that in addition more enduring chemical signposts are concurrently deposited along the recruitment trails. The latter substances function as orientation cues, so that long after the recruitment signal has vanished, motivated foragers can still follow the same track (Hölldobler, 1971d). Circumstantial evidence indicates that these cues originate at least in part from the Dufour's gland. We have evidence of species specificity in the mixture of compounds of the Dufour's glands of *Pogonomyrmex* (Regnier et al., 1973; Hölldobler and Regnier, unpublished observations). In addition, Hangartner et al. (1970) showed that *Pogonomyrmex badius* workers are able to distinguish the odor of their own nest material from that of other nests. In our most recent laboratory experiments we found that even trunk trails contain colony-specific chemical cues that enable the ants to choose the trails leading to their own nest as opposed to those leading to a neighboring colony. Furthermore, it was possible to demonstrate (Hölldobler, 1976b) that the use of chemically and visually marked trunk trails, which originate from recruitment trails, guarantees an efficient partitioning of foraging grounds. Trunk trails used by *Pogonomyrmex barbatus* and *P. rugosus* during foraging and homing have the effect of permitting the avoidance of aggressive confrontations between neighboring colonies of the same species. The trails channel the mass of foragers of hostile neighboring nests into diverging directions, before each ant pursues its individual foraging exploration. This system subtly partitions the foraging ground. Although foraging areas of conspecific colonies can overlap, aggressive interactions are usually less intense than at the core areas (trunk trails plus nest yards), which normally do not overlap and are vigorously defended.

African weaver ants (*Oecophylla longinoda*) employ a different technique for establishing and maintaining territories (Hölldobler and Wilson, 1977). Weaver ants are exceptionally abundant, aggressive, and territorial, a circumstance that makes them of significance in tropical forest ecology (Leston, 1970). We found that workers of *Oecophylla longinoda* recruit nestmates to previously unoccupied space by means of odor trails laid from the rectal gland, a hitherto unrecognized musculated organ located at the rear of the rectal sac. When colonies of *O. longinoda* are transferred from the field and confined to a potted citrus tree in the laboratory, the major workers patrol the available surrounding space restlessly. If a second tree is placed near the nest tree, groups of workers, orienting visually, mass on the nearest twig or branch in an attempt to reach the other tree by forming living bridges with their bodies. The longest living bridge we observed measured 17 cm. If they succeed, those crossing over begin to lay trails back and forth across the new space. Many return all the way to the nest, and while so doing lay trails directly across the bodies of nestmates making the living bridge (Fig. 13). A combination of chemical and tactile signals (but not the chemical trail alone) excites workers and induces them to move outward along the trail. This mode of communication, which we have termed *long-range recruitment,* results in an outpouring of additional workers onto the fresh space.

The discovery of recruitment to new space has led us to investigate by which cues the weaver ants differentiate between new and old areas. We found that a combination of chemical and visual cues are involved. For example we can release the recruitment process to new space simply by changing the visual surrounding, but also, although to a lesser degree, by changing the chemical make up of the environment. Furthermore we have found that the ants deposit their own chemical signposts, which, at least in part, originate from the rectal sac. These substances are different from those secreted from the rectal gland, and they serve as true territorial pheromones. We established that weaver ant colonies

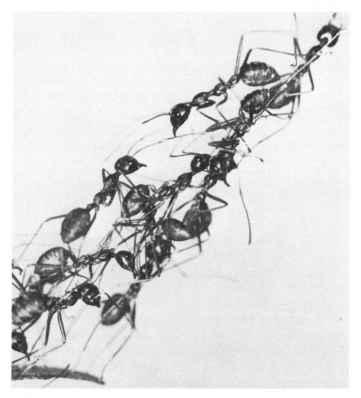

FIG. 13. Workers of the weaver ant *Oecophylla longinoda* form living bridges by linking their bodies into chains. The worker seen running over the upper portion of this bridge is laying an odor trail from her everted rectal gland directly onto the bodies of her nestmates. The trail will guide other members of the colony to a newly available foraging space. (From Hölldobler and Wilson, 1977.)

discriminate between the territorial signposts of their own colony and that of other colonies. A second form of communication in *Oecophylla longinoda* is referred to loosely as short-range recruitment (Hölldobler and Wilson, 1977). When workers encounter alien *Oecophylla* workers or other kinds of insects too large for them to seize, they chase the intruders through distances of 15 cm or more while dragging the end of the abdomen (but not the anus or acidopore) over the ground. In this way, the worker dispenses an attractant–arrestant pheromone from the sternal gland, located on the last abdominal sternite. Nestmates are attracted over distances of up to 10 cm to the area where the display occurred and tend to settle there in loose clusters. The result is a change in the overall spatial pattern of *Oecophylla* workers in those portions of the territory through which the intruders move, from random or weakly clumped distributions to moderately or strongly clumped distributions. During laboratory trials clusters of workers were able to restrain and subdue invaders in much shorter periods of time than were single defenders. Under prolonged stress from invaders, additional forces are recruited to the combat area with the aid of a conspicuous jerking motor display signal and the rectal-gland trail substance.

In the honey ant (*Myrmecocystus mimicus*) I discovered a still different territorial strategy (Hölldobler, 1976a). *Myrmecocystus mimicus* is abundant in the mesquite–acacia community in the southwestern United States, and like other members of its genus, it has a special honeypot caste, which functions as living storage containers. When their crops are filled to capacity, their gasters are expanded to almost the size of a cherry. Neighboring colonies of *M. mimicus* conduct territorial tournaments, in which hundreds of ants perform highly stereotyped display fights. These tournaments can last for several days, being interrupted only at night when the species is normally inactive. During the contest the ants walk high on legs held in a stilt position while raising the gaster and head. When two hostile workers meet, they turn to confront each other head on (Fig. 14a). Subsequently they engage in a more prolonged lateral display (Fig. 14b, c) during which each raises its gaster even higher and bends it toward its opponent. Simultaneously, the opponents drum their antennae intensively on each other's abdomen and kick each other with their forelegs. These exchanges are almost the only physical contact, although each ant seems to push sideways as if to dislodge the other one. After 10–30 sec one of the ants usually yields, and the encounter ends. The ants continue to move on stilt legs, quickly meet other opponents, and the whole ceremony is then repeated.

How do these territorial tournaments originate? When foragers venture into an alien territory, they encounter the residents at frequent intervals, whereupon they invariably commence a display fight. Subsequently, some scouts return to their colony while dragging their abdominal tips over the ground and thus summoning forces of their nestmates to the challenged territorial border. When the opposing worker forces meet, massive display tournaments ensue. Real physical fights usually end fatally for both opponents but occur only rarely. When one colony is considerably stronger than the other, the tournaments end quickly through sheer weight of numbers, and the weaker colony is raided. Of 28 territorial invasions observed, 5 ended with the raiding of the weaker colony. During these raids the queens were killed or driven off. The larvae, pupae, callow workers, and honeypot workers were carried or dragged to the nest of the raiders. This process required several days and terminated only when the raided colony ceased to exist. Field observations and laboratory experiments demonstrated that the surviving workers as well as the honeypots and brood of the raided colony were incorporated to a large extent into the raiders' nest. Since all cases of slave making in ants hitherto recorded have involved two different species, this is the first evidence for intraspecific slavery in ants. Experiments have shown that the territorial raids of *M. mimicus* are organized by an alarm-recruitment system. The ants

FIG. 14. The stereotyped display patterns of *Myrmecocystus mimicus*: (a) stilt walking and head-on confrontation; (b) beginning of lateral display; (c) full lateral display and antennal drumming. (From Hölldobler, 1976a.)

are alerted by a jerking motor display performed by the recruiting scouts, and they are subsequently guided to the combat area by a hindgut-pheromone trail laid by the scout ants.

VI. COMMUNICATION BETWEEN ANTS AND THEIR GUESTS

We have seen that the complex life within the insect society depends on the efficiency of many different forms of communication. It is therefore notable that a large number of solitary arthropods have acquired the capacity to provide the correct signals to these social insects. They have "broken the code" and are thereby able to take advantage of the benefits of the societies. Ant colonies contain an especially large number of these solitary arthropods. The guests, which are commonly known as myrmecophiles, include many members of the order Coleoptera (beetles) but also many mites, collembolans, flies, wasps, and members of other insect groups. In this section I will present several examples where it has been possible to analyze the mechanisms of interspecific communication between ants and their guests. Different species of myrmecophiles occupy different sites within an ant colony. Some species live along the trails of the ants, others at the garbage dumps outside the nest, others within the outermost nest chambers, while still others are found within the brood chambers (Hölldobler, 1971b, 1972, 1973a). In each case the requirements of interspecific communication are different.

Some of the most advanced myrmecophilic relationships are found in the staphylinid beetles *Lomechusa strumosa* and several species of the genus *Atemeles. Lomechusa strumosa* lives with the red slave-making ant *Formica sanguinea* in Europe. *Atemeles pubicollis,* also a European species, is normally found with the mound-making wood ant *Formica polyctena* during the summer. But in the winter it inhabits the nests of ants of the genus *Myrmica.* We know from the observations of Wasmann, made 60 years ago, that these beetles are both fed and reared by their host ants. The behavioral patterns of the larvae of these beetles are similar for the various species; in particular the larvae prey to a certain extent on their host ants' larvae. It is therefore astonishing that the brood-keeping ants not only tolerate these predators but also feed them as they do their own brood.

Both chemical and mechanical interspecific communication is involved in these unusual relationships. The beetle larvae show a characteristic begging behavior toward their host ants. As soon as they are touched by an ant, they rear upward and try to make contact with the ant's head. If they succeed, they tap the ant's labium with their own mouthparts (Fig. 15). This apparently releases regurgitation of food by the ant. The ant larvae beg for food in much the same way but less intensely.

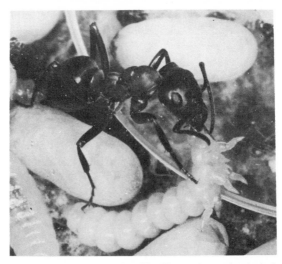

Fig. 15. Larva of *Atemeles* is given a droplet of food by an ant attendant in the brood chamber of a nest of *Formica* ants. (From Hölldobler, 1971b.)

By feeding ants on honey mixed with radioactive sodium phosphate it is possible to measure the social exchange of food in a colony. These experiments show that when myrmecophilous beetle larvae are present in the brood chamber they obtain a proportionately greater share of the food than the host-ant larvae. The presence of ant larvae does not affect the food flow to the beetle larvae whereas ant larvae always receive less food when they compete with beetle larvae. This finding suggests that the releasing signals presented by the beetle larvae to the brood-keeping ants may be more effective than those presented by the ant larvae themselves.

The beetle larvae are also frequently and intensely groomed by the brood-keeping ants; thus, it seemed probable that chemical signals are also involved in this interspecific relationship. The transfer of substances from the larvae to the brood-keeping ants could, in fact, be demonstrated by experiments with radioactive tracers. These substances are probably secreted by glandular cells, which occur dorsolaterally in the integument of each segment. The biological significance of the secretions was elucidated by the following experiments. Beetle larvae were completely covered with shellac to prevent the liberation of the secretion. They were then placed outside the nest entrance, together with freshly killed but otherwise untreated control larvae. The ants quickly carried the control animals into the brood chamber. The shellac-covered larvae, on the other hand, were either ignored or carried to the garbage dump. It was found that for adoption to be successful at least one segment of the larva must be shellac free. Furthermore, it was possible to show that after extracting all the secretions with acetone the larvae were no longer attractive. However, if the extracted larvae were contaminated with secretions from normal larvae, they once again became attractive. Even filter paper dummies soaked in such secretions were carried into the brood chambers.

In sum, the experiments show that the adoption of the beetle larvae and their care within the ant colony depend on chemical signals. It may be that the beetle larvae imitate a pheromone, which the ant larvae themselves use in releasing brood-keeping behavior in the adult ants. In obtaining food from the brood-keeping ants, however, the beetle larvae imitate and even exaggerate the food-begging behavior of the ant larvae (Hölldobler, 1967).

The question next arises of how the ant colony manages to survive the intense predation and food parasitism by the beetle larvae. Our observations have suggested a very simple answer. The beetle larvae are cannibalistic, and this factor alone is effective in limiting the number of beetle larvae in the brood chambers at any time. *Lomechusa* larvae normally occur singly throughout the brood chambers, in contrast to the ant larvae which are usually clustered together.

After a period of growth the beetle larvae pupate in the summer. At the beginning of autumn they eclose as adult beetles. The newly hatched *Lomechusa* beetles leave the ant nest and after a short period of migration seek adoption in another nest of the same host ant species. *Atemeles* beetles, on the other hand, migrate from the *Formica* nest, where they have been raised, to the nests of the ant genus *Myrmica*. They winter inside the *Myrmica* brood chambers and in the springtime return to a *Formica* nest to breed (Wasmann, 1910; Hölldobler, 1970a). The fact that the adult beetle is tolerated and is fed in the nests of ants belonging to two different subfamilies suggests that it is able to communicate efficiently in two different "languages."

The *Atemeles* face a major problem in finding their way from one host species to another. *Formica polyctena* nests normally occur in woodland, while *Myrmica* nests are found in the grassland around the woods. Experiments have revealed that when *Atemeles* leave the *Formica* nest they show high locomotor and flight activity and orientate toward light. This may well explain how they manage to reach the relatively open *Myrmica* habitat. Once they reach the grassland, the beetles must distinguish the *Myrmica* ants from among the other species present and locate their nests. Laboratory experiments have revealed that they identify the *Myrmica* nests by specific odors. Windborne species-specific odors are equally important in the spring movement back to the *Formica* nests.

Having found the hosts, the beetles must secure their own adoption. The process involves the four sequential steps depicted in Fig. 16. First, the beetle taps the ant lightly with its antennae and raises the tip of the abdomen toward it. The latter structure contains what I have called the *appeasement glands*. The secretions of these glands, which are immediately licked up by the ant, seem to

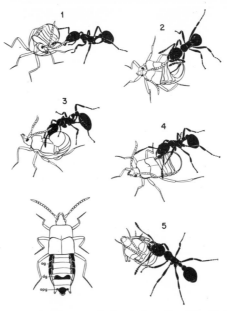

FIG. 16. Behavioral interactions between the beetle *Atemeles pubicollis* (white) and the ant *Myrmica laevinodis* (black) during the adoption process. (1 and 2) The beetle antennates and presents its appeasement glands (apg) to the ant. (3) After licking the ant moves around and licks the adoption glands (ag). (4) The beetle unrolls its abdomen and the ant picks the beetle up by the bristles associated with the adoption glands. (5) The ant carries the beetle into the nest; the beetle assumes a typical transportation posture. (From Hölldobler, 1969.)

suppress aggressive behavior. The ant is attracted next by a second series of glands along the lateral margins of the abdomen. The beetle now lowers its abdomen in order to permit the ant to approach. The glandular openings are surrounded by bristles. These are grasped by the ant and used to carry the beetle into the brood chamber. By experimentally occluding the openings of the glands, it could be shown that the secretion is essential for successful adoption. For this reason I have come to label them *adoption glands*. Thus, the adoption of the adult beetle, like that of the larva, depends on chemical communication. Again it is most probable that an imitation of a species-specific pheromone is involved (Hölldobler, 1970a).

Before leaving the *Formica* nest the *Atemeles* beetle must obtain enough food to enable it to survive the migration to the *Myrmica* nest. This it obtains by begging from the ants. The begging behavior is essentially the same toward both *Formica* and *Myrmica*. The beetle attracts the ant's attention by rapidly drumming on it with its antennae. Using its maxillae and forelegs it taps the mouthparts of the ant, thus inducing regurgitation (Fig. 17). As noted previously, the ants themselves employ a similar mechanical stimulation of the mouthparts to

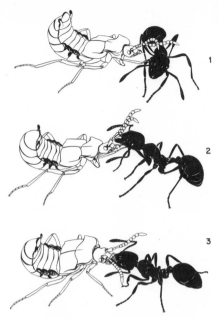

FIG. 17. The myrmecophilous beetle *Atemeles pubicollis* soliciting regurgitation in its host ant *Myrmica laevinodis*. (1) the beetle gains the attention of a worker ant by tapping it with its antennae and forelegs. (2) then the beetle stimulates the labium of the ant thereby releasing regurgitation (3). (From Hölldobler, 1970a.)

obtain food from one another. It is thus clear that *Atemeles* is able to obtain food by imitating these simple tactile food-begging signals.

Finally we can reflect on the significance of host changing as seen in the beetle *Atemeles*. There are good reasons for believing *Atemeles* first evolved myrmecophilic relationships with *Formica*. We can hypothesize that the ancestral *Atemeles* beetles hatched in *Formica* nests in the autumn and then dispersed, returning to other *Formica* nests only to overwinter. This pattern is seen in *Lomechusa* today (Wasmann, 1915; Hölldobler, 1972). However, in the *Formica* nest brood keeping ceases during the winter, and consequently social food flow is reduced. In contrast, the *Myrmica* colony maintains brood keeping throughout the winter. Thus, in *Myrmica* nests, larvae and nutrient from the social food flow are both available as high-grade food sources to the myrmecophiles. These observations, coupled with the fact that the beetles are sexually immature when they hatch, suggest why it is advantageous for the beetle to overwinter in *Myrmica* nests. In the *Myrmica* nest gametogenesis proceeds, and when spring comes, the beetles are sexually mature. They then return to the *Formica* nest to mate and lay their eggs. At this time the *Formica* are just beginning to raise their own larvae and the social food flow is again optimal. The life cycle and behavior of *Atemeles* is thus synchronized with that of its host ants in such a manner as to take maximum advantage of the social life of each of the two species.

The North American staphylinid myrmecophile *Xenodusa* has a similar life history. The larvae are found in *Formica* nests and the adults overwinter in the nests of the carpenter ants of the genus *Camponotus*. W. M. Wheeler (1911) first discovered this fact more than 50 years ago. It is undoubtedly significant that *Camponotus*, like *Myrmica*, maintains larvae throughout the winter. It may well be that the host-changing behavior of *Xenodusa* has the same significance as that discussed in *Atemeles*.

The myrmecophiles described so far all possess the necessary repertoire to enable them to live in the brood chambers of the ants' nests. These chambers constitute the optimal niche within an ant nest for a social food-flow parasite. Other myrmecophiles lacking the ability to communicate with their hosts to this degree tend to occupy other parts of the colony. For example, staphylinid beetles of the European genus *Dinarda* are usually found in more peripheral chambers of *Formica sanguinea*. It is also in the peripheral chambers of the nest that food exchange occurs between the foragers and the nest workers. Thus, at this site the *Dinarda* are able to participate in the social food flow. They obtain food in three ways. Occasionally they insert themselves between two workers exchanging food and literally snatch the food droplet from the donor's mouth. They also use a simple begging behavior in order to obtain food from returning food-laden foragers. The beetle approaches an ant and touches its labium surreptitiously. This usually causes the ant to regurgitate a small droplet of food. The ant, however, immediately recognizes the beetle as an alien and commences to attack it. At the first sign of hostility the beetle raises its abdomen and offers the ant the appeasement secretion. The secretion is quickly licked up by the ant, and almost immediately the attack ceases. During this brief interval the beetle makes its escape. Other groups of staphylinid beetles, for example, those of the genus *Pella*, live outside the nest on the garbage dumps or along the trails of the ants. Such myrmecophiles have evidently not developed any of the interspecific communication signals that would permit them to live inside the nest chambers. They do, however, possess and use the abdominal "appeasement glands" when attacked by the ants.

Some of the myrmecophiles prey on ants. For example, *Pella laticollis* lives near the trail of *Lasius fuliginosus* and hunts ants. When attacked by the ants it quickly provides the appeasement secretions. Then, it uses the moment's pause to jump on the back of the ant and to kill her by a bite between the head and thorax. The beetle next drags the ant away from the trail and devours it (Hölldobler, Möglich, and Maschwitz, unpublished observations).

Along the trails of *Lasius fuliginosus* are also to be found the nitidulid beetle *Amphotis marginata*. Acting as "highwaymen" in the ant world, these beetles

FIG. 18. The nitidulid beetle *Amphotis marginata* waits in ambush on the foraging trails of *Lasius fuliginosus* for food-laden workers. By stimulating the ant's mouthparts (1) the beetle causes it to regurgitate crop contents (2). The robbed ant frequently reacts aggressively, but passive defense (3) enables the armored beetle to weather the attack. (From Hölldobler, 1971b.)

successfully stop and obtain food from ants returning to the nest. Ants that are heavily laden with food are most easily deceived by the beetles' simple begging behavior. Soon after the beetle begins to feed, however, the ant realizes it has been tricked and attacks the beetle. The beetle then is able to defend itself simply by retracting its appendages and flattening itself on the ground. This mechanism gives the beetle adequate protection (Fig. 18). Laboratory experiments have shown that *Amphotis* locates the nests and the trails of *Lasius fuliginosus* by recognizing host-specific odors and the trail pheromones laid down by the ants (Hölldobler, 1968; Hölldobler, unpublished observations). Other myrmecophiles also utilize the chemically marked trails of their host species to locate the host nests or to follow the colony during emigrations. This is especially true for the myrmecophiles associated with army ants (Akre and Rettenmeyer, 1968). Moser (1964) reported that the myrmecophilic cockroach *Attaphila fungicola,* which lives in nests of the leaf cutter ant, *Atta texana,* follows artificial trails composed of the trail pheromone of the host ants.

In short, the success of the myrmecophiles depends largely on their ability to communicate with their hosts. Interspecific communication between a myrmecophile and its host might arise in evolution in two ways. First, we can think of the ant as a signal transmitter and the potential myrmecophile as a signal receiver. By the gradual evolutionary modification of its receptor system and behavior, the myrmecophile has succeeded in discriminating the transmitter's signals. In this way the myrmecophiles may have evolved the ability to recognize the odors of their specific hosts, the difference between host adults and larvae, and so forth. Second, the myrmecophile can be regarded as the signal transmitter and the potential host ant as the signal receiver. Beetle signals that induce social behavior in the ants have been favored in natural selection and very gradually improved. In both cases the ant's behavior serves as the model which the beetle mimics. The evolution of the myrmecophilous relationship therefore involves adaptive change in the potential myrmecophile only. By comparative analyses of the interspecific associations and communication mechanisms of closely related species it is possible to reconstruct a picture of the possible evolutionary pathways which led to the highly specialized social parasitic relationships in ant societies. The predatory behavior of *Pella laticollis* and the more primitive myrmecophilic behavior of *Dinarda dentata* may very well represent early evolutionary steps which have led in the end to the highly adapted myrmecophilic behavior of *Atemeles* and *Lomechusa.*

Acknowledgments

I would like to thank E. O. Wilson for reading the manuscript and my wife, Turid, for the illustrations. My own research, reported in this article, has been supported by grants from the Deutsche Forschungsgemeinschaft and the National Science Foundation of the United States.

References

Akre, R. D., and Rettenmeyer, C. W. 1968. Trail-following by guests of army ants (Hymenoptera: Formicidae: Ecitonini). *J. Kansas Entomol. Soc.* **41**, 165–174.

Alexander, R. D. 1975. Natural selection and specialized chorusing behavior in acoustical insects. *In* "Insects, Science and Society" (D. Pimental, ed.), pp. 35–77. Academic Press, New York.

Barlin, M. R., Blum, M. S., and Brand, J. M. 1976. Species-specificity studies on the trail pheromone of the carpenter ant, *Camponotus pennsylvanicus* (Hymenoptera; Formicidae). *J. Georgia Entomol. Soc.* **11**, 162–164.

Bergström, G., and Löfquist, J. 1973. Chemical congruence of the complex odoriferous secretions from Dufour's gland in three species of ants of the genus *Formica. J. Insect Physiol.* **19**, 877–907.

Blum, M. S. 1966. The source and specificity of trail pheromones in *Termitopone, Monomorium* and *Huberia,* and their relation to those of some other ants. *Proc. R. Entomol. Soc. London* **41**, 155–160.

Blum, M. S. 1974. Pheromonal sociality in the hymenoptera. *In* "Pheromones" (M. C. Birch, ed.), pp. 223–249. North-Holland Publ., Amsterdam.

Blum, M. S., and Wilson, E. O. 1964. The anatomical source of trail substances in formicine ants. *Psyche* **71**, 28–31.

Blum, M. S., Moser, J. C., and Cordero, A. D. 1964. Chemical releasers of social behavior. II. Source and specificity of the odor trail substances in four attine genera (Hymenoptera; Formicidae). *Psyche* **71**, 1–7.

Blum, M. S., Water, S. L., and Traynham, J. G. 1966. Chemical releasers of social behavior, VI: the relation of structure to activity of ketones as releasers of alarm for *Iridomyrmex pruinosus* (Roger). *J. Insect Physiol.* **12**, 419–427.

Blum, M. S., Crewe, R. M., Sudd, J. H., and Garrison, A. W. 1969. 2-Hexenal: isolation and function in a *Crematogaster (Atopogyne)* sp. *J. Georgia Entomol. Soc.* **4**, 145–148.

Bradshaw, J. W. S., Baker, P., and Howse, P. E. 1975. Multicomponent alarm pheromones of the weaver ant. *Nature* **258**, 230–231.

Brand, J. M., Duffield, R. M., MacConnell, J. G., Blum, M. S., and Fales, H. M. 1973. Caste-specific compounds in male carpenter ants. *Science* **179**, 388–389.

Buschinger, A. 1968. "Locksterzeln" begattungsbereiter ergatoider Weibchen von *Harpagoxenus sublaevis* Nyl. (Hymenoptera, Formicidae). *Experientia,* **24**, 297.

Buschinger, A. 1972. Giftdrüsensekret als Sexualpheromon bei der Ameise *Harpagoxenus sublaevis. Naturwissenschaften* **59**, 313–314.

Butenandt, A., Linzen, B., and Lindauer, M. 1959. Über einen Duftstoff aus der Mandibeldrüse der Blattschneiderameise *Atta sexdens rubropilosa* Forel. *Arch. Anat. Microscop. Morphol. Expr.* **48**, 13–19.

Cammaerts-Tricot, M. C. 1974. Piste et pheromone attractive chez la fourmi *Myrmica rubra. J. Comp. Physiol.* **88**, 373–382.

Cammaerts-Tricot, M. C. 1975. Ontogenesis of the defense reactions in the workers of *Myrmica rubra* L. (Hymenoptera: Formicidae). *Anim. Behav.* **23**, 124–130.

Carthy, J. D. 1950. Odour trails of *Acanthomyops fuliginosus. Nature (London)* **166**, 154.

Carthy, J. D. 1951. The orientation of two allied species of British ants, II: odour trail laying and following in *Acanthomyops (Lasius) fuliginosus. Behaviour* **3**, 304–318.

Dobrzanski, J. 1966. Contribution to the ethology of *Leptothorax acervorum* (Hymenoptera: Formicidae). *Acta Biol. Exp. (Warsaw)* **26**, 71–78.

Falke, J. 1968. Substanzen aus der Mandibeldrüse der Männchen von *Camponotus herculeanus.* Dissertation, Org. Chem. Institut der Universität Heidelberg.

Fletcher, D. J. C., and Brand, J. M. 1968. Source of the trail pheromone and method of trail laying in the ant *Crematogaster peringueyi. J. Insect Physiol.* **14**, 783–788.

Gabba, A., and Pavan, M. 1970. Researches on trail and alarm substances in ants. *In* "Communication by Chemical Signals" (J. W. Johnston, D. G. Moulton, and A. Turk, eds.), pp. 161–203. Appleton, New York.

Hangartner, W. 1967. Spezifitat und Inaktivierung des Spurpheromons von *Lasius fuliginosus* Latr. und Orientierung der Arbeiterinnen im Duftfeld. *Z. Vgl. Physiol.* **57**, 103–136.

Hangartner, W. 1969a. Trail laying in the subterranean ant *Acanthomyops interjectus*. *J. Insect Physiol.* **15**, 1–4.

Hangartner, W. 1969b. Structure and variability of the individual odor trail in *Solenopsis* (Formicidae). *Z. Vgl. Physiol.* **62**, 111–120.

Hangartner, W., and Bernstein, S. 1964. Über die Geruchsspur von *Lasius fuliginosus* zwischen Nest und Futterquelle. *Experientia* **20**, 392–393.

Hangartner, W., Reichson, J., and Wilson, E. O. 1970. Orientation to nest material by the ant *Pogonomyrmex badius* (Latreille). *Anim. Behav.* **18**, 331–334.

Haskins, C. P., and Whelden, R. M. 1965. "Queenless" worker sibship, and colony versus population structure in the formicid genus *Rhytidoponera*. *Psyche* **72**, 87–112.

Hingston, R. W. G. 1929. "Instinct and Intelligence." Macmillan, New York.

Hölldobler, B. 1967. Zur Physiologie der Gast-Wirt-Beziehungen (Myrmecophilie) bei Ameisen, I: Das Gastverhältnis der *Atemeles*- und *Lomechusa*-Larven (Col. Staphylinidae) zu *Formica* (Hym. Formicidae). *Z. Vgl. Physiol.* **56**, 1–21.

Hölldobler, B. 1968. Der Glanzkafer als "Wegelagerer" an Ameisenstrassen. *Naturwissenschaften* **55**, 397.

Hölldobler, B. 1969. Orientierungsmechanismen von *Atemeles pubicollis* Bris. bei der Wirtssuche. *Zool. Verh. Zool. Ges. Würzburg 1969, Zool. Anz.* **33**, 580–585.

Hölldobler, B. 1970a. Zur Physiologie der Gast-Wirt-Beziehungen (Myrmecophilie) bei Ameisen, II: Das Gastverhältnis der imaginalen *Atemeles pubicollis* Bris. (Col. Staphylinidae) zu *Myrmica* und *Formica* (Hym. Formicidae). *Z. Vgl. Physiol.* **66**, 215–250.

Hölldobler, B. 1970b. Chemische Verständigung im Insektenstaat. *Umschau* **70**, 663–669.

Hölldobler, B. 1971a. Sex pheromone in the ant *Xenomyrmex floridanus*. *J. Insect Physiol.* **17**, 1497–1499.

Hölldobler, B. 1971b. Communication between ants and their guests. *Scientific American* **224**, 86–93.

Hölldobler, B. 1971c. Recruitment behavior in *Camponotus socius* (Hym. Formicidae). *Z. Vgl. Physiol.* **75**, 123–142.

Hölldobler, B. 1971d. Homing in the harvester ant *Pogonomyrmex badius*. *Science* **171**, 1149–1151.

Hölldobler, B. 1972. Verhaltensphysiologische Adaptationen an ökologischen Nischen in Ameisennestern. *Verh. Dtsch. Zool. Ges.* **65**, 137–144.

Hölldobler, B. 1973a. Zur Ethologie der chemischen Verständigung bei Ameisen. *Nova Acta Leopold.* **37**, 259–292.

Hölldobler, B. 1973b. Chemische Strategie beim Nahrungserwerb der Diebsameise (*Solenopsis fugax* Latr.) und der Pharaoameise (*Monomorium pharaonis* L.). *Oecologia* **11**, 371–380.

Hölldobler, B. 1976a. Tournaments and slavery in a desert ant. *Science* **192**, 912–914.

Hölldobler, B. 1976b. Recruitment behavior, home range orientation and territoriality in harvester ants, *Pogonomyrmex*. *Behav. Ecol. Sociobiol.* **1**, 3–44.

Hölldobler, B. 1977a. The behavioral ecology of mating in harvester ants (Hymenoptera: Formicidae: *Pogonomyrmex*). *Behav. Ecol. Sociobiol.* **1**, 405–423.

Hölldobler, B. 1977b. Communication in social hymenoptera. *In* "How Animals Communicate" (T. Sebeok, ed.). Indiana Univ. Press, Bloomington, Indiana, pp. 418–471.

Hölldobler, B., and Haskins, C. P. 1977. Sexual calling behavior in primitive ants. *Science* **195**, 793–794.

Hölldobler, B., and Maschwitz, U. 1965. Der Hochzeitsschwarm der Rossameise *Camponotus herculeanus* L. (Hym. Formicidae). *Z. Vgl. Physiol.* **50**, 551–568.

Hölldobler, B., and Wilson, E. O. 1970. Recruitment trails in the harvester ant *Pogonomyrmex badius*. *Psyche* **77**, 385–399.

Hölldobler, B., and Wilson, E. O. 1977. Weaver ants: Social establishment and maintenance of territory. *Science* **195**, 900–902.

Hölldobler, B., and Wüst, M. 1973. Ein Sexualpheromon bei der Pharaoameise *Monomorium pharaonis* (L.). *Z. Tierpsychol.* **32**, 1–9.

Hölldobler, B., Möglich, M., and Maschwitz, U. 1973. *Bothroponera tesserinoda* (Formicidae): Tandemlauf beim Nestumzug. *Encycl. Cinematographica* (E 2040/1973), 3–14.

Hölldobler, B., Möglich, M., and Maschwitz, U. 1974. Communication by tandem running in the ant *Camponotus sericeus*. *J. Comp. Physiol.* **90**, 105–127.

Huwyler, S., Grob, K., and Viscontini, M. 1973. Identifizierung von sechs Komponenten des Spurpheromons der Ameisenart *Lasius fuliginosus*. *Helv. Chim. Acta* **56**, 976–977.

Huwyler, S., Grob, K., and Viscontini, M. 1975. The trail pheromone of the ant, *Lasius fuliginosus*: Identification of six components. *J. Insect Physiol.* **21**, 299–304.

Law, J. H., and Regnier, F. 1971. Pheromones. *Ann. Rev. Biochem.* **40**, 533–540.

LeMasne, G. M. 1952. Les échanges alimentaires entre adultes chez la fourmi *Ponera eduardi* Forel. *C. R. Acad. Sci. Paris* **235**, 1549–1551.

Leston, D. 1970. Entomology of the cocoafarm. *Ann. Rev. Entomol.* **15**, 273–295.

Leuthold, R. H. 1968a. Recruitment to food in the ant *Crematogaster ashmeadi*. *Psyche* **75**, 334–350.

Leuthold, R. H. 1968b. A tibial gland scent-trail and trail-laying behavior in the ant *Crematogaster ashmeadi* Mayr. *Psyche* **75**, 233–248.

Löfquist, J. 1976. Formic acid and saturated hydrocarbons as alarm pheromones for the ant *Formica rufa*. *J. Insect Physiol.* **22**, 1331–1346.

McGurk, D. J., Frost, J., Eisenbraun, E. J., Vick, K., Drew, W. A., and Young, J. 1966. Volatile compounds in ants: identification of 4-methyl-3-heptanone from *Pogonomyrmex* ants. *J. Insect Physiol.* **12**, 1435–1441.

Maschwitz, U. 1964. Gefahrenalarmstoffe und Gefahrenalarmierung bei sozialen Hymenopteren. *Z. Vgl. Physiol.* **47**, 596–655.

Maschwitz, U. 1975. Old and new trends in the investigation of chemical recruitment in ants. *In* "Pheromones and Defensive Secretions in Social Insects" (Ch. Noirot, P. E. Howse, and G. Le Masne, eds.), pp. 47–59. IUSSI, Dijon.

Maschwitz, U., Hölldobler, B., and Möglich, M. 1974. Tandemlaufen als Rekrutierungsverhalten bei *Bothroponera tesserinoda* Forel (Formicidae, Ponerinae). *Z. Tierpsychol.* **35**, 113–123.

Möglich, M., and Hölldobler, B. 1974. Social carrying behavior and division of labor during nest moving. *Psyche* **81**, 219–236.

Möglich, M., and Hölldobler, B. 1975. Communication and orientation during foraging and emigration in the ant *Formica fusca*. *J. Comp. Physiol.* **101**, 275–288.

Möglich, M., Hölldobler, B., and Maschwitz, U. 1974a. *Camponotus sericeus* (Formicidae): Tandemlauf beim Nestumzug. *Encycl. Cinematograph.* (E 2039-1974), 3–18.

Möglich, M., Maschwitz, U., and Hölldobler, B. 1974b. Tandem calling: A new kind of signal in ant communication. *Science* **186**, 1046–1047.

Moser, J. C. 1964. Inquiline roach responds to trail-marking substance of leaf-cutting ants. *Science* **143**, 1048–1049.

Moser, J. C., and Silverstein, R. M. 1967. Volatility of trail marking substance of the town ant. *Nature* **215**, 206–207.

Pain, J. 1973. Pheromones and hymenoptera. *Bee World* **54**, 11–24.

Regnier, F. E., and Wilson, E. O. 1968. The alarm defence system of the ant *Acanthomyops claviger*. *J. Insect Physiol.* **14**, 955–970.

Regnier, F. E., and Wilson, E. O. 1971. Chemical communication and "propaganda" in slave maker ants. *Science* **172**, 267–269.

Regnier, F. E., Nieh, M., and Hölldobler, B. 1973. The volatile Dufour's gland components of the harvester ants *Pogonomyrmex rugosus* and *P. barbatus*. *J. Insect Physiol.* **19**, 981–992.

Riley, R. G., Silverstein, R. M., and Moser, J. C. 1974a. Biological responses of *Atta texana* to its alarm pheromone and the enantiomer of the pheromone. *Science* **183**, 760–762.

Riley, R. G., Silverstein, R. M., and Moser, J. C. 1974b. Isolation, identification, synthesis and biological activity of volatile compounds from heads of *Atta* ants. *J. Insect Physiol.* **20**, 1629–1637.

Ruttner, F., and Ruttner, H. 1965. Untersuchungen über die Flugaktivität und das Paarungsverhalten der Drohnen, 2: Beobachtungen an Drohnensammelplätzen. *Z. Bienenforsch.* **8**, 1–18.

Ruttner, H., and Ruttner, F. 1972. Untersuchungen über die Flugaktivität und das Paarungsverhalten der Drohnen, 5: Drohnensammelplätze und Paarungsdistanz. *Apidologie* **3**, 203–232.

Strang, G. 1970. A study of honey bee drone attraction in the mating response. *J. Econ. Entomol.* **63**, 641–645.

Sudd, J. H. 1957. Communication and recruitment in Pharaoh's ant, *Monomorium pharaonis* (L.). *Anim. Behav.* **5**, 104–109.

Szlep, R., and Jacobi, T. 1967. The mechanism of recruitment to mass foraging in colonies of *Monomorium venustum* Smith, *M. subopacum* ssp. *phoenicium* Em., *Tapinoma israelis* For. and *T. simothi* v. *phoenicium* Em. *Insect Soc.* **14**, 25–40.

Szlep-Fessel, R. 1970. The regulatory mechanism in mass foraging and recruitment of soldiers in *Pheidole*. *Insect Soc.* **17**, 233–244.

Torgerson, R. L., and Akre, R. D. 1970. The persistence of army ant chemical trails and their significance in the ecitonine-ecitophile association (Formicidae: Ecitonini). *Melanderia* **5**, 1–28.

Traniello, J. F. A. 1977. Recruitment behavior, orientation and the organization of foraging in the carpenter ant *Camponotus pennsylvanicus* De Geer (Hymenoptera: Formicidae). *Behav. Ecol. Sociobiol.* **2**, 61–79.

Tumlinson, J. H., Silverstein, R. M., Moser, J. C., Brownlee, R. G., and Ruth, J. M. 1971. Identification of the trail pheromone of a leaf-cutting ant, *Atta texana*. *Nature* **234**, 348–349.

Tumlinson, J. H., Moser, J. C., Silverstein, R. M., Brownlee, R. G., and Ruth, J. M. 1972. A volatile trail pheromone of the leaf-cutting ant, *Atta texana*. *J. Insect Physiol.* **18**, 809–814.

Wasmann, E. 1910. Die Doppelwirtigkeit der *Atemeles*. *Dtsch. Entomol. Nat.* **1**, 1–11.

Wasmann, E. 1915. Neue Beitrage zur Biologie von *Lomechusa* und *Atemeles*, mit kritischen Bemerkungen über das echte Gastverhältnis. *Z. Wiss. Zool.* **114**, 233–402.

Wheeler, W. M. 1911. Notes on the myrmecophilous beetles of the genus *Xenodusa*, with a description of the larva of *X. cava* LeConte. *J. N.Y. Entomol. Soc.* **19**, 164–169.

Whelden, R. M. 1960. Anatomy of *Rhytidoponera metallica*. *Ann. Entomol. Soc. Am.* **53**, 793–808.

Wilson, E. O. 1958. A chemical releaser of alarm and digging behavior in the ant *Pogonomyrmex badius* (Latreille). *Psyche* **65**, 41–51.

Wilson, E. O. 1959a. Source and possible nature of the odor trail of fire ants. *Science* **129**, 643–644.

Wilson, E. O. 1959b. Communication by tandem running in the ant genus *Cardiocondyla*. *Psyche* **66**, 29–34.

Wilson, E. O. 1962. Chemical communication among workers of the fire ant *Solenopsis saevissima* (Fr. Smith): 1. The organization of mass-foraging; 2. An information analysis of the odor trail; 3. The experimental induction of social response. *Anim. Behav.* **10**, 134–164.

Wilson, E. O. 1965. Trail sharing in ants. *Psyche* **72**, 2–7.

Wilson, E. O. 1971. "The Insect Societies." Belknap, Harvard Univ. Press, Cambridge, Mass.

Wilson, E. O. 1975. Enemy specification in the alarm-recruitment system of an ant. *Science* **190**, 798–800.

Wilson, E. O. 1976. The organization of colony defense in the ant *Pheidole dentata* Mayr (Hymenoptera: Formicidae). *Behav. Ecol. Sociobiol.* **1**, 63–82.

Wilson, E. O., and Bossert, W. H. 1963. Chemical communication among animals. *Rec. Prog. Horm. Res.* **19**, 673–716.

Zwarlicki, C., and Morse, R. A. 1963. Drone congregation areas. *J. Apicult. Res.* **2**, 64–66.

Filial Responsiveness to Olfactory Cues in the Laboratory Rat

MICHAEL LEON

DEPARTMENT OF PSYCHOLOGY
MCMASTER UNIVERSITY
HAMILTON, ONTARIO, CANADA

I. INTRODUCTION

The relationship between a mother rat and her litter is characterized by a fine synchrony between the physiological, physical, and behavioral changes in the pups and the complementary changes in the mother. The development of the young depends on the mother providing the shelter, protection, and nurturance appropriate to the changing needs of the pups; the young must also alter their responses to the changing maternal care which they are offered.

Initially, the dam takes virtually total initiative in providing for the well-being of the young. At birth she licks and bites through the fetal membranes and cleans the pups thoroughly before they are placed in the maternal nest. She then assumes the nursing posture over the young, allowing them to suckle. If the young become displaced from the nest, perhaps by remaining attached to a nipple when the mother leaves, she retrieves the pups back to the nest (Rosenblatt and Lehrman, 1963; Sturman-Hulbe and Stone, 1929; Wiesner and Sheard, 1933), and she similarly transports the young away from the nest to a place of safety (Calhoun, 1962; Sturman-Hulbe and Stone, 1929). The mother facilitates elimination of urine and feces by the young by licking their anogenital region, builds and repairs the nest, determines the length of the nest bout, selects the environment in which the young remain, regulates their thermal and nurtural states, and defends them from predators and conspecifics (Calhoun, 1962; Friedman, 1975; Gelineo and Gelineo, 1951; Grota and Ader, 1969; Rosenblatt and Lehrman, 1963; Sturman-Hulbe and Stone, 1929; Wiesner and Sheard, 1933).

The pups literally are unable to see or hear, and their maintenance is probably aided by positive thigmo- and thermotaxis, which lead them to huddle together in the nest and allow them to contact the warm, furred mother for nursing (Alberts, 1976; Gustafsson, 1948). Their ability to respond to the environment matures rapidly over the following weeks; changes in the mother's behavior are congruent with this maturation. The mother, for example, spends less time in the nest as the young grow older, but at the same time, she provides increasing amounts of milk to the young, which remain dependent on her for their food intake even as they leave the nest (Babický et al., 1973; Grota and Ader, 1969; Rosenblatt and Lehrman, 1963). When the young become mobile they still maintain their intermittent nursing bouts by actively seeking out their dam or by rejoining their littermates in the nest. Eventually, when the mother becomes unresponsive to the demands of her litter during weaning, the young gradually assume physiological and behavioral independence and the weanlings no longer seek maternal care.

At each point in this intricate dyadic relationship, continual alterations occur in the behavior and physiology of the dam that complement the continually changing states of her growing young. In the discussion below, I describe those aspects of this finely synchronized relationship that are mediated, at least in part, by olfactory processes, concentrating on the use of volatile chemical cues by the rat pup during the alliance with the mother.

II. PUP RESPONSES TO OLFACTORY CUES

A. EARLY RESPONSES TO ODORS

Rats respond behaviorally to various noxious chemicals on Days 1–2 (Bolles and Woods, 1964; Small, 1899; Welker, 1964), although the responses to strong chemicals may not be mediated via the primary olfactory system (Alberts, 1976). Sniffing occurs in brief bursts in newborn rats and the frequency begins to rise sharply on Day 8. This behavior increases the airflow that passes over the olfactory receptors, and the sniffing rate reaches adult levels by Day 14 postpartum, coincident with the maturation of the neural basis for olfaction (Salas et al., 1969). Discrete head movements are noticeable beginning on Day 8, and coordinated patterns of vibrissae, nose, head and respiratory movements are present with each sniffing cycle (Welker, 1964).

Pups have been reported to react to maternal odor with an inhibition of gross motor activity as early as Day 2, and continuing through Day 12 (Shapiro and Salas, 1970). Direct observation of the pups in the experimental apparatus used to record pup movement, however, reveals that the transient inhibition of gross motor activity occurs as the pups raise their heads to sniff the air; the pups then typically orient themselves toward the odor source (Leon, unpublished observations). Similarly, Altman *et al.* (1973) observed that rat pups begin to orient toward their home cage odor from a distance of 30 cm as early as 3 days and by Day 8 the majority of pups orient toward their home cage most of the time.

Behavioral responses to odors associated with the mother and the nest are observed, therefore, at a time during the mother–litter relationship when the mother spends a large portion of the day in contact with her young (Croskerry *et al.*, 1976; Grota and Ader, 1969) and the pups are entirely dependent on the mother for their sustenance and care. The young are capable of responding to maternal odors quite early in life with gross behavioral movements (pivoting) to orient toward home odors, and also with finer orientating movements when in contact with their mother. This ability was first suggested when pups that were made anosmic either peripherally (using zinc sulfate) or centrally (by removal of the olfactory bulb) often failed to survive or did not gain as much weight as controls (Alberts, 1976; Kling, 1964; Pollack and Sachs, 1975; Singh and Tobach, 1975; Singh *et al.*, 1977; Tobach *et al.*, 1967).

B.   ORIENTATION TOWARD THE NIPPLE

Close behavioral observation of anosmic young indicate not only that they do not orient toward the mother and their littermates, but even when in contact with the mother they do not readily attach to a nipple (Alberts, 1976; Singh and Tobach, 1975; Singh *et al.*, 1977). It therefore appears as though the pups can not locate and attach to a nipple for suckling without chemical cues. Perhaps the reason that automated feeders are ineffective in inducing the young to suckle from them is that no natural chemical cues have been presented on the apparatus (i.e., Gustafsson, 1948).

When intact pups are presented with nipples that had been cleaned with organic solvents, the pups do not attach to the nipples, even if they brush over one with their snout. Simply allowing the organic solvents to evaporate without washing the nipple area, presumably leaving any natural chemical cues intact, does not interfere with approach and attachment to the nipples (Hofer *et al.*, 1976; Teicher and Blass, 1976). Moreover, the material taken from the nipple area is effective in reinstating nipple attachment on washed nipples and an extract from the saliva of the pups is similarly effective (Teicher and Blass, 1976).

While pups 4–5 days to 14 days of age utilize these cues for successful nipple attachment, a small number of pups made anosmic as early as three days postpartum, and most pups made anosmic in the second week postpartum, do live, albeit with a somewhat lowered rate of growth (see above). Therefore, although these chemical cues surrounding the nipple probably play an important role in the natural development of the mother–litter relationship, the older anosmic pups may be able to compensate, at least in part, for the loss of the chemical cues by utilizing other sensory information to obtain sustenance from their mother. The awake mother may also facilitate the establishment and maintenance of suckling by their offspring by behavioral means, while the anesthetized dam used in these studies is incapable of engaging in either gross or subtle interactions that might allow nipple attachment to occur in the absence of natural ventral odors. Since the probability of survival increases with the age at which the pups were made anosmic, it is possible that nonolfactory cues are reinforced by the mother's presence and that these stimuli maintain natural contact in these young rats in context wtih olfactory cues.

C. ORIENTATION TOWARD THE NEST

Altman *et al.* (1973) found that between Days 10 and 12 there was a sharp decrease in the latency of pups to go from an unfamiliar cage to their home cage and that the proportion of the pups successfully homing increased noticeably at this age. The pups responded to the odor of their isolated littermates, but oriented somewhat more quickly to the home cage odor (Altman *et al.* 1971).

Bolles and Woods (1964) observed as early as 2–3 days after birth that pups oriented toward the nest material in their home cage upon being scattered when the mother left the nest with her young still attached to her nipples. Gregory and Pfaff (1971) found that 12-day-old rats placed in an alley reliably moved into the area that contained their home cage bedding in preference to clean bedding, although some show the preference at an earlier age. Older pups (13–19 days old) preferred to move to home cage bedding rather than bedding taken from a virgin female, but no preference was demonstrated for home cage bedding over bedding from another lactating female and her litter. Landauer *et al.* (1976) extended these findings by demonstrating that while 12-day-old pups prefer the odor of their home cage, 16-day-old rats investigate home and strange cage bedding equally, and 21-day-old pups prefer the bedding of a strange mother and litter to their own.

D. ORIENTATION TOWARD THE MOTHER

1. *Maternal Attractiveness*

If nest material attracts pups by means of an olfactory cue, it is likely that the mother herself is imparting an odor to the bedding. Bolles and Woods (1964) observed one rat pup to crawl a distance away from its littermates toward its mother on Day 4 postpartum; this instance is the sole report of a pup approaching a mother in the first week of life. Donaldson (1924) and Farris (1950) first observed this type of behavior at about 10 days postpartum. Small (1899) noted a 12-day-old pup that crawled to its mother from the nest and began to suckle.

The importance of odor emitted by lactating females in eliciting this approach behavior was substantiated by Nyakas and Endröczi (1970). Mother rats were separated from their young and placed in an arm of a U maze. Their Day 10 pups were allowed to approach either arm of the maze, and most went to the mother on each trial. These pups preferred the mother to a virgin female, a male, or the mother's urine. It was established that the mother emitted an attractive cue not emitted by other adult rats, and the question of the nature of the attractant was then addressed. Pups did not prefer either arm of the maze when a temperature differential was established in the maze, suggesting that thermal cues were not critical for attracting the pups. The role of olfactory cues was clarified by placing a mother in one arm of the maze and a virgin female in the other, then removing them, leaving their odors behind. The pups still chose the side previously occupied by the mother, of necessity utilizing only odor stimuli. Then the ability of the pups to utilize olfactory cues was inhibited by local anesthesia of the nasal mucosa. Even when the mother was present in one arm of the maze, the young demonstrated no preference for that side. Only when olfactory cues were present, and young were able to detect them did they approach the maternal odor.

In a parallel study, Leon and Moltz (1971) tested the responses of 16-day-old young to different odors in an olfactory discrimination apparatus (Fig. 1), which consists of a start box leading to a triangular open field, ending in a shallow cliff beyond which lay two visually concealed goal compartments. Forced air was passed from a central source through each goal compartment, and up the cliff, to

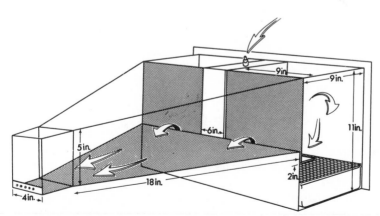

FIG. 1. The olfactory discrimination apparatus used to determine olfactory preferences by allowing the young to approach either goal box and descend the cliff, thereby registering a choice.

permit the delivery of olfactory cues to pups in the start chamber. The pups are allowed to descend the cliff of either goal compartment to register a choice. Of the 16-day-old pups 93% chose their own mother in preference to a virgin female, and 99% chose their mother rather than an empty goal box. Both their own and strange mothers were approached equally when placed in the different goal boxes simultaneously, and unfamiliar colony mothers were approached when opposed to an empty goal box.

The olfactory nature of this attractant was demonstrated by showing that pups would not choose their mother preferentially if they were upwind of her, but would approach a goal box that she had previously occupied. Also, the pups did not approach their mother more frequently than a virgin female when all airborne chemical cues were eliminated.

The term *maternal pheromone,* which we have labeled this olfactory substance, will be used in our discussion in the original sense of chemical communication between conspecifics (Karlson and Butenandt, 1959).

2. The Pheromonal Bond

Little evidence of attraction to either mother or virgin female was seen in 1 or 10-day-old pups, despite their ability to register a choice with a locomotor response. Between Days 12 and 14 there was a pronounced increase in the proportion of pups approaching their mother, the attraction remaining high until Day 27. By Day 41 the choice was essentially random. This pattern of pheromonal bond development is particularly interesting, since the young begin to leave the nest at the time that the bond develops and are weaned at its termination (Leon and Moltz, 1972).

Of course, testing young with their own mother at different ages after birth confounded the separate tracing of the ontogeny of pup responsiveness to the pheromone with the ability of their mother to emit the attractant. I discuss the development of pheromone emission in the mother and then address the problem of the development of the approach response to it in the young.

In order to observe the capability of pheromone emission by mother rats, 16-day-old colony pups, which were shown to be highly attracted to maternal pheromone, were used to detect the presence of the odor. We observed whether they approached colony mothers at different lactational ages or colony virgins. The 16-day-old test pups did not exhibit a significant preference for the mothers until Day 14 of lactation, but then they continued to be highly attracted to them through Day 21, and by Day 27 the response had waned. Mother rats, therefore, emit their attractant odor during the third and fourth weeks postpartum (Leon and Moltz, 1972).

Pups of different ages were then tested once with the odor of the Day 16 mothers that served as a standard, attractive pheromone source. The young began to approach the odor at 12–14 days, and they continued to respond to the odor

until the attraction waned at 27 days (Leon and Moltz, 1972). A striking synchrony exists between the pup approach response and maternal pheromone emission, as young pups orient to the what are probably low concentrations of maternal odor emitted during the first two weeks postpartum, then begin to approach
the stronger odor until pheromone emission declines at 4 weeks after birth.

3. Source of Odor Emission

Before further investigation of the mechanism controlling the time of
pheromone emission, one must know from what source, as well as by what
mechanism, the odor is emitted into the external environment. In an effort to
identify the source of the odor, various excretions of the Day 16 mother were
presented to the Day 16 colony pups to determine which were capable of attracting the mobile young. The urine of the mothers did not attract the young, but the
anal excreta was as attractive as the mother herself. The anal excreta collected
from virgin females, however, was not effective in attracting pups (Leon, 1974).

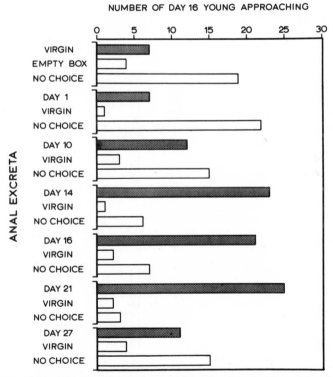

FIG. 2. The number of the 30 16-day-old colony pups that approached the anal excreta of a virgin
female or that of mothers at different points in lactation.

Recalling the pattern of maternal pheromone emission, one would expect the anal excreta of mothers of different lactational ages to change in its ability to attract test pups, just as the attractiveness of the mother herself changes during the postpartum period. The young begin to prefer the anal excreta of lactating females to virgin female excreta when the dams are 14 days postpartum, the attraction lasting until Day 27 (Fig. 2). The pattern of response elicited by the anal excreta alone is virtually the same as that of the mother herself (Leon, 1974).

If one examines the material defecated by females during a 3-hr period, one finds that on Day 1, when the anal excreta is not attractive to the pups, the amount defecated is similar in a mother and a virgin. There is a sharp increase in amount of anal excreta defecated by Day 10–14 mothers and it remains high

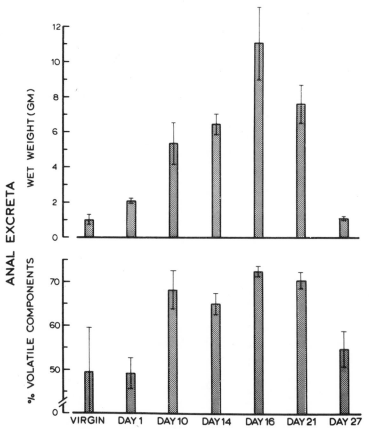

Fig. 3. The weight and proportion of volatile components of the anal excreta defecated in a 3-hr period from virgin and lactating mothers.

throughout the period that the pheromonal bond exists. The weight of the defecated material declines at Day 27, when pheromone emission ends (Fig. 3).

The anal excreta of pheromone-emitting mothers also differs qualitatively from that of Day 1 or Day 27 mothers or virgin females. The most obvious difference is that in addition to the familiar, formed, dry, black feces, these attractive mothers excrete large quantities of a semisolid, light-colored, unformed substance. This material, known as caecotrophe, is formed in the caecum of rats (Harder, 1949) and the increased caecotrophe defecation is associated with a rise in the volatile components of the maternal anal excreta.

4. Site of Odor Synthesis

The caecum is a large structure in the rat pouching out at the junction of the small and large intestine, which becomes enlarged during lactation (Fell et al., 1963). A digested mass enters the caecum from the small intestine, and the material that is pushed into the distal section of the caecum serves as a substrate for bacterial growth. When it is defecated, it is called caecotrophe. The material from the proximal section of the caecum is passed through the large intestine and anus as feces. The caecotrophe passes through the large intestine with relatively little water loss and is eaten by adult rats directly from the anus (Harder, 1949; Lutton and Chevallier, 1973). The caecotrophe then mixes with the food in the stomach and small intestine (Harder, 1949), where the bacteria contained in the caecotrophe are critical for effective diet utilization and nutrition (Hoetzel and Barnes, 1966; Mikelson, 1956). Harder (1949, p. 104) suggested that the caecotrophe "must have a special aroma which is more attractive to the animals" if adults were to discriminate the caecotrophe from feces for caecotrophy. Virgin female rats consume virtually all of the caecotrophe that they may emit, but lactating females produce large amounts of caecotrophe that they do not consume immediately. The excess caecotrophe is one obvious difference between those females that attract pups and those that do not, and it seems probable that the caecotrophe is the specific portion of the anal excreta that serves as the substrate for pheromone emission. In fact, when the feces portion of the anal excreta is separated and presented to the test young, they find it relatively unattractive, while the caecotrophe alone is as attractive as the entire anal excreta. The caecotrophe, then, carries the odor to the environment. Since the caecum is the site at which the anal excreta is differentiated into caecotrophe and feces, it seems quite possible that this structure is the site of pheromone synthesis.

If the odor is synthesized in the caecum and not, for example, by an anal gland that marks the caecotrophe but not the feces, then the pheromone might be present in the unexcreted caecal material itself. In a study designed to test this possibility, pups were highly attracted to the caecal contents of Day 16 mothers, indicating that secretions of the anal glands are not critical for the attraction. Moreover, material taken from the gastrointestinal tract above the caecum was also unattractive to young, adding further support to the proposal that the site of synthesis is the caecum itself (Leon, 1974).

Since both lactating and nonlactating adult rats produce caecotrophe in their caecum, the attractive odor might be present in the caeca of both mothers and virgins. The material taken from virgin females as well as from adult males was highly attractive to the pups, suggesting that the odor is synthesized in the caecum of all adult rats. Although the caecotrophe portion of the anal excreta is typically consumed by adult rats, if one collects some unconsumed caecotrophe from these rats, it is highly attractive to pups (Leon, unpublished observations).

Since both lactating and nonlactating rats synthesize the odor, the difference in the attractiveness of lactating mothers seems to arise from the differential emission of uningested caecotrophe. One possibility for this difference could be that mother rats simply reingest less of the caecotrophe that they defecate, with the remainder forming the medium for pheromone transmission. A more likely explanation is that lactating females reingest as much or more of their caecotrophe, but there is enough of an increase in the amount of caecotrophe defecated that a proportion of the substance remains unconsumed and carries the attractant to the environment. Some support for this suggestion lies in the fact that the rat alimentary canal, particularly the caecum, greatly increases in length and weight during lactation (Boyne *et al.*, 1953; Campbell and Fell, 1964; Cripps and Williams, 1975; Fell *et al.*, 1963; Poo *et al.*, 1939; Souders and Morgan, 1957). The gastrointestinal tract processes large amounts of feed at an increased rate (Adams *et al.*, 1976) during the time of pheromone emission. Further, after about Day 10, this increase in food consumption by the lactating mother is not accompanied by a weight gain (Anderson and Turner, 1963; Brody and Nisbet, 1938; Cole and Hart, 1938; Cotes and Cross, 1954; Fell *et al.*, 1963; Fleming, 1976; Menaker & Navia, 1973; Ota and Yokoyama, 1967a, b; Slonaker, 1925; Wang, 1925; see Fig. 4).

The food intake of mothers may reach two to three times that of virgin females, and the increased processing of these large amounts of food might very well lead to increased defecation and uningested caecotrophe that determine the appearance of maternal pheromone. Although a strong correlation exists between the high levels of food consumption and increased amounts of excess caecotrophe that attracts the pups, the necessity of such intake patterns had not been established. Leon (1975) limited the amount of food that lactating females were allotted and observed the effects of this rationing procedure on the defecation of caecotrophe and on the emission of the pheromone. Since nonlactating females do not emit pheromone when eating 20 gm of food each day, mother rats had their food rationed at several different amounts without disrupting lactation. They received 50, 40, 35, or 30 gm of food each day, and on Day 16 postpartum were tested for their attractiveness to pups. Maternal pheromone was inhibited in those mothers allowed to eat only 30 gm of food, while the mothers ingesting 50

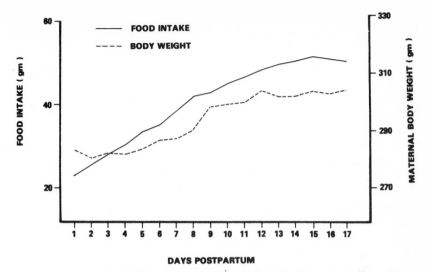

FIG. 4. The food intake and body weight of a group of 10 Wistar mothers nursing litters of 8 pups and ingesting Purina Laboratory chow.

gm were highly attractive. Not surprisingly, there was a direct relationship between the amount of food consumed and the weight of anal excreta defecated. Moreover, with an increase in food intake there was an increase in excess caecotrophe emitted, as measured by the proportion of volatile components as well as by qualitative examination of the anal excreta.

The maternal pheromone starts being emitted just about the time that the mother's weight gain stabilizes although food intake continues to rise toward the end of the second postpartum week. An experiment was done to determine whether the amount of food eaten by mothers on Day 8, even though it is considerably elevated over that of virgins, was sufficient to induce pheromone emission on Day 16. The prediction was that mothers would not be attractive on Day 16 when allowed to ingest only the amount they had been eating on Day 8, each day through Day 16. It was found that mothers whose food intake was maintained on Day 8 amounts were not attractive to pups, whereas mothers that were able to eat at liberty were highly attractive. Therefore, it is a result of the great amount of food that is eaten during the second week of lactation that excess caecotrophe is emitted.

5. Stimulus Control of Pheromone Emission

Mother rats nursing their litters are quite sensitive to the stimulation they receive from the pups. For example, there is a strong correlation between the size of the mother's litter and the amount of food she consumes. The dam also increases her diet consumption and produces increasing quantities of milk as the pups get older. When pup stimulation is removed at the time of weaning, her food intake goes down (Ota and Yokoyama, 1967a, b). The period of pheromone emission occurs during the above period when the mother increases her consumption of food while her body weight remains stable.

If the stimulation from the pups induces the high levels of food intake that are shown to be essential for excess caecotrophe defecation, then by altering the amount of pup stimulation that a mother receives one should be able to alter her ability to emit maternal pheromone. Mothers nursing one-day-old pups eat relatively small quantities of food, defecate little or no excess caecotrophe, and do not attract pups. Day 16 mothers that have been nursing developing pups for over two weeks, and consequently are eating large quantities of food, are highly attractive to pups (Leon, 1975; see Figs. 2, 3, and 4). Moltz and Leon (1973) allowed mothers to nurse only one-day-old young by replacing their litters each day with newly born foster litters: these mothers never experienced the stimulation of developing pups and neither consumed large quantities of food nor defecated excess caecotrophe (Leon, unpublished observations). Control mothers received a new foster litter of advancing age each day.

When tested in the olfactory discrimination apparatus on Day 16 postpartum, the 16-day-old pups did not approach the mothers that had nursed only Day 1 pups, and clearly preferred the control mothers, demonstrating that maternal pheromone emission depends on appropriate pup stimulation.

It was not possible to advance the onset of pheromone production by substituting Day-10 pups for a mother's newly born young, testing when she was 6 days postpartum and the litter she was raising was 16 days old. Perhaps in both experimental situations the litter stimulation at the time of testing was inappropriate or insufficient to induce the emission of excess caecotrophe carrying the maternal pheromone.

Would the termination of pheromone emission also be blocked by inappropriately aged litters? Although maternal responsiveness to developing pups wanes until weaning occurs after the fourth postpartum week, a mother will continue to nurse younger foster litters when they are substituted before the female's own litter induces a decline in lactation (Bruce, 1961; Nicoll and Meites, 1959; Selye and McKeown, 1934; Thatcher and Tucker, 1968; Wiesner and Sheard, 1933). Not only is maternal behavior prolonged when a mother rat is kept with young pups, but the mother continues to lactate and to ingest great quantities of food (Tomogane et al., 1976a). One might expect then that these females would defecate more caecotrophe than they reingested and would, therefore, emit maternal pheromone.

Moltz et al. (1974) maintained mothers with 14- to 21-day-old foster litters after the mothers had begun to emit the pheromone. These mothers continued to emit the pheromone till 53 days postpartum, while control mothers kept with appropriately aged pups stopped after Day 27 postpartum. When the pup stimulation is such that lactation continues with the accompanying increase in food intake, pheromone emission can be prolonged. Holinka and Carlson (1976) also were able to extend the period of maternal pheromone emission by means by changing the age of the litters that the mothers nursed. They were also able to inhibit pheromone emission by introducing older pups to mothers. In this case the older pups presumably induced a decline in lactation with its concomitant fall in diet consumption, as is characteristic of mothers no longer nursing their young (Ota and Yokoyama, 1967b).

6. Endocrine Control of Pheromone Emission

In the rat mother, ovarian, adrenal, and hypophyseal hormones have all been shown to be dependent on pup stimulation for their secretion during lactation (Amenomori et al., 1970; Grota and Eik-Nes, 1967; Grosvenor, 1964a, b; Merchant, 1974; Zarrow et al., 1972). I will first explore the possibility that one of these hormones may be essential for maternal pheromone emission, and then determine whether they act through the elevation of food intake in mother rats.

Leon and Moltz (1973) found that postpartum adrenalectomy, ovariectomy or the combined operation had little effect on the attractiveness of mother rats when these dams reared litters of healthy foster pups. However, mothers with reduced prolactin release from the adenohypothesis by means of daily morning injections of ergocornine hydrogen maleate, a drug found to reduce the release of pituitary prolactin in vivo (Lu et al., 1971; Shaar and Clemens, 1972; Wuttke et al., 1971), were unattractive to test pups when they were given the opportunity to approach them in the discrimination apparatus. Prolactin injections given concurrently with the ergot derivative successfully reversed the inhibition of pheromone emission, specifically indicating the importance of prolactin for odor emission. It is important to note that all the mothers in all groups behaved maternally to their foster young, despite surgical or pharmacological intervention (Leon and Moltz, 1973; Numan et al., 1972).

Prolactin, assayed during lactation, is elevated for an extended period (Amenomori et al., 1970; Merchant, 1974) preceding and during the onset of pheromone emission (Leon and Moltz, 1972). During early stages of lactation, suckling by the pups serves as the main stimulus for the release of prolactin by the mother (Amenomori et al., 1970; Terkel et al., 1972). However, by Day 14, and continuing through Day 21, a period coincident with the development of pheromone emission (Leon and Moltz, 1972), exteroceptive (i.e., nonsuckling) pup stimuli release prolactin in the mother (Grosvenor, 1965; Grosvenor et al., 1970; Mena and Grosvenor, 1972; Moltz et al., 1969).

Prolactin titers in mothers are sensitive both to inadequate as well as incongruent pup stimulation, for when a disparity exists between the postpartum age of the mother and the chronological ages of the foster young, there is a decline in prolactin response to the young (Bruce, 1961; Grosvenor *et al.,* 1970). Perhaps only when mother and young are matched—only when the mother's postpartum physiological condition is in step with the age-related stimulus characteristics of her young—do the sustained high prolactin levels necessary for the appearance of pheromone emission occur. When parturient females are kept with Day 1 pups for 16 days, they did not emit the pheromone, presumably because the pup stimulation induced relatively low levels of prolactin, that were unable to stimulate the emission of the pheromone (Moltz and Leon, 1973). Day 10 pups given to parturient females were unable to promote the onset of odor emission, when the pups were 16 days old and the mother was 6 days postpartum presumably because the incongruent pup stimuli did not release sufficient prolactin, or did so too briefly to stimulate pheromone emission. Congruently, extended lactation induced by continuous replacement of foster litters keeps prolactin levels elevated, and pheromone emission is prolonged after the time of natural weaning when prolactin levels normally decline (Amenomori *et al.,* 1970; Moltz *et al.,* 1974; Tomogane *et al.,* 1976b). These data indicate the pheromone to be under the ultimate stimulus control of the young—the appropriate stimuli releasing the high sustained levels of prolactin necessary for pheromone emission.

Parturient females were given injections of ergocornine (Leon, 1974), ergonovine, or CB154 (Leon, unpublished observations) to reduce prolactin release (Fluckiger and Kovacks, 1974; Shaar and Clemens, 1972), and were offered healthy pups of appropriate age daily. At 16 days postpartum, their anal excreta was collected after 3 hr of isolation, when it was tested for its attractive capability. As predicted, no caecotrophe was present in the defecated material, and it was not approached by the Day 16 test young. Prolactin replacement therapy, which restored the attractiveness of the material, resulted in excess caecotrophe being defecated. That emission and not synthesis was dependent on the presence of high levels of prolactin was demonstrated by taking material directly from the caecum where the odor is produced. This material was highly attractive in prolactin-blocked mothers, while their anal excreta remained unattractive.

Both mothers and virgins synthesize the attractant odor, but the lactating females have high plasma concentrations of prolactin and emit the odor, while the virgins have low prolactin levels and do not release the pheromone. When maternal prolactin levels are suppressed, they are similar to virgin females with naturally low prolactin concentrations since neither emits the odor, despite its synthesis. Maternal pheromone is maternal only in the sense that lactating females alone secrete sufficient amounts of prolactin to induce excess caecotrophe defecation that attracts mobile young.

7. *Prolactin, Food Intake, and Pheromone Emission*

How does prolactin induce the defecation of excess caecotrophe that serves as the vehicle for pheromone emission? Prolactin could either inhibit reingestion of caecotrophe by lactating females, or it could induce their increased eating and drinking patterns and thereby cause large enough amounts of caecotrophe to be defecated, to preclude full reingestion of the caecotrophe. Mothers are ingesting large quantities of food during periods that they begin to emit excess caecotrophe. These intake patterns are dependent on the presence of the young (Ota and Yokoyama, 1967a), perhaps by stimulating lactation, the metabolic demands of which might provoke elevated food consumption by the mother. Maternal ingestive patterns though, may not be induced directly by the metabolic demands of milk production. Cotes and Cross (1954) severed the galactophores of mother rats, a procedure that probably reduced the metabolic demands of lactation by inhibiting milk delivery to the pups while maintaining the stimuli associated with developing young, which were fostered each day. Nevertheless, the same pattern of a continuing increase in food intake was observed, and the authors concluded that the stimuli associated with suckling were sufficient to cause the increased food intake. Fleming (1976) also found an elevation in food intake after inhibition of milk flow.

Recall that (1) suckling and nonsuckling stimuli associated with the young induce the release of prolactin in the postpartum female rat (Amenomori et al., 1970; Grosvenor, 1965; Grosvenor et al., 1970; Mena and Grosvenor, 1972); (2) direct assay of prolactin in lactating females has shown high plasma levels of this hormone throughout the first three postpartum weeks (Amenomori et al., 1970); and (3) high levels of prolactin are essential for excess caecotrophe, and therefore maternal pheromone emission (Leon and Moltz, 1973). It seemed possible that pups could stimulate maternal food consumption by causing the release of prolactin by their suckling, which, in turn, stimulates increased food intake, resulting in the defecation of excess caecotrophe, which serves as the substrate for pheromone synthesis and the vehicle for its emission.

Studies by Tindal (1956), Fleming (1976), Grosvenor (1956), and Tomagane et al., (1975) have demonstrated that when prolactin release is suppressed by ergot derivatives in postpartum females, food intake is depressed. Using the same dose and injection regimen of ergocornine that inhibited excess caecotrophe defecation in lactating mothers, Leon (unpublished observations) was able to suppress food intake to the levels of virgin females. Ovariectomy, adrenalectomy, or the combined operation did not produce such an alteration in diet consumption (Fleming, 1977; Leon, unpublished observations; Ota and Yokoyama, 1967a). Furthermore, prolactin replacement therapy (50 IU per day in PVP; see Morishige & Rothchild, 1972) partially restored elevated food intake of intact mothers (Leon, unpublished observations, Fig. 5; Tomagane et al., 1975). The effects of ergocornine were not due to its antiadrenergic properties since ergonovine, which does not inhibit these neurotransmitters (Grollman, 1965; Nickerson, 1970), was equally effective in reducing food intake in mother rats. Finally, the influence of prolactin on food intake is probably not mediated by its effect on galactopoiesis, since females whose nipples are sealed, but who

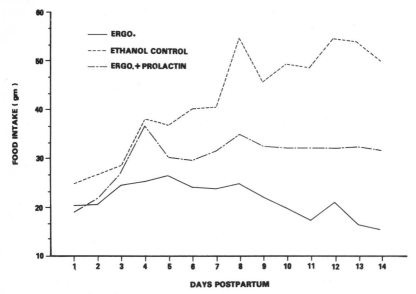

FIG. 5. Food intake of mother rats kept with foster litters of 8 pups on Purina diet and receiving daily injections of ergocornine (0.5 mg per day), ergocornine plus prolactin (25 IU, 2 times per day, suspended in PVP), or control injections.

continue to receive suckling stimulation consume elevated levels of their diet and produce excess caecotrophe that carries the attractive maternal pheromone (Leon, unpublished observations).

Using another approach, Leon (1974) gave daily injections of prolactin to virgin female rats in an effort to approximate that aspect of the maternal state that is critical for pheromone emission. After 16 days of injections, Day 16 colony test pups chose between the prolactin-treated and the saline-treated females. Eighty percent of the pups approached the prolactin-injected females, demonstrating the effectiveness of these hormone injections in inducing maternal pheromone emission. The food and water intake and weight gain observed in the prolactin-treated rats was virtually identical in pattern, although not in magnitude, to that of lactating females (Fig. 6). Prolactin induced a sharp rise in weight gain until Day 12, after which time the rate of body weight gain stabilized, while the food intake remained elevated. The quantitative and qualitative measures of the anal excreta revealed the defecation of uningested caecotrophe in the prolactin-treated females, but not in the control animals. Thus, it is not the absolute levels of food intake, weight gain and caecotrophe defecation, but the relationship between these processes that determines whether the attractant is emitted.

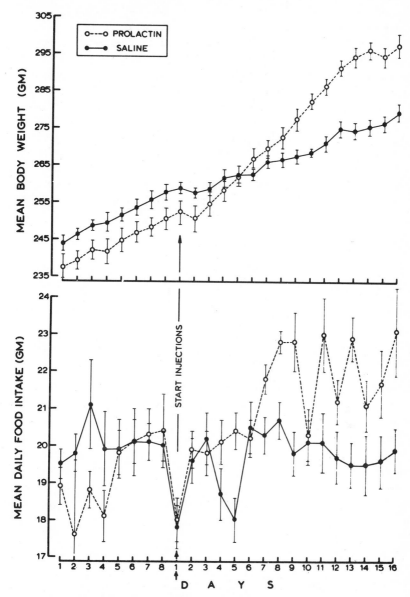

FIG. 6. The body weight and food intake of virgin female rats injected with either prolactin (25 IU, 2 times per day in saline) or with the saline vehicle alone.

Koranyi *et al.* (1977) have shown that pups elicit the release of prolactin in virgins that have become maternal after continuous exposure to foster pups (Rosenblatt, 1967). The elevated levels of prolactin should stimulate the release of the attractant odor. Virgin females after being subjected to such pup stimulation emitted the odor (Leidahl and Moltz, 1975), achieving through pup stimulation that which was previously shown with prolactin injections.

Male rats are similar to virgin females in that both synthesize the attractant in their caecum, have low endogenous levels of prolactin, eat relatively small amounts of food, gain weight gradually, defecate little caecotrophe that remains uningested, and do not attract pups (Leon, unpublished observations). However, while females experience naturally elevated levels of plasma prolactin during lactation, males never are subjected to this endogenous state. Exogenous prolactin can cause the female system to emit excess caecotrophe, carrying the attrac-

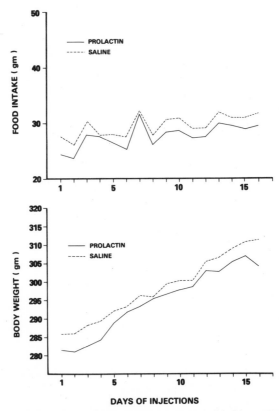

FIG. 7. The body weight and food intake of male rats injected with either prolactin (25 IU, 2 times per day in saline) or with the saline vehicle alone.

tive odor into the environment, but the same treatment does not induce a change in male food intake or weight gain, or attractant emission (Leon, unpublished observations, Fig. 7; Li et al., 1949; Pfaff, 1969). Similarly, males that become maternal after being exposed continuously to foster pups (Leon et al., 1973; Rosenblatt, 1967) do not emit the pheromone as do females (Leidahl and Moltz, 1975).

Male rats, however, will emit the odor after the infusion into their caecum of bile taken from females that are emitting the pheromone. Bile taken from mothers not emitting the pheromone, either due to lactational age or to prolactin suppression, was not capable of stimulating pheromone emission (Moltz and Leidahl, 1977).

Since intact males synthesize the attractant odor, the implications of these data must bear on the mechanism of its emission. The mother rat that emits the odor consumes large quantities of food, which is moved through the gastrointestinal tract at an elevated rate (Adams et al., 1976).

It is likely that a substance in bile is secreted at high levels in response to increased food intake, which facilitates the transport through the gastrointestinal tract of material that becomes feces and caecotrophe. Prolactin-suppressed and recently parturient mothers do not consume large amounts of food and would not be expected to produce this increase in hepatic secretion. Therefore, while the bile of pheromone-emitting mothers might elevate the rate of gastrointestinal transport, producing increased, and perhaps excess caecotrophe emission, mothers eating relatively small amounts of food should secrete bile that is ineffective in this regard.

8. Microbial Control of Pheromone Synthesis

Caecal material serves as a substrate for the growth of enteric microorganisms (Raibaud et al., 1966), and the volatile chemicals produced by microbial metabolism appear to be the source of the attractive odor. To test this idea the growth of caecal bacteria was inhibited by allowing mother rats to ingest the antibiotic, neomycin sulfate. These females did not attract pups in the olfactory discrimination apparatus, whereas mothers ingesting a solution not containing the antibiotic were preferred by a large majority of the young. Tetracyclene, another antibiotic that inhibits microbial growth by a different mode of action, had effects similar to those of neomycin (Leon, 1974).

Although these data suggest a role of caecal bacteria in pheromone production, they do not indicate whether the presence of the microbial population during lactation is essential for the synthesis of the pheromone, or its emission. To determine if synthesis was inhibited by the antibiotic, the contents of the caecum, the site of odor synthesis, were obtained from both neomycin and control mothers and tested for their attractiveness to pups. Pups preferred caecal contents from control mothers over that from neomycin-treated mothers, indicating that the synthesis of the pheromone was inhibited rather than its emission. There was no difference in the weight or proportion of volatile components of the anal excreta defecated over a 3-hr period by neomycin or control mothers indicating that emission of anal excreta was not altered by drug treatment. Neomycin was also capable of inhibiting the attractive capability of virgin caecal contents, supporting the hypothesis that the mechanism for odor synthesis is similar in both lactating and nonlactating adults.

While these data strongly supported a microbial mode of synthesis of the attractant, it was possible that the antibiotic substance might have nullified the attractive odor by direct chemical action either in the gastrointestinal tract, or by some action elsewhere in the body. A nonmicrobial explanation for the synthesis of the pheromone cannot be excluded by these data. The caecal bacteria therefore were deprived of their medium for growth in order to interfere with bacterial function indirectly without the use of pharmacological agents. The growth of microbial organisms requires raw carbohydrates in the caecum; if sucrose, which is completely absorbed above the level of the caecum, is the only constituent carbohydrate in the maternal diet, caecal bacterial function is inhibited for want of an appropriate growth medium (Fredericia *et al.*, 1927; Guerrant *et al.*, 1935, 1937; Hopkins and Leader, 1946; Roscoe, 1927). Mothers fed this sucrose-based diet attracted neither their own pups nor pups raised with mothers that ingested Purina Laboratory Chow. No preference was demonstrated for the caecal contents of sucrose-diet mothers. The reinstatement of carbohydrates in the caecum by means of the addition of starch to the experimental diet restored the attraction of the mother rats (Leon, 1974). Thus, when caecal bacteria function was disrupted, either by direct antibiotic action, or indirectly by withdrawal of an adequate growth medium, the pheromone is not synthesized.

The mechanism for synthesis therefore depends on microbial functioning, and the mechanism for emission depends on developing pups inducing high levels of

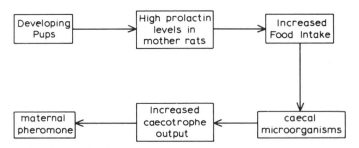

FIG. 8. A model for maternal pheromone synthesis and emission. Developing pups stimulate prolonged, high levels of prolactin in their mothers, and these lactating females consume large quantities of food. The odor is produced in the caecum by enteric microorganisms and is transmitted to the external environment by the defecation of caecotrophe, which is not reingested.

prolactin that induce increased food consumption and caecotrophe defecation, carrying the pheromone. A model of pheromone synthesis and emission is represented in Fig. 8.

9. Dietary Control of Pheromone Synthesis

The synthesis of maternal pheromone is dependent on the action of the caecal microorganisms on the substrate supplied by the food eaten by the lactating rat (Section II.D.8). Since rats consume a wide variety of foods, however, the substrate within the caecum would be expected to change with different diets. The consumption of qualitatively different diets would result in differential growth of enteric bacterial populations (Draser et al., 1973; Porter and Rettger, 1940; Rettger & Horton, 1914; Smith, 1965), and the metabolic products synthesized on the different substrates would also be altered (Fred et al., 1921; Lampen and Peterjohn, 1951). It therefore seemed entirely likely that dissimilar diets might alter the synthesis of maternal pheromone by changing caecal bacterial population patterns with their differing volatile metabolic products. It should be noted that except for special experimental diets, all colony mothers were fed the same Purina Laboratory Chow diet.

The existence of different diet-dependent maternal odors could be demonstrated by means of a behavioral assay only if the approach response of mobile pups was specific to the maternal odors of dams eating a particular diet. If that were the case, then the pups could serve to identify the different maternal odors by their differential approach responses. Accordingly, mothers were permitted access to either of two diets, arbitrarily referred to as Diets A and B, and their young were subsequently observed systematically for their preference for the odor emitted in the excreta of mothers fed either diet (Leon, 1975).

A choice then was offered to both Diet A and Diet B pups. They were allowed to choose between the anal excreta of two colony mothers, one that had been eating Diet A and the other, Diet B. The young showed a clear preference for the odor emitted by mothers that had been eating the same diet as their own mothers. Therefore, even though mothers eating both diets emitted an attractant, the attraction was specific to the odor with which the pups had previous experience.

Pups raised by mothers eating Diet A overwhelmingly preferred the odor of the anal excreta defecated by colony Diet A mothers to that of Diet A virgins. Diet B pups showed the same response pattern for Diet B maternal anal excreta when compared to that of Diet B virgin females. These data confirm the original finding that 16-day-old pups approach the odor emitted in the anal excreta of same diet mothers (Leon, 1974; Leon and Moltz, 1971).

It was possible that the specificity of the pheromonal bond shown by the young might have been a reflection of a greater relative attraction for the familiar odor over the unfamiliar. That is, although Diet B pups preferred Diet B maternal odor, they might have approached Diet A maternal odor if the former was not present in the test situation. This possibility was examined by allowing Diet B pups to choose between the anal excreta of Diet A mothers and Diet A virgins in the test situation, while Diet A pups were given the appropriate, opposite choice.

Neither Diet A nor Diet B pups demonstrated a preference for mothers over virgins that had been eating a diet different from their own mothers, even in the absence of their familiar maternal odor. There is a specificity involved in the pheromonal bond that is dependent on the kind of food the mother is eating and the particular odor that the young experience. Clearly, the pheromone is not an innate, species-typic releaser, but rather the approach behavior appears to be an individually learned response on the part of the pups to the specific odor of the mother. Although all mobile rat pups may be attracted to the odor of lactating mothers, their response is guided by the familiarity of the emitted odor. The form of the pheromonal response is therefore species-typic, but the pheromonal bond exists only in terms of individual experience.

III.   ONTOGENY OF ATTRACTION IN RAT PUPS

The attraction of pups to the particular odor of the mother must be established through experience with that odor, but by what mechanism does the approach response develop? It is possible that pups approach the first maternal odor to which they are exposed. Pups raised with a mother that did not emit any maternal pheromone might be responsive to the odor of either Diet A or B fed mothers in the test situation. Mothers fed the sucrose-based diet (Diet S) do not produce an attractant (Section II.D.8). Pups raised with these mothers are not attracted to Diet S mothers, but more significantly, they are not attracted to the odor of Diet A mothers either. Even without the possible interference of Diet B odor in Diet B raised pups, there is no attraction to Diet A in these pups, and the same is true with respect to possible interference of Diet A in the pups' responses to Diet B (Leon, 1975).

Would pups raised with a mother that did not produce an attractant develop a responsiveness to the maternal pheromone of other mothers eating another diet if they were given the appropriate exposure to that odor? Diet S mothers that did not produce the pheromone were allowed to raise pups either in an isolated room, or in a room that housed 20–40 mothers eating Diet A and producing a salient odor highly attractive to their progeny. When tested for their approach behavior to either the odor of the Diet A mothers or virgins, the isolated Diet S pups showed no attraction to the odor, but those Diet S pups reared in its presence overwhelmingly chose the maternal attractant. Clearly, the exposure of maternal pheromone to pups while being nurtured by their non-pheromone-producing mother was quite effective in establishing a pheromonal attraction to a specific maternal odor.

The above findings all suggest an important role for experience in the ontogeny of pup attraction to maternal pheromone, but the question remains as to the nature of the experience necessary for approach responses to the odor to develop. Young rats seek the warmth and the nourishment (Gustafsson, 1948) that constitute critical facets of maternal care. These unconditional stimuli elicit unconditioned approach responses, and the maternal pheromone may function as a conditioned stimulus that elicits approach behavior after many paired repetitions with warmth and nourishment. It is possible, however, that association of maternal odor with maternal warmth, contact and feeding are not necessary for the development of the tendency of pups to approach the odor of the dam. The possibility exists that simple exposure to the odor of a mother in the absence of any primary reinforcement is sufficient to produce a tendency to approach that odor.

Leon *et al.* (1977) allowed pups to be reared by a Diet S mother that did not produce an attractive maternal odor. Such pups are not attracted to odors of mothers fed either Diet A or B, upon initial exposure. From Days 1 to 19, the pups were taken from their own mother and isolated in an apparatus where they received either filtered air, or the odor of a Day 16–21 mother that was ingesting Purina Laboratory Chow and emitting maternal pheromone. On Day 20, the Diet S-reared pups were tested for their response to Day 16–21 anal excreta of Purina-fed dams. Those litters that had been preexposed to the maternal odor in the absence of contact with the mother approached the maternal odor with as great a probability as pups actually reared by Purina mothers. Diet S pups exposed to fresh air did not develop the attraction. Simple exposure without any reinforcement from the mother is sufficient to establish normal responsiveness to maternal pheromone (Fig. 9).

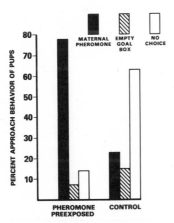

Fig. 9. The proportion of pups preexposed to either maternal pheromone or fresh air that approached the maternal pheromone.

The naturally occurring odors synthesized by dams are limited to the odors produced by caecal microorganisms. The possibility exists, however, that the developing rat will respond also to a wide range of preexposed odors when exposed to an arbitrary odor. This phenomenon has been reported several times in several species (Carter, 1972; Carter and Marr, 1970; Cornwell, 1975; Mainardi *et al.*, 1965; Marr and Gardner, 1965; Marr and Lilliston, 1969), but in these studies the odors were associated with other features of the mother (Cheal, 1975). The mechanisms responsible for increased attraction of preexposed artificial odors may differ from that underlying the development of approach to maternal pheromone.

We therefore exposed pups to an arbitrary odor (peppermint) in isolation, to determine whether the development of attraction as a result of simple exposure is limited to the class of odors produced in the caecum of the maternal rat (Leon *et al.*, 1977). Pups exposed to fresh air in isolation demonstrated a significant avoidance of the peppermint odor, but pups that were preexposed overwhelmingly preferred the odor. Simple exposure to an arbitrary odor, even one not produced by a lactating female, is sufficient to render that odor attractive to the pups, even if it is initially, inherently aversive.

Postnatal exposure of young mammals to either a naturally occurring or arbitrary stimulus, in the absence of any obvious reinforcement, is sufficient to enhance the attractiveness of that stimulus in affiliative situations. Extrapolation from these findings suggests that a simple nonassociative mechanism supports the development of approach responses in pups.

Perhaps, as a general rule, simple familiarity with a given stimulus will enhance the relative attractiveness of that stimulus to a young animal. It is possible that for young mammals, as for adults (Barnett, 1958; Mitchell, 1976), novel stimuli are inherently aversive. Placement of a subject in a test situation to which it has not been previously exposed introduces that individual to a wealth of novel, and therefore, aversive stimuli. In such a situation, that portion of the test environment containing salient, familiar cues would be least novel and consequently least aversive. The young organism might therefore be expected to seek out the source of familiar cues in the novel environment. On this model, the apparent attractiveness of the familiar odor is reinterpreted as a reduced unattractiveness of that stimulus in an environment composed of unfamiliar aversive elements. The reduced aversiveness resulting from exposure might be attributed either to reduced saliance of the preexposed stimulus (Rescorla, 1971) or to a "learned safety" process (Rozin and Kalat, 1971; Siegel, 1974).

Many of the requisite conditions for the acceptance of this model have been met in experimental analyses and observations of the mother–litter interaction. First, there is an increase in exploratory and sniffing behavior in young rats about the time of onset of the pheromonal bond (Bolles and Woods, 1964; Welker,

1971). Furthermore, when placed in an unfamiliar environment away from mothers and siblings, young rats demonstrate a striking increase in locomotor activity concurrent with the time that they approach maternal pheromone (Bronstein and Dworkin, 1974; Campbell *et al.*, 1969; Campbell and Mabry, 1972; Randall and Campbell, 1976; Feigly *et al.*, 1972; Goodrick, 1975; Hofer, 1973a, b, 1975; Leon and Moltz, 1972; Moorcroft, 1971; Moorcroft *et al.*, 1971; Tobach *et al.*, 1967).

The young rat responds to a novel environment devoid of familiar odors by moving. Presumably its efforts would take it out of the situation (if the test environments were not enclosed), thereby increasing the probability of encountering the mother, siblings, nest, or their residual cues. These responses to novel areas are persistent, and do not readily habituate (Bronstein *et al.*, 1974; Feigly *et al.*, 1972; Goodrick, 1975) although habituation to mildly nociceptive stimulation is present as early as Day 1 (File and Plotkin, 1974; File and Scott, 1976).

Second, one would expect that the presence of the mother with her familiar odor would subdue the young. Hofer (1975, 1976) and Randall and Campbell (1976) have observed just such a phenomenon.

The third expectation is that if the maternal pheromone was the agent that familiarized the environment, then pups deprived of the ability to utilize those cues would show elevated locomotor activity, even in the presence of their mother in the home cage. Pups made anosmic either by surgical disruption of the olfactory system or by chemical destruction of the olfactory epithelium respond as though they were in a novel environment, when they are actually in the presence of their mothers and littermates (Alberts, 1976; Hofer, 1975, 1976; Singh and Tobach, 1975; Singh *et al.*, 1977). This striking phenomenon is independent of the thermal or nutritive loss engendered by the anosmic pups, for when both parameters are maintained, the enhanced locomotor activity remained when the pups were made anosmic or separated from the mother (Hofer, 1973a,b; Randall and Campbell, 1976).

It is also consistent with this model of pup behavior that locomotor activity is subdued when the pups are placed with their littermates while the mother is absent (Randall and Campbell, 1976). Leon (1974) has shown that pups are marked with the odor of their mother, and that pups will approach their littermates' odor in the olfactory discrimination apparatus. When pup odor is suppressed either by raising the pups with a mother that is incapable of marking the young (Leon, 1974), or by washing and drying the pups that are to be used as goal stimuli, littermates are not attracted to each other in the test situation (Leon, unpublished observations). Alberts (1976) also found that anosmic pups tend not to aggregate as do their intact counterparts.

Using what may be a more subtle indication of distress, Oswalt and Meier (1975) found that rat pups would emit more ultrasonic vocalizations when placed over clean bedding material than on home nest material. These data suggest the sensitivity of young rats to unfamiliar environments and complement the gross behavioral evidence gathered from rat pups in a novel environment.

A critical test of this model would be to present maternal pheromone to the pups, either in a familiar or unfamiliar situation and to observe whether they approach the odor. One might expect a decrement in the approach response in a familiar environment, while pups placed in a novel environment should readily approach the same odor. Members of a litter therefore were (1) preexposed to the olfactory discrimination apparatus, (2) preexposed to a different novel environment, or (3) allowed to remain with the mother. On Day 20 postpartum, the maternal pheromone was presented in the test situation.

Those pups given experience in the testing environment either did not approach the odor, or took much longer to make a choice, while the other pups approached the odor with alacrity. These data suggest that young rats approach the maternal odor primarily because it is the most familiar, and hence, least aversive stimulus in an unfamiliar situation (Jans, Galef, and Leon, unpublished observations).

IV. WEAKENING OF THE PHEROMONAL BOND

Pups start to approach the maternal odor before the second week postpartum, and continue to do so until weaning (Babický et al., 1970, 1973). During this period, when the pheromonal bond is functional, the mother and mobile pups continue to engage in periodic nursing bouts. The maternal pheromone may serve to attract the pups to the mother and to effect these reunions by maintaining litter cohesion, keeping the young in the nest.

While I have discussed the basis for the onset and maintenance of approach behavior, I have not yet dealt with the mechanisms underlying the decline of approach to the maternal pheromone. To study this, we first determined more precisely the age at which the preference of developing pups for maternal pheromone declines (Leon and Behse, 1977). Pups were tested on Days 21–27 to trace the decline of the approach response. Those pups of 30 tested at each age that chose maternal and virgin odors or made no choice are shown in Fig. 10. It is clear that 21–24-day-old pups were still highly responsive to the maternal odor, while responsiveness dropped off sharply at Day 25, and continued to decline until Day 27. Was this decline based upon changes in the mother or upon changes in the young? Moltz et al. (1974) allowed the pups to be cared for by foster mothers of 14–21 days postpartum that may have continued to act maternally and to emit maternal pheromone at a time when the natural mother had ceased pheromone emission and parental care. Neither these pups nor normally reared

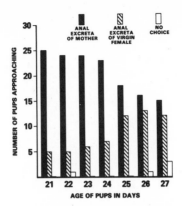

FIG. 10. The number of 30 pups, Days 21–27 postpartum, to approach the maternal pheromone, the odor of a virgin female, or that made no choice.

young approached the maternal pheromone at 27 days of age. Recall, however, that Holinka and Carlson (1976) inhibited odor emission in mothers by substituting older pups for the natural litters, and, since no measure of continuation of odor emission was taken by Moltz, Leidahl and Rowland, their data are difficult to interpret. Nevertheless, the cessation of the approach response by Day 27 postpartum may be due to some change occurring in the weanling pups, rather than to a change in odor emission.

Leon (1974) suggested that the change responsible for the decline of the weanling's approach to maternal odor might be related to the onset of caecotrophe production in weanlings. Young rats develop the same intestinal flora as their mother (Smith, 1965) by ingesting their mother's anal excreta (Leon, 1974). Since initially they also ingest the same food as their mothers (Galef and Clark, 1972), probably they produce a caecotrophe odor quite similar to their mothers'. Weaned rats begin to approach their own caecal odor coincident with the time at which their mother stops emitting her attractant. If caecal maturation is associated with cessation of approach to maternal odor, one should observe the development of caecal odor production in weanlings that parallels their decline in approach to maternal pheromone. Our next studies were aimed at determining when the young begin to produce caecotrophe and how this affects their response to maternal odor. We could determine the age at which the caecum becomes an organ capable of producing an attractant odor by exposing 16-day-old pups to the odor of the caecal contents of weanlings of various ages in the olfactory discrimination apparatus. The development of the attractiveness of the caecal material taken from weanling pups is traced in Fig. 11.

A gross examination of the caeca showed that they were relatively undeveloped on Day 21, contained little semidigested food, and the olfactory dis-

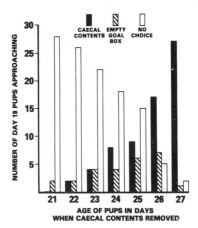

FIG. 11. The number of 30, 19-day-old colony pups that approached the odor of the caecal contents taken from pups 21–27 days postpartum.

crimination test revealed that their contents did not attract the test pups. There is a large increase in the proportion of test pups that approach the odor of the caecal material by Day 26, and it is only at Day 27 that the proportion is similar to that evoked by adult caecal material. The growth of attractiveness of the caecal material from Days 21 to 27 is highly correlated with the cessation of the pups' response to the maternal odor.

If maturation of caecal odor production is not only correlated with, but in fact causes the cessation of the approach response to maternal caecal odor, then it should be possible to extend the period during which the young are responsive to maternal pheromone by preventing maturation of caecal function in weanling rats. Caecal odor production was prevented in two ways: by surgical removal of the caecum, and by dietary suppression of caecal microorganisms.

On Day 25 postpartum, pups were subjected to either a caecectomy or to a sham operation. On Day 30, each of the weaned pups was isolated from its mother and then allowed to approach material pheromone. Caecectomized pups approached the odor, while the sham operates did not.

In the second condition, pups were weaned onto their mother's sucrose-based diet (Diet S) that would not allow the growth of the caecal microorganisms that synthesize the odor. Then, they were exposed to, and became familiar with, the maternal odor of Purina-fed mothers. The decline in responsiveness to the Purina maternal odor by Diet S-weaned pups then was compared to the decline demonstrated by Purina-weaned young that had developed an attraction to the same Purina maternal odor but had a normal maturation of caecal function. The prediction was that, while the Purina-reared weanlings should have ceased responding to the odor at 30 days postpartum, those with caecal odor inhibition would still approach the maternal attractant at that time.

These predictions were confirmed: 30-day-old pups eating the sucrose diet and exposed to Purina maternal odor continued to approach that odor, while Purina-reared pups no longer approached it. Caecal odor development in weanlings therefore is critical for the cessation of attraction to the maternal caecal odor (Leon and Behse, 1977).

We can speculate about the actual mechanism by which the development of caecal odor synthesis and emission by the weanling causes the reduction in their attraction to the maternal odor. As mothers decrease the emission of their attractive odor, the pups begin their own caecal odor and transfer their attraction to it.

V. Functional Aspects of the Pheromonal Bond

While under the care of the mother, the young not only receive her physical protection and nurturance, but the pups and nest are marked with the caecal odor of their mother, the communicative value of which lingers in her absence. Her odor may confer a familiar olfactory environment around the young, suppressing neophobic responses in the maternal environment by decreasing its novelty. As the mother ceases to emit her odor, the young begin to emit their own odor, which might maintain the familiarity of the weanling's immediate surroundings. This process would facilitate the development of independence by the weanlings by eliminating their dependency on the mother for providing a familiar olfactory environment.

Several investigators have suggested that the importance of an animal being surrounded by its own odor lies in its "confidence" value to the individual by marking the area as "safe" (Ewer, 1968; Mykytowicz, 1973). The onset of production of a rat's own odor may be particularly effective in increasing the familiarity of its immediate environment, decreasing its inherent neophobic responses to the stimuli with which they are inundated.

The "confidence" or reduction in neophobic responses induced by the odor of the individual would allow the rat to set up and defend a home area, an ability that is crucial for successful reproduction. Resident rats will typically repel intruders successfully, a behavior dependent on their ability to discriminate their odors from those of conspecifics (Alberts and Galef, 1973; Telle, 1966). When male rabbits are placed in an unfamiliar pen, one will become dominant if its anal excreta is present (Mykytowicz, 1973). Perhaps the development of the capacity to emit an individual odor allows the weanling to engage in social responses necessary for interactions with conspecifics. The emission of an individual's own odor would also allow others in its clan to identify it for appropriate social behavior.

Complete physiological and behavioral changes occur in the pups during the last week of the mother–litter interaction:

1.   The cessation of the approach response is well correlated with the gradual but steady weaning of the rats from milk to solid food.

2.   The young rats, born with a sterile gut, are inoculated by the end of the third week with the microorganisms of the mother, presumably by the ingestion of her anal excreta (Smith, 1965).

3.   The young continue to suckle until the end of the fourth postpartum week, despite their ability to be weaned soon after the second week.

4.   The milk that the young continue to ingest probably suppresses the activity of the caecal biota until weaning has occurred, by altering the pH of the alimentary canal (Hopkins and Leader, 1946). The sucrose-based diet that was used to block caecal function in the weanlings has essentially the same constituents as dried milk, with the exception that lactose is its only carbohydrate rather than sucrose. Diets in which lactose is the sole carbohydrate do not completely inhibit caecal function, but allow the growth of some microorganisms (Hopkins and Leader, 1946; Morgan and Yudkin, 1962). A diet that included milk would allow slow development of the caecal biota while supplying the nutrients that the caecal microorganisms do not yet produce.

5.   The onset of the reingestion of caecotrophe by the pups must accompany the total reliance on solid food, since caecal bacteria play a critical role in solid food utilization and nutrition.

Since the milk constitutes, in terms of calories, a negligible portion of the diet of the weanling who has been ingesting solid food since about Day 16 (Babický *et al.,* 1970, 1973), it is possible that the milk provides the vitamins (probably thiamin) that the full caecal microorganism population will synthesize after weaning (Hopkins and Leader, 1946). The milk would allow the young to grow maximally, while suppressing the growth of caecal bacteria, as well as the onset of caecal function and coprophagy, thereby delaying the self-sufficiency of the young.

Continued investment of maternal care in the young may have been selected for maintaining optimal physical growth in the young until they are fully capable of the maximal diet utilization and nutrient production; occurring with the onset of caecal function. Early weaning, even as late as 25 days postpartum, has subsequent detrimental effects on the young (Hahn, 1973; Kraus *et al.,* 1967; Macho *et al.,* 1970; Ogle and Kitay, 1974).

The continued dependence of the young on the mother's milk, coupled with their continued attraction to her, may allow the mother to engage in nonnurtural maternal behaviors (Galef and Clark, 1976). These behaviors may allow transmission of information from mother to young about the physical and social relationships that exist in their immediate environment. This information would allow the optimal utilization of the resources that surround the young.

While the dam increases her reproductive success by supporting maximal pup growth and providing information for them about their immediate environment, she will eventually lose more than she gains in terms of her parental investment in that particular litter with respect to her future reproductive attempts. At the same time, the young should continue to seek the mother's food and protection. Weaning should occur at a time when the young have a maximal probability of growing and reproducing, and at a time that minimizes the delay in future parental reproduction (Trivers, 1974). Presumably, these criteria are reached at the end of the fourth postpartum week, when the pheromonal bond is dissolved.

The maternal pheromone, while important for a specific period in the life of the young rat, is clearly only one of the stimuli that are involved in the growth and maturation of the pups. The first two weeks may find the maternal nest odors and her ventral odors as prepotent cues, only to be replaced in importance by the maternal pheromone which in turn may be replaced by other cues. The timely changes in behavior observed in developing rats indicate that they are not becoming more perfect adults, but are uniquely adapting to the problems at each point in maturation. The fine synchrony that characterizes the pheromonal bond is a reflection of the close interaction between mother and litter that is essential for the success of the reproductive process.

Acknowledgments

I would like to thank J. Brewster, B. G. Galef, Jr., and B. Woodside for their helpful comments. The preparation of this chapter was supported in part by NRC Grant A8578.

References

Adams, S. P., Ajam, I. K., Matthews, B. F., and Sullivan, P. B. 1976. Increased gastric emptying and intestinal mobility in lactating mice. *J. Physiol.* **257**, 57P–58P.

Alberts, J. R. 1976. Olfactory contributions to behavioral development in rodents. In "Mammalian Olfaction, Reproductive Processes and Behavior," (R. Doty, ed.), pp. 67–94. Academic Press, New York.

Alberts, J. R., and Galef, B. G., Jr. 1973. Olfactory cues and movement: Stimuli mediating intraspecific aggression in the wild Norway rat. *J. Comp. Physiol. Psychol.* **85**, 233–242.

Altman, J., Sudarshan, K., Das, G. D., McCormick, N., and Barnes, D. 1971. The influences of nutrition on neural and behavioral development. III. Development of some motor, particularly locomotor, patterns during infancy. *Dev. Psychobiol.* **4**, 97–114.

Altman, J., Brunner, R. L., Bulut, F., and Sudarshan, K. 1973. The development of behavior in normal and brain-damaged infant rats studied with homing (nest-seeking) as motivation. "Drugs and the Developing Brain" (A. Vernadakis and J. N. Weiner, eds.), pp. 321–348. Plenum, New York.

Amenomori, Y., Chen, C. L., and Meites, J. 1970. Serum prolactin levels in rats during different reproductive states. *Endocrinology* **86**, 506–510.

Anderson, R. R., and Turner, C. W. 1963. Feed consumption during lactation and involution in Sprague–Dawley Rolfsmeyer rats. *Proc. Soc. Exp. Biol. Med.* **113**, 334–336.

Babický, A., Ošťádalová, I., Pařízek, J., Kolář, J., and Bibr, B. 1970. Use of radiosotope techniques for determining the weaning period in experimental animals. *Physiol. Bohemoslov.* **19**, 457–467.

Babický, A., Pařízek, J., Ošťádalová, I., and Kolář, J. 1973. Initial solid food intake of young rats in nests of different sizes. *Physiol. Bohemoslov.* **22**, 557–566.

Barnett, S. A. 1958. Experiments on "neophobia" in wild and laboratory rats. *Br. J. Psychol.* **49**, 195–201.

Bolles, R. C., and Woods, J. 1964. The ontogeny of behaviour in the albino rat. *Anim. Behav.* **12**, 427–441.

Boyne, A. W., Chalmers, M. I., and Cuthbertson, D. P. 1953. The balance and partition of nitrogen in the pregnant and lactating rat. *Hoppe-Seyler's Z. Physiol. Chem.* **295**, 424–435.

Brody, S., and Nisbet, R. 1938. A comparison of the amounts and energetic efficiencies of milk production in rat and in dairy cow. Research Bulletin 285 of the University of Missouri Agricultural Experiment Station, pp. 5–30.

Bronstein, P. M., and Dworkin, T. 1974. Replication: The persistent locomotion of immature rats. *Bull. Psychon. Soc.* **4**, 124–126.

Bronstein, P. M., Neiman, H., Wolkoff, F. P., and Levine, M. J. 1974. The development of habituation in the rat. *Anim. Learn. Behav.* **2**, 92–96.

Bruce, H. M. 1961. Observations on the suckling stimulus and lactation in the rat. *J. Reprod. Fertil.* **2**, 17–34.

Calhoun, J. B. 1962. "The Ecology and Sociology of the Norway Rat." U.S. Public Health Service, Bethesda, Maryland.

Campbell, B. A., Lytle, L. D., and Fibiger, H. C. 1969. Ontogeny of adrenergic arousal and cholinergic inhibitory mechanisms in the rat. *Science* **166**, 637–638.

Campbell, B. A., and Mabry, P. D. 1972. Ontogeny of behavioral arousal: A comparative study. *J. Comp. Physiol. Psychol.* **81**, 371–379.

Campbell, R. M., and Fell, B. F. 1964. Gastrointestinal hypertrophy in the lactating rat and its relation to food intake. *J. Physiol. (London)* **171**, 90–97.

Carter, C. S. 1972. Effects of olfactory experience on the behavior of the guinea pig *Cavia porcellus*. *Anim. Behav.* **20**, 54–60.

Carter, C. S., and Marr, J. N. 1970. Olfactory imprinting and age variables in the guinea pig *Cavia porcellus*. *Anim. Behav.* **18**, 238–244.

Cheal, M. 1975. Social olfaction: A review of the ontogeny of olfactory influences on vertebrate behavior. *Behav. Biol.* **15**, 1–25.

Cole, H. H., and Hart, G. H. 1938. The effect of pregnancy and lactation on growth in the rat. *Am. J. Physiol.* **123**, 589–597.

Cornwell, C. A. 1975. Golden hamster pups adapt to complex rearing odors. *Behav. Biol.* **14**, 175–188.

Cotes, M. P., and Cross, B. A. 1954. The influence of suckling on food intake and growth of adult female rats. *J. Endocrinol.* **10**, 363–367.

Cripps, A. W., and Williams, V. J. 1975. The effect of pregnancy and lactation on food intake, gastrointestinal anatomy and the absorptive capacity of the small intestine in the albino rat. *Br. J. Nutr.* **33**, 17–32.

Croskerry, P. G., Smith, G. K., Leon, L. N., and Mitchell, E. A. 1976. An inexpensive system for continuously recording maternal behavior in the laboratory rat. *Physiol. Behav.* **16**, 223–225.

Donaldson, H. H. 1924. "The Rat: Data and Reference Tables," 2nd ed. Wistar Institute, Philadelphia.

Draser, B. S., Crowther, J. S., Goddard, P., Hawksworth, G., Hill, M. J., Peach, S., and Williams, R. E. O. 1973. The relationship between diet and gut microflora in man. *Proc. Nutr. Soc.* **32**, 49–52.

Ewer, R. F. 1968. "Ethology of Mammals." Plenum, New York.

Farris, E. J. (ed.). 1950. "The Care and Breeding of Laboratory Animals." Wiley, New York.

Feigly, D., Parsons, P., Hamilton, L., and Spear, N. 1972. Development of habituation to novel environments in the rat. *J. Comp. Physiol. Psychol.* **79**, 443–452.

Fell, B. F., Smith, K. A., and Campbell, R. M. 1963. Hypertrophic and hyperplastic changes in the alimentary canel of the lactating rat. *J. Pathol. Bact.* **85**, 179–188.

File, S., and Plotkin, H. C. 1974. Habituation in the neonatal rat. *Dev. Psychobiol.* **7**, 121–127.

File, S., and Scott, E. 1976. Acquisition and retention of habituation in the preweanling rat. *Dev. Psychobiol.* **9**, 97–107.

Fleming, A. S. 1976. Control of food intake in the lactating rat: Role of suckling and hormones. *Physiol. Behav.* **17**, 841–848.

Fleming, A. 1977. Effects of estrogen and prolactin on ovariectomy-induced hyperphagia and weight gain in female rats. *Behav. Biol.* **3**, 417–423.

Fluckiger, E., and Kovacs, E. 1974. Inhibition by 2-Br-alpha-ergocryptine-mesilate (CB 154) of suckling-induced pituitary prolactin depletion in lactating rats. *Experientia* **30**, 1173.

Fred, E. B., Peterson, W. H., and Anderson, J. A. 1921. The characteristics of certain pentose-destroying bacteria, especially as concerns their action on arabinose and xylose. *J. Biol. Chem.* **48**, 385–412.

Fredericia, L. S., Freudenthal, P., Gudjonnson, S., Johansen, G., and Schoubye, N. 1927. Refection, a transmissible change in the intestinal content, enabling rats to grow and thrive without vitamin B in the food. *J. Hyg.* **27**, 70–102.

Friedman, M. I. 1975. Some determinants of milk ingestion in suckling rats. *J. Comp. Physiol. Psychol.* **89**, 636–647.

Galef, B. G., Jr., and Clark, M. M. 1972. Mother's milk and adult presence: Two factors determining initial dietary selection by weanling rats. *J. Comp. Physiol. Psychol.* **78**, 220–225.

Galef, B. G., Jr., and Clark, M. M. 1976. Non-nurturent functions of mother–young interaction in the Agouti (*Dasyprocta punctata*). *Behav. Biol.* **17**, 255–262.

Gelineo, S., and Gelineo, A. 1951. Sur la thermoregulation du rat nouveau et la temperature du nid. *C. R. Acad. Sci. Paris* **232**, 1031–1032.

Goodrick, C. L. 1975. Adaptation to novel environments by the rat: Effects of age, stimulus intensity, group testing and temperature. *Dev. Psychobiol.* **8**, 287–296.

Gregory, E. H., and Pfaff, D. W. 1971. Development of olfactory guided behavior in infant rats. *Physiol. Behav.* **6**, 573–576.

Grollman, A. 1965. "Pharmacology and Therapeutics," 6th ed. Lea and Febiger, Philadelphia.

Grosvenor, C. E. 1956. Some effects of ergotamine tartrate upon lactation in the rat. *Am. J. Physiol.* **186**, 211–215.

Grosvenor, C. E. 1964a. Effect of suckling upon pituitary growth hormone (STH) concentration in the lactating rat. *Physiologist* **7**, 150.

Grosvenor, C. E. 1964b. Influence of the nursing stimulus upon thyroid hormone secretion in the lactating rat. *Endocrinology* **75**, 15–21.

Grosvenor, C. E. 1965. Evidence that exteroceptive stimuli can release prolactin from the pituitary gland of the lactating rat. *Endocrinology*, **76**, 340–342.

Grosvenor, C. E., Maiweg, H., and Mena, F. 1970. A study of factors involved in the development of the exteroceptive release of prolactin in the lactating rat. *Horm. Behav.* **1**, 111–120.

Grota, L., and Ader, R. 1969. Continuous recording of maternal behavior in *Rattus norvegicus*. *Anim. Behav.* **17**, 722–729.

Grota, L., and Eik-Nes, K. B. 1967. Plasma progesterone concentrations during pregnancy and lactation in the rat. *J. Reprod. Fertil.* **13**, 83–91.

Guerrant, N. B., Dutcher, R. A., and Tomey, L. F. 1935. Die bedrutung de darmbaktierien fur den vitamin haushalt des organismus. *J. Biol. Chem.* **110**, 233–243.

Guerrant, N. B., Dutcher, R. A., and Brown, R. A. 1937. Further studies concerning formation of B-vitamins in digestive tract of rats. *J. Nutr.* **13**, 305–315.

Gustafsson, P. 1948. Germ-free rearing in rat. *Acta Pathol. Microbiol. Scand. Suppl.* **72–75**, 1–130.

Hahn, P. 1973. Immediate and late effects of premature weaning and of feeding a high fat or high carbohydrate diet to weanling rats. *J. Nutr.* **103**, 690–696.

Harder, W. 1949. Zur Morphologie und Physiologie des Blinddarmes der Nagetiere. *Verh. Dtsch. Zool. Ges.*, **2**, 95–109.

Hoetzel, D., and Barnes, R. H. 1966. Contributions of the intestinal microflora to the nutrition of the host. *Vitam. Horm.* **24**, 115–171.

Hofer, M. A. 1973a. Maternal separation affects infant rat behavior. *Behav. Biol.* **9**, 629–633.

Hofer, M. A. 1973b. The role of nutrition in the physiological and behavioral effects of early maternal separation on infant rats. *Psychosom. Med.* **35**, 350–359.

Hofer, M. A. 1975. Studies on how early maternal separation produces behavioral change in young rats. *Psychosom. Med.* **37**, 245–264.

Hofer, M. A. 1976. Olfactory denervation: Its biological and behavioral effects in infant rats. *J. Comp. Physiol. Psychol.* **90**, 829–838.

Hofer, M. A., Shair, H., and Singh, P. 1976. Evidence that maternal ventral skin substances promote suckling in infant rats. *Physiol. Behav.* **17**, 131–136.

Holinka, C. F., and Carlson, A. D. 1976. Pup attraction to lactating Sprague–Dawley rats. *Behav. Biol.* **16**, 489–505.

Hopkins, E. G., and Leader, V. R. 1946. On refection in rats and on the nature of the growth promoted by the addition of small quantities of milk to vitamin free diets. *J. Hyg.* **44**, 149–157.

Karlson, P., and Butenandt, A. 1959. Pheromones (ectohormones) in insects. *Ann. Rev. Entomol.* **4**, 39–58.

Kling, A. 1964. Effects of rhinencephalic lesions on endocrine and somatic development in the rat. *Am. J. Physiol.* **206**, 1395–1400.

Koranyi, L., Phelps, C. P., and Sawyer, C. H. 1977. Changes in serum prolactin and corticosterone in induced maternal behavior in rats. *Physiol. Behav.* **18**, 287–292.

Kraus, M., Krecek, J., and Popp, M. 1967. The development of corticosterone production by the adrenal gland in normally and prematurely weaned rats. *Physiol. Bohemoslov.* **16**, 120–127.

Lampen, J. A., and Peterjohn, H. R. 1951. Studies on the specificity of the fermentation of pentoses by *Lactobacillus pentosus*. *J. Bacteriol.* **62**, 281–292.

Landauer, M. R., Carr, W. J., and Marasco, E. 1976. Responses of preweanling rats to home cage vs. strange cage bedding. Paper presented at a meeting of the East. Psychol. Soc., New York.

Leidahl, L. C., and Moltz, H. 1975. Emission of the maternal pheromone in the nulliparous female and failure of emission in the adult male. *Physiol. Behav.* **14**, 421–424.

Leon, M. 1974. Maternal pheromone. *Physiol. Behav.* **13**, 441–453.

Leon, M. 1975. Dietary control of maternal pheromone in the lactating rat. *Physiol. Behav.* **14**, 311–319.

Leon, M., and Behse, J. 1977. Dissolution of the pheromonal bond: Waning of approach response by weanling rats. *Physiol. Behav.* **18**, 393–397.

Leon, M., and Moltz, H. 1971. Maternal pheromone: Discrimination by pre-weanling albino rats. *Physiol. Behav.* **7**, 265–267.

Leon, M., and Moltz, H. 1972. The development of the pheromonal bond in the albino rat. *Physiol. Behav.* **8**, 683–686.

Leon, M., and Moltz, H. 1973. Endocrine control of the maternal pheromone in the postpartum female rat. *Physiol. Behav.* **10**, 65–67.

Leon, M., Numan, M., and Moltz, H. 1973. Maternal behavior in the rat: Facilitation through gonadectomy. *Science* **179**, 1018–1019.

Leon, M., Galef, B. G., Jr., and Behse, J. 1977. Establishment of pheromonal bonds and diet choice in young rats by odor pre-exposure. *Physiol. Behav.* **18**, 387–391.

Li, C. H., Ingle, D. J., Prestrud, M. C., and Nezamis, J. E. 1949. Lack of effect of lactogenic hormone upon organ weights, nitrogen and phosphorus balance, and the fat and protein content of liver and carcass in male rats given lactogenic hormone. *Endocrinology* **44**, 454–457.

Lu, R. H., Koch, F., and Meites, H. 1971. Direct inhibition by ergocornine of pituitary prolactin release. *Endocrinology* **89**, 229–233.

Lutton, C., and Chevallier, F. 1973. Coprophagie chez le rat blanc. *J. Physiol. Paris* **66**, 219–228.

Macho, L., Strbak, V., and Strzovcov, A. 1970. Thyroid and adrenal function in prematurely weaned rats. *Physiol. Bohemoslov.* **19**, 77–82.

Mainardi, D., Marsan, M., and Pasquali, A. 1965. Causation of sexual preferences of the house mouse. The behavior of mice reared by parents whose odor was artificially altered. *Atti. Soc. Ital. Sci. Nat.* **104**, 325–338.

Marr, H. M., and Gardner, L. E. 1965. Early olfactory experience and later social development in the rat: Preference, sexual responsiveness and care of young. *J. Genet. Psychol.* **107**, 167–174.

Marr, J. N., and Lilliston, L. G. 1969. Social attachment in rats by odor and age. *Behaviour* **33**, 277–282.

Mena, F., and Grosvenor, C. E. 1972. Effect of suckling and of exteroceptive stimulation upon prolactin release in the rat during late lactation. *J. Endocrinol.* **52**, 11–22.

Menaker, L., and Navia, J. M. 1973. Appetite regulation in the rat under various physiological conditions: The role of dietary protein and calories. *J. Nutr.* **103**, 347–352.

Merchant, F. W. 1974. Prolactin and luteinizing hormone cells of pregnant and lactating rats as studied by immunohistochemistry and radioimmunoassay. *Am. J. Anat.* **139**, 245–267.

Mikelson, O. 1956. Intestinal synthesis of vitamins in the non-ruminant. *Vitam. Horm.* **14**, 1–95.

Mitchell, D. 1976. Experiments on neophobia in wild and laboratory rats: A reevaluation. *J. Comp. Physiol. Psychol.* **90**, 190–197.

Moltz, H., and Leidahl, L. C. 1977. Bile, prolactin and the maternal pheromone. *Science* **196**, 81–83.

Moltz, H., and Leon, M. 1973. Stimulus control of the maternal pheromone in the lactating rat. *Physiol. Behav.* **10**, 69–71.

Moltz, H., Levin, R., and Leon, M. 1969. Prolactin in the postpartum rat: Synthesis and release in the absence of suckling stimulation. *Science* **163**, 1083–1084.

Moltz, H., Leidahl, L., and Rowland, D. 1974. Prolongation of pheromonal emission in the maternal rat. *Physiol. Behav.* **12**, 409–412.

Moorcroft, W. H. 1971. Ontogeny of forebrain inhibition of behavioral arousal in the rat. *Brain Res.* **35**, 513–522.

Moorcroft, W. H., Lytle, L. D., and Campbell, B. A. 1971. Ontogeny of starvation-induced behavioral arousal in the rat. *J. Comp. Physiol. Psychol.* **75**, 69–67.

Morgan, T. B., and Yudkin, J. 1962. The vitamin-sparing action of sorbitol, sugars and related substances. *Vitam. Horm.* **20**, 39.

Morishige, W. K., and Rothchild, I. 1974. Temporal aspects of the regulation of corpus luteum function by leuteinizing hormone, prolactin and placental luteotrophin during the first half of pregnancy in the rat. *Endocrinology* **95**, 260–274.

Mykytowicz, R. 1973. Reproduction of mammals in relation to environmental odors. *J. Reprod. Fertil. Suppl.* **19**, 433–446.

Nickerson, M. 1970. Drugs inhibiting adrenergic nerves and structures innervated by them. *In* "The Pharmacological Basis of Therapeutics" (L. S. Goodman and A. Gilman, eds.), pp. 549–584. Collier-MacMillan, Toronto.

Nicoll, C. S., and Meites, J. 1959. Prolongation of lactation in the rat by litter replacement. *Proc. Soc. Exp. Biol. Med.* **101**, 81–82.

Numan, M., Leon, M., and Moltz, H. 1972. Interference with prolactin release and the maternal behavior of female rats. *Horm. Behav.* **3**, 29–38.

Nyakas, C., and Endröczi, E. 1970. Olfaction guided approaching behavior of infantile pups to the mother in a maze box. *Acta Physiol. Acad. Sci. Hung.* **38**, 59–65.

Ogle, T. F., and Kitay, J. I. 1974. Effects of premature weaning on adrenal function in intact and gonadectomized rats. *J. Endocrinol.* **63**, 489–496.

Oswalt, G. L., and Meier, G. W. 1975. Olfactory, thermal and tactile influences on infantile ultrasonic vocalization in rats. *Dev. Psychobiol.* **8**, 129–135.

Ota, K., and Yokoyama, A. 1967a. Body weight and food consumption of lactating rats: Effect of ovariectomy and of arrest and resumption of suckling. *J. Endocrinol.* **38**, 251–261.

Ota, K., and Yokoyama, A. 1967b. Body weight and food consumption of lactating rats nursing various sizes of litters. *J. Endocrinol.* **38**, 263–268.

Pfaff, D. 1969. Sex differences in food intake changes following pituitary growth hormone or prolactin injections. *Proc. 77th Annu. Conv. Am. Psychol. Assoc. Washington, D.C.* **4**, 211–212.

Pollack, E. I., and Sachs, B. D. 1975. Male copulatory behavior and female maternal behavior in neonatally bulbectomized rats. *Physiol. Behav.* **14**, 337–343.

Poo, L. J., Lew, W., and Addis, T. 1939. Protein anabolism of organs and tissues during pregnancy and lactation. *J. Biol. Chem.* **128**, 69–77.

Porter, J. R., and Rettger, L. F. 1940. Influence of diet on the distribution of bacteria in the stomach, small intestine and caecum of the white rat. *J. Infect. Dis.* **66**, 104–110.

Raibaud, P., Dickinson, A. B., Sacquat, E., Charlier, H., and Moquot, G. 1966. The microflora of the alimentary tract of the rat. II. Quantitative study of various genera of microorganisms present in the stomach and intestines of conventional rats. Quantitative variations from one individual to another and as a function of age. *Ann. Inst. Pasteur* **110**, 861–876.

Randall, P. K., and Campbell, B. A. 1976. Ontogeny of behavioral arousal in rats: Effect of maternal and sibling presence. *J. Comp. Physiol. Psychol.* **90**, 453–459.

Rescorla, R. A. 1971. Summation and retardation tests of latent inhibition. *J. Comp. Physiol. Psychol.* **75**, 77–8ŀ.

Rettger, L. F., and Horton, G. P. 1914. A comparative study of the intestinal flora of white rats kept on experimental and ordinary mixed diets. *Zentralbl. Bakteriol. I. Abt. Orig.* **73**, 362–372.

Roscoe, M. H. 1927. Spontaneous cures in rats reared upon diet devoid of vitamin B and anti-neurotic vitamin. *J. Hyg.* **27**, 103–107.

Rosenblatt, J. S. 1967. Non hormonal basis of maternal behavior in the rat. *Science* **156**, 1512–1514.

Rosenblatt, J. S., and Lehrman, D. S. 1963. Maternal behavior of the laboratory rat. *In* "Maternal Behavior in Mammals" (H. L. Reingold, ed.), pp. 8–57. Wiley, New York.

Rozin, P., and Kalat, J. W. 1971. Specific hungers and poison avoidance as adaptive specializations of learning. *Psychol. Rev.* **78**, 459–486.

Salas, M., Guzman-Flores, C., and Shapiro, S. 1969. An ontogenetic study of olfactory bulb electrical activity in the rat. *Physiol. Behav.* **4**, 699–703.

Selye, H., and McKeown, T. 1934. Further studies on the influence of suckling. *Anat. Rec.* **60**, 323–332.

Shaar, C. J., and Clemens, J. A. 1972. Inhibition of lactation and prolactin secretion in rats by ergot alkaloids. *Endocrinology* **90**, 285–288.

Shapiro, S., and Salas, M. 1970. Behavioral response of infant rats to maternal odor. *Physiol. Behav.* **5**, 815–817.

Siegel, S. 1974. Flavor preexposure and "learned safety." *J. Comp. Physiol. Psychol.* **87**, 1073–1082.

Singh, P. J., and Tobach, E. 1975. Olfactory bulbectomy and nursing behavior in rat pups. *Dev. Psychobiol.* **8**, 151–164.

Singh, P. J., Tucker, M., and Hofer, M. 1977. Effects of nasal ZnSO$_4$ irrigation and olfactory bulbectomy on rat pups. *Physiol. Behav.* **17**, 373–382.

Slonaker, J. R. 1925. The effect of copulation, pregnancy, pseudopregnancy and lactation on the voluntary activity and food consumption of the albino rat. *Am. J. Physiol.* **71**, 362–394.

Small, W. S. 1899. Notes on the psychic development of the young white rat. *Am. J. Psychol.* **11**, 80–100.

Smith, H. W. 1965. The development of the flora of the alimentary tract in young animals. *J. Pathol. Bact.* **90**, 495–513.

Souders, H. J., and Morgan, A. F. 1957. Weight and composition of organs during the reproductive cycle in the rat. *Am. J. Physiol.* **191**, 1–7.

Sturman-Hulbe, M., and Stone, C. P. 1929. Maternal behavior in the albino rat. *J. Comp. Psychol.* **9**, 203–237.

Teicher, M. H., and Blass, E. M. 1976. Suckling in newborn rats: Eliminated by nipple lavage, reinstated by pup saliva. *Science* **193**, 422–424.

Telle, H. J. 1966. Bietrag zur Kenntnis der Verhaltensweise von Ratten, vergleichend dargestellt bei, *Rattus norvegicus. Z. Angew. Zool.* **53**, 129–196.

Terkel, J., Blake, C. A., and Sawyer, C. H. 1972. Serum prolactin levels in lactating rats after suckling or exposure to ether. *Endocrinology* **91**, 49–53.

Thatcher, W. W., and Tucker, H. A. 1968. Intensive nursing and lactational performance during extended lactation. *Proc. Exp. Biol. Med.* **128**, 46–48.

Tindal, J. S. 1956. Effect of ergotamine and dihydroergotamine on lactation in rats. *J. Endocrinol.* **14**, 268–274.

Tobach, E., Rouger, Y., and Schneirla, T. C. 1967. Development of olfactory function in the rat pup. *Am. Zool.* **7**, 792.

Tomogane, H., Ota, K., and Yokoyama, A. 1975. Suppression of progesterone secretion in lactating rats by administration of ergocornine and the effect of prolactin replacement. *J. Endocrinol.* **65**, 155–161.

Tomogane, H., Ota, K., Unno, H., and Yokoyama, A. 1976a. Changes in body weight, milk production, food and water consumption and vaginal smears in rats during prolonged lactation. *Endocrinol. Jpn.* **23**, 129–136.

Tomogane, H., Ota, K., and Yokoyama, A. 1976b. Duration of diestrus period and secretion of progestins during prolonged lactation in the rat. *Endocrinol. Jpn.* **23**, 137–141.

Trivers, R. L. 1974. Parent-offspring conflict. *Am. Zool.* **14**, 249–264.

Wang, G. H. 1925. The changes in the amount of daily food-intake of the albino rat during pregnancy and lactation. *Am. J. Physiol.* **71**, 736.

Welker, W. R. 1964. Analysis of sniffing of the albino rat. *Behaviour* **22**, 223–244.

Wiesner, B. P., and Sheard, N. M. 1933. "Maternal Behaviour in the Rat." Oliver and Boyd, Edinburgh.

Wuttke, W., Cassell, E., and Meites, J. 1971. Effects of ergocornine on serum prolactin to LH and on hypothalamic content of PIF and LRF. *Endocrinology* **88**, 737–741.

Zarrow, M. X., Schlein, P. A., Denenberg, V. H., and Cohen, H. A. 1972. Sustained corticosterone release in lactating rats following olfactory stimulation from the pups. *Endocrinology* **91**, 191–196.

A Comparison of the Properties of Different Reinforcers*

JERRY A. HOGAN

DEPARTMENT OF PSYCHOLOGY
UNIVERSITY OF TORONTO
TORONTO, CANADA

AND

T. J. ROPER†

DEPARTMENT OF EXPERIMENTAL PSYCHOLOGY
UNIVERSITY OF CAMBRIDGE
CAMBRIDGE, ENGLAND

*The order of authorship was determined by a coin toss. The sections on food, water, heat, locomotor activity, and nest material were written initially by Roper; the sections on aggression, sex, and ESB by Hogan. However, all sections of the contribution were thoroughly discussed and edited jointly, and we both take responsibility for the final version.

†Present address: School of Biological Sciences, The University of Sussex, Falmer, Brighton, Sussex BN1 9QG, England.

I. Introduction

    The concept of reinforcement is used in experimental psychology to explain changes in behavior that reflect what we call learning, and also to explain the continued occurrence of responses after they have been acquired. Most studies of reinforcement use rats or pigeons as subjects, food or electric shock as reinforcer, and the Skinner box or maze as test environment (Mackintosh, 1974), but it is often assumed that principles and theories derived from such studies are applicable to other species, other reinforcers, other apparatus, and even to behavior in the animal's natural habitat (for references see Seligman, 1970; Shettleworth, 1972).

In recent years this assumption of generality has been subjected to intensive experimental analysis, with the result that many workers now question its validity (e.g., Rozin and Kalat, 1971; Garcia et al., 1972; Seligman and Hager, 1972; Shettleworth, 1972; Hinde and Stevenson-Hinde, 1973). Most attention has focused on questions concerning the response that is being reinforced or the relation between the response and the reinforcer. For example, Shettleworth (1975) has considered whether all responses within the animal's repertoire are equally reinforcible. while others (e.g., Bolles, 1970; Stevenson-Hinde, 1973) have asked whether certain responses are more or less compatible with certain reinforcers.

One aspect of this problem that has received relatively little attention is whether all reinforcers affect instrumental learning in the same way. More and more reports have been appearing in which reinforcers other than food have been used. In many of these reports, results have been different from what would have been expected had food been used. The major purpose of our contribution is to examine these different reinforcers per se. We shall consider only positive reinforcers, and restrict our review to instrumental conditioning.

We begin by considering the variety of events that have been claimed to be reinforcers, and then discuss in detail a number of reinforcers about which more information is available: presentation of food, water, heat, and electrical stimulation of the brain; and the opportunity to engage in wheel running, nest building, sexual behavior, and aggressive behavior. Where reinforcing properties are a matter of controversy, we first review evidence that the event in question really is a reinforcer. We then discuss data on acquisition, extinction, magnitude of reinforcement, and fixed-ratio schedules. In the course of preparing the review, it became clear that many of the differences among reinforcers could be best understood in terms of differences among the motivational systems associated with each reinforcer. We therefore include information about "motivational" variables, such as deprivation, satiation, and priming. In some cases we are led to discuss theoretical issues unique to one reinforcer. Finally, we consider some of the general questions that arise from our analysis, including the relevance of the data to theories of what makes a reinforcer reinforcing. We conclude that with respect to learning, similar principles probably apply to all the reinforcers we have examined, but that with respect to performance, it is necessary to consider each reinforcer within the context of its own motivational system.

A. THE VARIETY OF REINFORCERS

A positive reinforcer is usually defined operationally as an event that, when made contingent on a response, increases the frequency of that response (Skinner, 1938). Some workers require that the term "reinforcer" be applied only to stimuli, on the grounds that presentation of a stimulus is what the experimenter actually controls. Other workers, however, have taken a less operational approach and use the term to refer to internal events or to particular activities that occur in reinforcing situations. We shall use the term in whichever way seems most natural in any particular case, without implying that we support any particular position on this issue. We return to the question of identifying the precise reinforcing event in Section X, General Discussion.

In the past two decades, literally hundreds of studies have been published that claim to show that some event or other in some species or other meets the operational definition of a reinforcer. These include stimuli that fulfill some obvious physiological need in appropriately deprived animals, such as food, water, heat, cold, oxygen, and various drugs; the opportunity to engage in various species-specific activities such as pecking, gnawing, grooming, hoarding, sand digging, nest building, pup retrieving, courting, copulating, fighting, and running; the opportunity to explore; stimuli that seem biologically relevant to the species at hand such as sweet tastes, conspecific bird song, or an imprinting stimulus; electrical stimulation of the brain; and any stimulus change at all. Reviews of some of this literature are given by Tapp (1969), Glickman (1973), and Bolles (1975).

Many of these studies were undertaken to prove or disprove some particular theory of reinforcement, with the result that systematic studies of the properties of particular reinforcers are relatively rare. Other studies have used only one or a few animals, and statistical treatment of the data is often absent. Further, many events claimed to be reinforcers have, at best, weak effects on responding, so that most interest has been concentrated on whether the event is a reinforcer at all. This seems to be particularly true of so-called "sensory" reinforcers such as light onset and bird song, where reinforcing effects have frequently been found to be highly variable within or between subjects (e.g., Kish, 1966; Stevenson-Hinde, 1973).

Still another problem has been pointed out by Berlyne (1969). A stimulus may satisfy the operational definition of a reinforcer by at least two means other than by the kind of response strengthening usually thought to occur in learning. First, it may increase the animal's general level of activity (or, a particular motivational state), so that the rate at which the operant is emitted by chance increases; second, it may elicit the response either through an unlearned reflex, or through a conditioned association. To eliminate these possibilities and demonstrate a true reinforcing effect, two groups of animals must be trained under conditions of contingent and noncontingent reinforcement, respectively, and then tested in extinction. In addition, Berlyne and others suggest that there should be a minimum interval (e.g., 24 hr) between training and testing, on the grounds that learning is generally thought to involve a change in behavior that lasts for hours or days, rather than for minutes or seconds. Very few studies of reinforcers, especially those using free-operant rather than discrete-trials procedures, include the controls recommended by Berlyne. The most frequent control is to measure unreinforced rate of responding ("operant level") in the naive animal, and compare it with the subsequent reinforced rate; but this controls neither for an increase in general activity nor for response elicitation. An increase in general activity is sometimes controlled for by the use of a yoked subject, or a second manipulandum that does not deliver reinforcement, but a distressingly large number of studies lack control procedures altogether.

The particular reinforcers we have chosen to review are the ones for which the most systematic data are available, and for which many of the methodological criticisms apply least. Nonetheless, gaps in the evidence and methodological weakness are still a problem in some cases, and this is mentioned when appropriate.

B. The Analysis of Reinforcers

In preparing the review, we found it helpful to distinguish learning from differences in asymptotic learned behavior. A process of learning occurs during acquisition and extinction, and the primary data reflect changes in responding over consecutive trials. (In a free-operant situation, a "trial" means the events leading up to and including the delivery of one reinforcement). Attention is focused on questions such as: How many trials does it take for responding to reach a certain level? Or: What is the shape of the learning curve? Studies of the effects of changing amount or schedule of reinforcement, on the other hand, are usually concerned with asymptotic performance of the learned response under different conditions, and the period of transition from one condition to another is usually ignored.

Within the area of asymptotic performance we may distinguish two further classes of effect, that we shall refer to as *patterning* and *regulatory* effects, respectively. By "patterning" effects we mean differences in the fine structure of operant responding. For example, a fixed-ratio (FR) schedule of food reinforcement (see below) typically generates a steplike pattern of responding from one reinforcement to the next; but as we shall see, this pattern is not obtained with certain other reinforcers. Similarly, increases in amount of food reinforcement usually result in predictable changes in certain measures of response rate; but other reinforcers may not produce similar effects.

By "regulatory" effects we mean differences in responding that seem related to the long-term regulation of the associated motivational system. On an FR schedule, the animal must make a specified number of responses to obtain each reinforcement (e.g., on an FR 5 schedule, a reinforcement is delivered following every fifth response). Other things being equal, it follows that if the FR value is increased, then reinforcement rate must decline, because a finite time is required to make each response. Consequently, if the session is so short that the animal works continuously at an asymptotic rate, the number of reinforcements obtained per session must necessarily be inversely related to FR size. However, if the session is long enough to allow the animal to obtain as many reinforcements as it wants, four alternatives are possible:

1.   The animal may continue to respond until it has obtained as many reinforcements as it would have obtained on FR 1, in which case number of responses must increase in proportion to FR size.

2.   It may stop when it has made as many *responses* as it would have made on FR 1, in which case number of reinforcements will decline in proportion to FR size.

3.   It may do something in between these two extremes, in which case number of responses per session will increase, and number of reinforcements fall, to an intermediate extent.

4.   It may make *fewer* responses per session than it would have made on FR 1, in which case number of reinforcements will decline even more precipitously than in (2).

Precisely the same logic may be applied if instead of increasing the work requirement for each reinforcement, we decrease the reinforcement size. At one extreme the animal may increase its response output so as to obtain the same total amount of the reinforcing commodity as it would have obtained with the larger reinforcement size; at the other, it may make fewer responses, in which case it will receive a much smaller total amount of the reinforcer per session.

We describe these possible outcomes as reflecting different degrees of *compensation* for changes in FR size or in amount of reinforcement. If total amount of the reinforcer received per session remains constant, compensation is said to be complete; if number of responses per session remains constant, compensation is said to be zero; and if response output falls, compensation is said to be negative. Most of our discussion of regulatory effects centers around the question of whether animals do tend to compensate for changes in FR schedule or in amount of reinforcement, by means of appropriate changes in response output. As we shall see, compensation appears to be better with some reinforcers than with others, and in Section X, we consider what this may mean.

In order to clarify the distinction between *patterning* effects and *regulatory* effects, we shall reserve the term *rate of responding* for short-term asymptotic rate (usually responses per minute). When we mean *number of responses per session,* we say so. Failure to make this distinction has sometimes led to confusion. For example, Collier *et al.* (1972) found that ''rate'' of responding with food as reinforcer was inversely related to reinforcement size, whereas previous operant studies had shown a direct relationship. However, Collier *et al.* (1972)

tested rats in their home cages for 24 hr per day, so that the animals were obliged to earn all their food by lever pressing, whereas previous investigators had tested rats in Skinner boxes for limited sessions, in which all available time was spent obtaining food. In the former case the rats compensated for increases in reinforcement size by decreasing the number of responses made per day, so that *overall* rate of responding was inversely related to reinforcement size. Had Collier and co-workers recorded short-term asymptotic rate of responding, they might well have discovered the typical direct relationship.

II. Food as Reinforcer

A. Acquisition

There is general agreement, with respect to discrete-trials studies using a variety of apparatus, that rate of acquisition and asymptotic level of responding are inversely related to delay of reinforcement, and directly related to amount of reinforcement and to deprivation level (for reviews see Kimble, 1961; Mackintosh, 1974; and Bolles, 1975). But even within the restricted methodology of learning theory, the magnitude of the effect produced by these variables covers a wide range.

Little else can be said about acquisition with any certainty. In a typical alleyway study, rats run faster in successive trials, and approach asymptotic speed after 20–30 trials. There is often wide variation between individuals within an experiment (e.g., Mackintosh, 1974, p. 147), as well as between experiments, however.

In free-operant studies, acquisition of a response such as lever pressing is usually encouraged by an active training procedure (*shaping*), after some degree of pretraining (e.g., "magazine training," see Ferster and Skinner, 1957). Because there has been no attempt to standardize either pretraining or training procedures, and because the most popular method of shaping relies heavily on the skill of the experimenter, the majority of free-operant studies give no useful information about acquisition.

A few experimenters have attempted to circumvent these problems by simply placing the animal in the box and leaving it to discover the significance of the lever. Where data are available from such studies, they generally concur with the results of discrete-trials procedures. Speed of acquisition varies enormously between individuals, but Skinner (1932, 1936) has claimed that suitably pretrained animals can learn to lever press in a single trial.

This brief review shows that acquisition is subject to a host of known variables, and possibly to even more unknown ones, which means that comparing results from different studies using food as the reinforcer can be difficult indeed.

It follows that precise comparisons among reinforcers can only be made on the basis of results obtained under strictly similar conditions, preferably *within* individual studies.

B. EXTINCTION

The major variables whose effects on extinction have been studied are: distribution of trials (massed versus spaced); number of acquisition trials; amount of reinforcement; delay of reinforcement; and schedule of reinforcement during acquisition. The literature is reviewed by Mackintosh (1974), whose conclusions can be crudely summarized as follows: resistance to extinction increases up to a point with number of training trials, but is reduced by overtraining; it is directly related to intertrial interval during training, and to delay of reinforcement; it is inversely related to amount of reinforcement; and it is enhanced by the use of intermittent, rather than continuous, schedules of reinforcement during training (the "partial reinforcement effect"). In addition there is some evidence that rate of extinction is inversely related to deprivation level (see Bolles, 1975), but the effect is at best small. There is also evidence that increasing the effortfulness of the response results in more rapid extinction, but interpretation of this effect is a matter of dispute (Kimble, 1961).

If these generalizations are accepted, they suggest that variables that increase the strength of responding during acquisition do not necessarily retard extinction, and may actually enhance it. In particular, increases in number of acquisition trials and in reinforcement size, and decreases in delay of reinforcement all enhance responding during acquisition, but result in more rapid extinction. The relevance of this point will become more obvious when we consider unitary explanations of differences between reinforcers.

Extinction is a notoriously variable phenomenon, and the literature is replete with counterexamples. As with acquisition, therefore, comparisons among reinforcers can only be made on the basis of carefully controlled studies, and even then apparent differences between reinforcers may lend themselves to a variety of interpretations.

C. AMOUNT OF REINFORCEMENT

1. Patterning Effects

It is generally supposed that larger amounts of reinforcement lead to increased vigor of responding, both in the alleyway and, with intermittent schedules, in the Skinner box (e.g., Pubols, 1960; Mackintosh, 1974). However, the generality of this conclusion is quite restricted. There is good evidence, in rats, that speed of running in a straight alley is directly related to amount of food reinforcement (Logan, 1960; Pubols, 1960), and that rate of responding on fixed-interval (FI) schedules is directly related to concentration of sucrose solution (Guttman, 1953). However, Lowe *et al.* (1974) found that response rate on an FI schedule did not vary with the concentration of a milk reward, and it decreased on an FR schedule. They also showed that postreinforcement pause duration increased with concentration of the reinforcer on both schedules. In pigeons, several studies have failed to show a clear relationship between response rate and duration of food presentation on variable interval (VI) or FR schedules (e.g., Keesey and Kling, 1961; Neuringer, 1967; Powell, 1969). Powell found that postreinforcement pause duration was inversely related to duration of reinforcement, a result that contradicts that of Lowe *et al.* (1974) in rats.

Several authors have pointed out that there are different ways of varying amount of reinforcement (e.g., duration of access to food, weight of food, number of pieces of food), but there is still no agreement as to which manipulation is preferable (see Kling and Schrier, 1971, for a thoughtful discussion of this issue). There may be species differences in the preferred dimensions of reinforcement size, and even within species the quality of the reinforcer may be important. Thus, rats responding on FI schedules seem to perform differently for sucrose and for milk (see above). Immediate metabolic reactions to a particular reinforcer may be one determinant of the postreinforcement pause. Sensory attractiveness may also affect responding (see Kling and Schrier, 1971). Most of these factors are ignored by most investigators, so it is not surprising that the literature is full of inconsistencies.

A final effect is that larger amounts of reinforcement support responding to higher fixed ratios, when ratio is increased either between or within sessions (e.g., Hodos and Kalman, 1963).

2. Regulatory Effects

Surprisingly few studies address the question of whether animals compensate for changes in reinforcement size by proportionately changing their response output. Rozin and Mayer (1961a) found that, in goldfish, the number of lever presses per day on an FR 1 schedule was inversely related to size and calorific value of the reinforcement pellets. The fish thus tended to respond so as to obtain a constant weight of food or calorific input per day, but few data are given and there was clearly considerable variability between fish.

No directly comparable experiment has been done with rats, but Collier and Jennings (1969) made two concentrations of sucrose solution available to rats for 30 min per day, on a series of FR schedules from 10 to 320. As Fig. 1 shows, the number of reinforcements per session (Fig. 1a) was inversely related to sucrose concentration at FR 10 and FR 20, but directly related at higher ratios. The total amount of sucrose obtained per day (Fig. 1b) was greater with the higher concentration at all ratios, and was proportionately greater the higher the FR. Thus, the rats compensated partially for the differences in concentration at low ratios, and

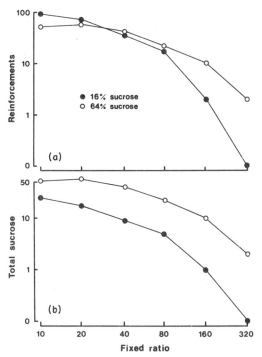

FIG. 1. Number of reinforcements per session (a), and total amount of sucrose received (b), as a function of FR size, in rats working for two different concentrations of sucrose solution. (Data from Collier and Jennings, 1969.)

negatively at high ones. Whether they would compensate completely on an FR 1 schedule is not known.

D. FIXED-RATIO SCHEDULES

1. *Patterning Effects*

Fixed-ratio schedules typically generate a steplike cumulative record (e.g., Ferster and Skinner, 1957). The duration of the postreinforcement pause is directly related to FR size (Felton and Lyon, 1966; Powell, 1969), but response rate within each ratio run remains relatively constant (Ferster and Skinner, 1957; Powell, 1969; Barofsky and Hurwitz, 1968). It follows that increases in FR size result in decreases in reinforcement rate, though in sessions of restricted length there is no consistent effect on response rate (Felton and Lyon, 1966; Killeen, 1969; Powell, 1969). Postreinforcement pause duration also increases in less deprived animals (Sidman and Stebbins, 1954). At very high ratios, breaks may appear within response runs, the runs may show positive or negative acceleration, and the postreinforcement pauses may become very long. Performance is then said to show *ratio strain*. This occurs at ratios of a few hundred in pigeons pecking for grain, but rather earlier in rats working for solid food pellets.

2. Regulatory Effects

Collier *et al.* (1972) allowed rats to lever press for food for 24 hr a day in their home cages, on an ascending series of FR schedules from 1 to 240. The results are shown in Fig. 2. The number of responses per day (Fig. 2a) increased in

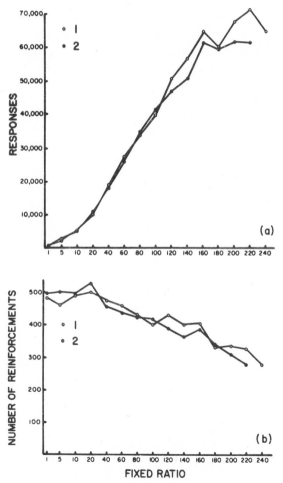

FIG. 2. Number of responses emitted (a) and reinforcements received (b) per day, as a function of FR size, in two rats working for food reinforcement. (From Collier, Hirsch, and Hamlin, 1972. Copyright Brain Research Publications. Reproduced by permission.)

proportion to FR size up to about FR 20, so that number of reinforcements per day (Fig. 2b) remained constant. Between FR 20 and 160, the number of responses continued to increase, but not enough to prevent a gradual decline in number of reinforcements. After FR 160, number of responses reached an asymptote, so that number of reinforcements declined even more steeply. Thus, the rats compensated completely for increases in the ratio up to FR 20, then compensated less and less, and eventually not at all. Compensation was achieved partly by increases in response rate, but mainly by spending more time working for food: the authors report that at FR 160 the rats were spending 14 hr a day lever pressing. It seems likely that response output then became asymptotic because time was a limiting factor. In spite of the reduction in food intake the rats maintained their body weights up to FR 80, indicating that they were able, within limits, to compensate physiologically as well as behaviorally.

The number of reinforcements obtained per session as a function of FR size, on log–log coordinates, for a number of studies comparable to the one just described are shown in Fig. 3. Session length ranged from 24 hr to 30 min, but in all cases there was reason to suppose that it was not a limiting factor, at least at

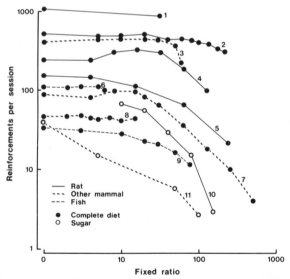

FIG. 3. Number of reinforcements obtained per session as a function of FR size, on log–log coordinates, with food as reinforcer. Data are from the following studies: (1) Logan (1964); (2) Collier, Hirsch, and Hamlin (1972); (3) Hirsch and Collier (1974a); (4) King and Gaston (1976); (5) Teitelbaum (1957); (6) Hogan et al. (1970); (7) Hamilton and Brobeck (1964); (8) Roper (1975a); (9) Rozin and Mayer (1964); (10) Collier and Jennings (1969); (11) Smart (1970). The subjects were rats, except for (3) guinea pig; (6) Siamese fighting fish; (7) rhesus monkey; (8) and (11) mouse; (9) goldfish.

low ratios. The reinforcer was a solid, complete diet pellet except in the case of Curves 10 (sweetened glucose pellet) and 11 (sucrose solution). In the majority of cases compensation was complete or nearly complete at low ratios, but failed gradually at higher ones. Thus, the results reported by Collier et al. (1972) (which are represented by Curve 2) have considerable support from other studies. There is some suggestion of poorer compensation with sugar (Curves 10 and 11) than with complete diet as reinforcer. In a few cases (e.g., Curves 3 and 10) compensation actually became negative at high ratios, that is, number of reinforcements declined faster than FR schedule increased, indicating that number of responses must have declined.

Compensation is affected by a number of variables other than FR size. Collier and Jennings (1969) covaried FR schedule, sucrose concentration, and lever weight, and found that compensation was better with a more concentrated solution and with an intermediate lever weight. Collier et al. (1972) found that complete compensation continued to a higher ratio (FR 160) when rats were allowed to take as many pellets as they wanted at each reinforcement, than when each reinforcement consisted of a single pellet. The authors imply that better performance occurred in the former case because the schedule interfered to a lesser extent with the rat's natural pattern of feeding, but the difference might equally well be attributed to the larger reinforcement size, or to the smaller number of responses required per day.

A number of studies (e.g., Teitelbaum, 1957; Hamilton and Brobeck, 1964; King and Gaston, 1976) have shown that hypothalamically obese rats and monkeys are unusually poor at compensating for increases in FR schedule, and Mrosovsky (1964, 1968) reports that the same is true of hibernating dormice. Roper (1975a) found that in mice, compensation was better at a higher level of deprivation, and with a reduced distance between the response key and the food dispenser. Finally, Lea and Roper (1977) showed that compensation was poorer in rats working for complete diet pellets when sucrose pellets were concurrently available on an FR schedule, than when there was no alternative food available, and poorer still when complete diet pellets were concurrently available.

Compensation is thus affected by many of the variables that affect local pattern of responding. Changes in amount of reinforcement, deprivation level, lever weight, obesity, and distance between manipulandum and reinforcer dispenser, all of which are known to affect rate of responding on at least some schedules, all affect degree of compensation, and in all cases, a change that would be expected to reduce response rate had the effect of diminishing compensation. Furthermore, as noted in the previous section, duration of the postreinforcement pause, rather than running response rate, varies with FR size, and in several of the studies reviewed above, poor compensation was associated with prolonged postreinforcement pausing rather than with within-run pausing. Finally, breaks in responding reminiscent of "ratio strain" were sometimes seen at about the point at which number of responses per session leveled off or began to decline (e.g., Collier *et al.*, 1972, Fig. 10). All this suggests that patterning effects and regulatory effects may be causally related.

E. FEEDING AS A MOTIVATIONAL SYSTEM

We comment here briefly on two issues that are particularly relevant to our main theme, and discuss in slightly more detail a third. Sources for further information on feeding include Cofer and Appley (1964), Grossman (1967), Teitelbaum (1971), Bolles (1975), Silverstone (1976), and Novin *et al.* (1976).

1. Internal versus External Control of Feeding

Until recently, the study of hunger and feeding behavior has been dominated by the concepts of homeostasis and the reflex. The conventional assumption has been that abstinence from eating causes a physiological need state within the animal, which in turn elicits eating; and conversely, intake of food causes reciprocal changes, which inhibit eating. Hence, periods of eating alternate with periods of noneating.

In spite of recent criticisms (e.g., Collier *et al.*, 1972), we feel that this "depletion–repletion" model still has much to recommend it, especially when applied to long-term *regulation* of food intake, as opposed to short-term *control* (cf. Le Magnen, 1971). Thus, animals are efficient at regulating their body weight and composition over long periods of time, despite all manner of experimental interference (e.g., dilution of food, imposition of restricted feeding schedules, removal of various sources of feedback). On the other hand, in the depletion–repletion model, by focusing on reflexlike responses to changes in internal variables, one tends to overlook factors such as learning, incentive properties of the food, social facilitation, and early experience, all of which are now known to be important determinants of food intake. We wish to emphasize simply that feeding is controlled by both internal and external factors, or in the language of classical learning theory, is both driven and elicited (Bindra, 1969).

2. Food Deprivation as a Motivational Variable

Procedurally, hunger is almost invariably induced by limiting the animal's food intake, as would be expected in view of the dominant position of the depletion–repletion model. Typically, rats or pigeons are tested at about 80% of their predeprivation body weight. Thus, in almost all studies of food reinforcement or of feeding behavior the subjects are not merely hungry, but are quite severely starved, at least in comparison with caged controls. Consequently, the results of such studies may be quite misleading from the viewpoint of normal food intake, and our notions of the efficacy of food as a reinforcer may be exaggerated (Roper, 1975a). (On the other hand, it might be argued that freely fed, caged animals are obese by "normal" standards. Unfortunately, there is no such thing as a "normal" environment for a laboratory rat.) At the very least, it is lax to use the word "hungry" to refer both to an animal that has voluntarily abstained from eating for a few hours, and to one that is chronically under-nourished.

3. Motivational Aspects of Hypothalamic Obesity

As already noted, rats and monkeys that have become obese as a result of ventromedial hypothalamic lesions perform poorly on FR and other intermittent schedules of reinforcement. This is relevant to the problem of comparing food with other reinforcers, because it has been suggested that the poor performance of obese animals can be explained by saying that they find food only weakly reinforcing (Hogan et al., 1970), or that their motivation is low (Miller et al., 1950; Teitelbaum, 1961). Hence, the performance of obese animals may provide a model against which to assess whether other reinforcers can usefully be described as "weak," in the sense of resembling weak food reinforcement (Shettleworth, 1972).

A number of recent studies shed doubt on the validity of this argument, by showing that obese animals perform as well as or better than controls under certain circumstances (for a review see King and Gaston, 1976). Some authors have pointed out that the animals in early studies were not deprived to equal percentage of preoperative body weight, and have shown that obese animals perform almost as well as normals when deprived to this criterion. Others (e.g., King and Gaston, 1973, 1976) emphasize that performance can be further enhanced by exposure to preoperative training on intermittent schedules. Furthermore, obese animals show evidence of heightened "affective" reactions to various novel stimuli, and are hyperreactive to handling, shock, frustrative nonreward, changes in the reinforcement schedule, and the palatability of the food. Since hyperreactivity to quinine-adulterated food is also greatly reduced by preoperative training (Singh, 1974), King and Gaston (1976) suggest that pretraining may improve performance on intermittent schedules by reducing the animal's hyperreactivity to aversive aspects of such schedules. Thus, they suggest that at least part of the performance deficit seen in nonpretrained, obese animals is caused by a change in the animal's response to novel stimuli, and has nothing directly to do with hunger motivation or the reinforcing strength of food. Whether or not this hypothesis survives remains to be seen: the point is that explanations of poor operant performance in terms of weakness of reinforcement or level of motivation may prove oversimplified, or perhaps quite misleading, in the face of more detailed analysis.

III.   WATER AS REINFORCER

A.   ACQUISITION

Most early studies with water as reinforcer proceeded on the assumption that the drive properties of thirst resemble those of hunger. The discovery that this was in some respects grossly true using the obstruction apparatus (Warner, 1928), maze (Elliott, 1929; Omwake, 1933) and Skinner box (Skinner, 1936) did little to stimulate more detailed comparison, and the assumption of similarity is now so strong that the authors of textbooks do not always state which reinforcer was used in a particular case.

Nevertheless, there are indications, even in the earliest literature, that the reinforcing properties of food and water are not identical. Hull (1933) and Wickens *et al.* (1949) tested rats that had been deprived of food or water for equal lengths of time in a T maze, and found that the food-reinforced, food-deprived animals acquired a position habit more slowly than the water-reinforced, water-deprived ones. Since the food-reinforced animals ran faster, the difference could not be explained simply by saying that thirst was a stronger drive than hunger. The position is further complicated by the finding that hungry rats perform better than thirsty ones in a complex, multiple T maze (Bruce, 1935), but that the order of performance is reversed if the animals are given a small amount of the appropriate reinforcer before being placed in the maze (Bruce, 1938). Since Hull (1933) and Wickens *et al.* (1949) did not adopt the latter procedure, this result does not clarify the contradiction between their results and those of Bruce (1935, 1938).

Bruce (1935) also noted that the hungry and thirsty rats showed markedly different initial behavior in the maze, the hungry ones having a "faster and better method of attack in solving the maze problem" (p. 177). Pursuing this issue, Petrinovich and Bolles (1954) and Bolles (1958) found that water-reinforced rats were indeed superior in acquiring a position habit in a T maze (cf. Hull, 1933; Wickens *et al.*, 1949), but that food-reinforced ones were superior in a response alternation. Furthermore, they were able to attribute this difference to a tendency to perseverate from trial to trial in the thirsty animals, as opposed to a tendency to alternate in the hungry ones. However, the results of yet another study (Bolles and Petrinovich, 1956), in which rats subjected to various degrees of both hunger *and* thirst were run for food or water in a T maze, suggest that the crucial factor is not a difference in the motivational state or the nature of the reward per se, but in the overall deprivation level. Thus, rats suffering reduced body weight tended to alternate regardless of the reward, whereas those whose weight was normal did not. The differences between food- and water-reinforced performance seen in most of the previous studies therefore can be attributed to the fact that the levels of water deprivation did not result in reduced body weight, whereas the levels of

food deprivation did. There is thus some factual support for our earlier suggestion (p. 168) that the behavior of chronically deprived animals may differ from
that of "hungry" ones (see also Eisman *et al.*, 1960).

The one exception to this explanation is Bruce's finding that water-reinforced
performance is more susceptible to an appetizer effect, and this may represent a
qualitative difference between the reinforcers or their associated motivational
systems (see also Gallistel, 1973, p. 195; Hunsicker and Reid, 1974).

Turning to a different question, Logan and Spanier (1970) suggest that asymptotic, water-reinforced performance is less sensitive to delay of reinforcement
than is food-reinforced responding. Appropriately deprived rats were run in a
straight alley for food or water, and retained in the goal box for 1 or 30 sec prior
to the delivery of reinforcement. The greater delay of reinforcement resulted in
slower running in both groups, but the difference was less marked in the water-
reinforcement case: the water-deprived animals ran faster in the 30-sec condition·
than did the food-deprived ones, even though they ran less fast in the 1-sec
condition. The authors suggest that the water-deprived rats were able to bridge
the delay more successfully because they tended to sniff or lick at the water cup
during the delay, whereas the food-deprived ones explored the goal box. Thus, a
difference in instrumental performance may be attributable to a difference in the
fine structure of the behavior associated with a particular reinforcer or drive state.

B. EXTINCTION

Macdonald and de Toledo (1974) trained rats to press a lever or run down an
alley for continuous or intermittent food or water reinforcement, and then measured responding during extinction. With both tasks, extinction was more rapid
and the partial reinforcement effect was smaller when water had been used as
reinforcer during training, than when food had been used. This result is not
explicable in terms of a difference in motivational level, response rate, or amount
of reinforcement during training, because a difference in either direction in any
one of these parameters would not be expected to produce both the observed
effects. For example, if water were equivalent to a small amount of food, it
would be expected to produce a smaller partial reinforcement effect, but slower
extinction (see p. 162).

Macdonald and de Toledo's (1974) study is a good example of how two
reinforcers might be directly compared, but unfortunately their results have been
questioned. First, a number of authors have obtained large partial reinforcement
effects with water as reinforcer, comparing continuous-reinforcement and
partial-reinforcement groups of rats in straight alleys (see Shanab *et al.*, 1975;
Seybert and Gerard, 1976; Seybert *et al.*, 1976; and references cited by them).
Second, Seybert and Gerard argue that the amount of water reinforcement was
unusually small, and the performance measure idiosyncratic, in Macdonald and

de Toledo's study; and they showed that the partial reinforcement effect was indeed attenuated substantially when these conditions were replicated (for other methodological criticisms of Macdonald and de Toledo, see Shanab *et al.*, 1975). Finally, Seybert and Gerard (1976), and Seybert *et al.* (1976) showed that sequential variables and reinforcement size affected a partial water-reinforcement effect in the same way as they are known to do with food reinforcement. These results not only undermine those of Macdonald and de Toledo: they provide additional evidence that the properties of food and water are similar.

On the other hand, an experiment by Levy and Seward (1969) indirectly supports Macdonald and de Toledo's claim. They deprived rats of both food and water; ran them in a double runway for food followed by food, food followed by water, water followed by food, or water followed by water; and then tested them with the first reinforcer absent. With food followed by food, omission of the first reinforcer induced faster running in the second alley, a so-called "frustration effect" (Amsel and Roussel, 1952; Amsel, 1958, 1962); and Levy and Seward intended to examine this effect using different reinforcers in the two alleys. Contrary to expectation, they found an equal frustration effect in the food–food and food–water groups, and no effect at all in the water–water and water–food groups. Thus, the effect depended on the nature of the initial reinforcer, and not on its identity or otherwise with the second reinforcer. Their result thus supports the contention that withholding expected water reinforcement has less effect on behavior than does withholding expected food (Shettleworth, 1972). Clearly, however, the experiment should be repeated with different amounts of water reinforcement and different levels of deprivation before it can be considered conclusive.

It is worth noting that, despite the criticisms of Seybert, Shanab, and their colleagues, none of their experiments directly compares food-reinforcement and water-reinforcement groups of rats. Consequently, their results do not directly challenge those of Macdonald and de Toledo, or of Levy and Seward. What is required is a careful study in which parameters such as amount of reinforcement are varied systematically for both reinforcers, in otherwise identical conditions. If it proves possible by this means to produce identical results with food and water, this is prima facie evidence that the two reinforcers have qualitatively similar properties (cf. Shettleworth, 1972).

C. AMOUNT OF REINFORCEMENT

1. Patterning Effects

Studies using straight alleys (Kintsch, 1962) and mazes (Wike and Farrow, 1962) have shown faster acquisition and better asymptotic performance with larger volumes of water reinforcement, thus confirming what would be expected on the basis of food-reinforcement studies. In both cases, however, amount of reinforcement was confounded with time in the goal box, since the animals were confined until they had consumed all the water. In a study designed to separate these variables, Robbins (1969) allowed rats to drink from tubes of different diameters for varying lengths of time. He found a correlation between running speed and duration of reinforcement, but none between running speed and amount consumed. In contrast, food-reinforcement studies suggest that duration of food availability affects responding less than amount eaten (see p. 163).

Numerous studies have varied amount of reinforcement by varying the concentration of sucrose solutions, and have consistently found that more concentrated solutions lead to faster running in alleys (e.g., Goodrich, 1960; Kraeling, 1961; Knarr and Collier, 1962; Snyder, 1962), or to higher rates of lever pressing in a Skinner box (e.g., Guttman, 1953). Since it is generally assumed that food and water reinforcement have equivalent effects, the question has not arisen as to whether sucrose solution more nearly resembles one or the other, but there is evidence that it may differ from condensed milk (see p. 163) and from water (see below, p. 175).

2. Regulatory Effects

Logan (1964) reports results from a single rat that was required to lever press for water in its home cage on an FR 8 schedule, with different amounts (volumes) of reinforcement. Compensation for changes in amount of reinforcement was incomplete, but was better with larger volumes (cf. Collier and Jennings, 1969). Complete compensation might have occurred with a lower fixed ratio (see p. 163).

D. FIXED-RATIO SCHEDULES

1. Patterning Effects

A number of studies have examined FR performance with water reinforcement (see below), but we have found no report of the detailed pattern of responding. Assuming that any gross peculiarity would have been noticed, we conclude that responding for water resembles broadly responding for food.

2. Regulatory Effects

The number of reinforcements obtained per day at different fixed ratios for five separate studies is shown in Fig. 4. In Studies 1–4, water was the reinforcer, and the animals were tested continuously in their home cages; in Study 5, the reinforcer was sucrose solution, and was available for 30 min per day. The species used include rat, guinea pig, and Mangabey monkey.

The general form of the curves resembles those of Fig. 2, with a gradually more marked failure to compensate as ratio size increases. There is a possible difference from the food-reinforcement results in that compensation is never

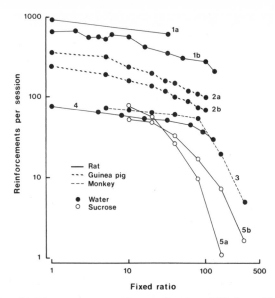

FIG. 4. Number of reinforcements per session as a function of FR size, with water or sucrose solution as reinforcer. Data are from the following studies: (1a) Logan (1964), 0.1 ml per reinforcement; (1b) Logan (1964), 0.4 ml per reinforcement; (2a) Hirsch and Collier (1974b), 10 sec access per reinforcement; (2b) Hirsch and Collier (1974b), 20 sec access per reinforcement; (3) Findley (1959); (4) King and Gaston (1976); (5a) Collier and Jennings (1969), 16% sucrose solution; (5b) Collier and Jennings (1969), 64% sucrose solution.

complete, even at very low ratios (compare Fig. 4 with Curves 2, 3, 4, 6, 7, and 8 of Fig. 2). This may indicate that the species in question are more able to compensate for reduced water intake by other means (e.g., by reducing water loss) than is the case with food intake.

On the other hand, the relatively poorer compensation with water might simply reflect a quantitative difference in reinforcement size or motivational level, since there is no *a priori* way of knowing how much water is equivalent to a 45-mg food pellet, or how many hours of water deprivation are equivalent to, say, 23 hr of food deprivation. Logan (1964) attempted to equate motivational level and amount of reinforcement by requiring rats to work for all their food and water in their home cages, on concurrent FR schedules. Amount of reinforcement was adjusted so that the number of responses made per day for food was equal to the number made for water, on an FR 1 schedule; and since the animals were not deprived of either commodity, motivation was in some sense equal. Under these conditions, compensation for increases in FR size was poorer for water than for food. Thach (1970), applying the same procedure, obtained a similar result in the rhesus monkey. Thus, there is some reason to suppose that water differs intrinsically from food in the extent to which it supports behavioral compensation for increased work requirement.

Failure to compensate has also been reported using a schedule in which a fixed cumulative duration of lever-switch closure was required per reinforcement (Allison, 1976), and using different lever weights on FR and FI schedules (Logan, 1964; Collier and Knarr, 1966). King and Gaston (1976) have shown that hypothalamic hyperphagic rats perform poorly for water on FR schedules, as they also do for food (see p. 169).

In Studies 1, 2, and 5 of Fig. 4, amount of reinforcement was varied as well as schedule. In Study 5, compensation was better with the more concentrated of two sucrose solutions (i.e., Curve 5b is flatter than 5a); but no such effect was obtained with different durations of access to water (Studies 1 and 2). Since there is evidence that rats are able to distinguish different durations of access to water (see p. 173), this may constitute a nontrivial difference between the two reinforcers.

E.   Drinking as a Motivational System

Much of what was said about the control and regulation of eating applies also to drinking. Thus, theories of thirst have centered mainly around homeostasis and internal control, and deprivation is the most common motivational procedure; but the importance of external stimulus factors is also apparent. For reviews see Cofer and Appley (1964), Andersson (1966), Grossman (1967), Fitzsimons (1971), Blass (1975), Bolles (1975), and Blass and Hall (1976).

In many species hunger and thirst are interrelated. In rats, pigeons, and doves, food or water deprivation results in a self-imposed decrease in drinking or eating, respectively. Collier and others (e.g., Collier and Knarr, 1966; Collier and Levitsky, 1967; Collier and Squibb, 1967) have suggested that this helps to speed up weight loss, which is thought to be desirable because it reduces the rate of expenditure of the commodity of which the animal is primarily deprived (see also p. 183). However, it may be mistaken to say that the food-deprived rat is in any sense water deprived, because digestion itself accounts for a large proportion of the water requirement. Hence, food-deprived animals may merely refuse to drink water which they no longer need. Furthermore, not all species react to food deprivation by decreasing their intake of water: the reverse is the case in various species of desert rodents (Wright, 1976), some strains of mice (Kutscher, 1974), and male rabbits (Cizek, 1961). This may be related to the fact that these species normally obtain some or all of their water from food, so that when deprived of food they must increase their direct intake of water. However, this cannot account for the amount of water ingested in all cases.

As already noted (p. 170), water-reinforced responding is unusually sensitive to a priming effect. There is also evidence that within-session satiation curves obtained with water reinforcement are less regular than those obtained with food in rats (Skinner, 1936) and cats (Smith and Smith, 1939).

IV. HEAT AS REINFORCER

A. ACQUISITION

Radiant heat or warm air has been claimed to reinforce operant responding in rats (Weiss, 1957), mice (Baldwin, 1968), pigs (Baldwin and Ingram, 1968), dogs (Cabanac, 1972), primates (Carlisle, 1966a, 1971), chicks (Wasserman, 1973), doves (Budgell, 1971), and lizards (Kemp, 1969; Regal, 1971) maintained at low ambient temperatures, and cold air or water has been claimed to reinforce lever-pressing in rats (Epstein and Milestone, 1968; Krisst and Sechzer, 1969), dogs (Cabanac, 1972), and goldfish (Rozin and Mayer, 1961b; Rozin, 1968) maintained at high temperatures. Few of these studies utilized controls adequate for an unambiguous demonstration of a reinforcing effect, but the fact that rate of lever pressing varies in the expected manner with ambient temperature (Weiss and Laties, 1960), hypothalamic temperature (Satinoff, 1964; Carlisle, 1966b), and rectal temperature (Adair, 1971) suggests that the animals were indeed working for heat or cold.

In most studies no formal training procedure was used: the animal was simply placed in a Skinner box at an appropriate environmental temperature, and left to discover the significance of the manipulandum. Using this procedure, Weiss (1957) and Weiss and Laties (1960, 1961) found that shaved rats began to lever press quite suddenly when their skin temperatures had fallen to a particular value, and that performance rapidly reached a consistent high level. Wasserman (1973) found that key pecking for heat in chicks could be induced by autoshaping in as few as eight trials, but Budgell (1971) reports considerable difficulty in shaping the same response in doves. These results suggest that in most cases heat reinforcement can support acquisition at least as well as food or water. It is worth noting that in most studies the ambient temperature was low (or high) enough to be lethal. Thus heat or cold reinforcement is even more immediately essential for survival in the experimental conditions than is food or water.

B. EXTINCTION

Leeming (1968) extinguished a rearing response for heat in rats, after training with a variety of fixed-interval schedules and amounts of reinforcement. Resistance to extinction was not related to fixed-interval duration in any clear manner (i.e., there was no partial reinforcement effect), and was positively related to reinforcement duration. Both of these results conflict with food reinforcement studies. However, training consisted of only a single 36-min session, so the anomalous performance may merely reflect inadequate acquisition.

C. AMOUNT OF REINFORCEMENT

1. *Patterning Effects*

Various studies (cited below) have shown that response rate is inversely related to duration or intensity of heat reinforcement, a result opposite to that typically obtained with food or water. This apparent contradiction can be resolved by considering the nature of the reinforcer and of the motivational system. Unlike food, heat reinforcement counteracts the antecedent conditions of drive (by increasing the ambient temperature) directly and instantaneously (Weiss and Laties, 1960); and conversely, its effects dissipate soon after reinforcement is terminated (Carlisle, 1966a), so that responding does not satiate within the session. Assuming that the animal responds so as to maintain a preferred average ambient temperature, it follows that both minute-to-minute response rate and number of responses per session will be inversely related to reinforcement size. In other words, short-term response rate with heat reinforcement is equivalent to long-term response rate (number of responses per day or week) with food, and any positive incentive effect of large reinforcement size is likely to be hidden by adverse short-term satiety effects.

Nevertheless, a number of authors have expressed concern that heat reinforcement violates what are considered to be general laws of performance. Leeming (1968) reasoned that if very short bursts of heat were delivered on an intermittent schedule, the satiety effects of different amounts of reinforcement should be minimized, thus allowing differences in incentive value to emerge. He therefore allowed rats to work for short but intense bursts of heat on FI 10-, 40-, and 60-sec schedules, and varied reinforcement duration between 0 and 0.35 sec. A positive relationship between response rate and reinforcement size emerged only in the FI 10-sec group, and the FI 60-sec group showed no increase in responding over unreinforced control animals.

2. *Regulatory Effects*

Corbit (1970) shows data from three studies in which shaved rats were required to lever press for different amounts of heat reinforcement. In all cases the animals tended to compensate for differences in reinforcement size; but with small reinforcements responding was inadequate to maintain a constant calorific input. The results thus resemble those of food and water studies. Weiss and Laties (1960, 1961) and Carlisle (1966a) showed that rats suffered a decline in body temperature with short durations of reinforcement, so their failure to compensate behaviorally was not due to more efficient utilization of the available heat. The same authors have obtained similar results by varying intensity rather than duration of reinforcement, but Carlisle suggests that the function relating heat input to reinforcement size differs in detail according to whether duration or intensity is the independent variable (unfortunately the data were not subjected to statistical analysis).

Poor compensation has also been reported in pigs (Baldwin and Ingram, 1968) and genetically hairless mice (Baldwin, 1968), but Carlisle (1966a) found almost perfect compensation in squirrel monkeys. Furthermore, cynomolgus (*Macaca fascicularis*) and pig-tailed (*M. nemestrina*) macaques maintained a constant body temperature over a range of reinforcement durations (Carlisle, 1971), and shaved rats maintained a constant hypothalamic temperature over a range of intensities (Carlisle, 1968), on schedules in which heat was delivered for as long as the lever was depressed. Finally, Corbit (1970) reports that good compensation occurred with fully furred rats using cool air as reinforcer on a similar schedule. The reasons for some of these contradictions remain obscure. Carlisle (1966a) suggested that the squirrel monkeys in his study performed better than the rats because their pelage was left intact, but his subsequent result with shaved rats (Carlisle, 1968) disconfirms this hypothesis. It may be the case that relatively larger amounts of reinforcement were used for the monkeys, since compensation is known to improve with increases in reinforcement size.

The finding that compensation is better when the animal is given precise control over reinforcement duration is less puzzling, and is consistent with results using food (Collier *et al.*, 1972) and activity (Collier and Hirsch, 1971) as reinforcers. As Corbit (1970) points out, a reinforcement of fixed duration may be too short or too long for the animal's immediate needs, and hence is likely to be less reinforcing, or possibly even aversive (for example, too much heat might be painful). For whatever reason, however, we can conclude that under certain conditions, at least some species can compensate for changes in amount of heat reinforcement at least as well as they can compensate for changes in amount of food or water.

D. FIXED-RATIO SCHEDULES

1. Patterning Effects

Carlisle (1969) allowed shaved rats to lever press for 3-sec bursts of heat on a series of FR schedules from 1 to 20. Responding was sporadic even at the lowest ratios, with long pauses after reinforcements and breaks within response runs, and it broke down altogether at about FR 15. With food reinforcement, this sort of performance would be expected only at much higher ratios, or in poorly motivated animals. A number of rats died of cold during the experiment, so the result can hardly be blamed on insufficient need for heat, but as with hunger, performance could be related to drive by an inverted-U function.

Carlisle later (1970) tested rats on various chain schedules, that is, schedules in which completion of one requirement brought another into operation. In one case, using a two-lever apparatus, an FR n schedule was programed on one lever, the completion of which caused onset of a signal light, and made the second lever operative for 1 min. During this minute, the second lever delivered 3-sec bursts of heat on an FR 1 schedule. Thus each time it completed the fixed ratio, the rat could obtain up to 20 heat reinforcements, rather than just one as in a conventional FR schedule. Under these conditions Carlisle obtained normal fixed-ratio performance up to about FR 64. This is grossly similar to the performance of rats reinforced with single food pellets, but one would expect responding to ratios of a few hundred in rats reinforced with food on a comparable chain schedule.

2. Regulatory Effects

In the first experiment reported above, Carlisle (1969) obtained failure to compensate for increases in FR size over the whole range of schedules (Fig. 5, Curve 1b). A squirrel monkey also tested on conventional FR schedules showed complete compensation up to FR 5, but not thereafter (Fig. 5, Curve 1a). Performance was not improved by increasing the reinforcement size or decreasing the ambient temperature.

Substantially better compensation was obtained with the chain schedule (Fig. 5, Curve 2a). Note that number of reinforcements per session was lower with the chain schedule than with the conventional FR, because more heat was obtained each time the ratio was completed. In the same study, results were reported from

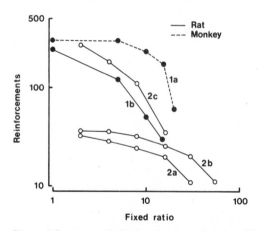

Fig. 5. Number of heat reinforcements obtained per hour, as a function of FR size. Data are from the following studies: (1a) Carlisle (1969), monkey; (1b) Carlisle (1969), rat; (2a) Carlisle (1970), rat, heterogeneous chain FR n FR 1 (1 min) schedule; (2b) Carlisle (1970), homogeneous chain FR n FR 1 (1 min) schedule; (2c) Carlisle (1970), heterogeneous chain FR n FR 1 schedule.

two other chain schedules. In the first, both components of the chain operated on the same lever, and this gave marginally better compensation than the two-lever schedule (Fig. 5, Curve 2b). In the second, both levers again were used, but the second delivered only one 3-sec burst of heat each time the ratio on the first was completed. This schedule thus resembled a conventional FR, except that the final response had to be made on a second lever, and, like the conventional FR, it gave poor compensation (Fig. 5, Curve 2c).

Carlisle concludes that FR performance is improved by increasing the overall density of reinforcement, but not simply by making the rat go to another lever to collect reinforcement, or by accompanying reinforcement with a visual discriminative stimulus. In some respects these results parallel those of studies with brain stimulation as reinforcer (see Section IX), but even with the most effective chain schedule, compensation was inferior to that obtained with food or water. As with food reinforcement, the results also suggest that "patterning" and "regulatory" effects go hand in hand, in that poor local control over responding was associated with poor compensation.

A minor question that remains to be answered is: Why did compensation improve when the chain schedule was used, but not when reinforcement size was increased? A possible reason is that prolonged or intense bursts of heat may be aversive (see below).

E. THERMOREGULATION AS A MOTIVATIONAL SYSTEM

Like hunger and thirst, thermoregulation has generally been treated as a homeostatic system (e.g., Corbit, 1970; Cabanac, 1972; Bligh, 1973); but unlike hunger and thirst, thermoregulatory imbalances can be rectified either behaviorally or autonomically (at least within limits). Broadly speaking, the rule determining which mechanism is used seems to be: use behavior first, but when the behavioral response becomes too difficult, use autonomic means (Adair and Wright, 1976; see also Cabanac, 1972, p. 25). Thus, we prefer to light a fire or turn on the air conditioner, rather than shiver or sweat.

Regarded in this light, some of the apparent inconsistencies in the data begin to make sense. For example, several studies suggest that with heat as reinforcer, compensation for increases in FR size, or for decreases in amount of reinforcement, is unusually susceptible to disruption at moderate fixed ratios or with small reinforcements. This may be because autonomic regulation of temperature becomes more efficient when reinforcement size is very small, or FR size moderately large. Again, the chain schedule may be superior in maintaining behavioral regulation because a series of small reinforcements is likely to bring the animal's temperature back to the preferred level with greater precision than is a single large one. The same is true of schedules in which reinforcement duration is controlled by response duration (see p. 178). Thus, behavioral regulation is more effective the smaller the difference between the required temperature and the temperature produced by a reinforcement, and this may be why short durations of reinforcement are relatively ineffective, and why in extreme conditions animals die of hypothermia rather than lever press. An additional factor in death from hypothermia may be adaptation of cold sensations.

V. Locomotor Activity as Reinforcer

A. Acquisition and Extinction

In the studies cited below, rats were confined to a wheel or treadmill fitted with a retractable lever, and reinforcement was delivered by releasing a brake or switching on a motor to drive the apparatus. Formal training seems to be unnecessary, and there are no detailed accounts of acquisition or extinction. Premack (1965) showed that wheel running would increase the probability of various operants above their unreinforced levels, but other studies have lacked control procedures. Since wheel running is increased by food deprivation (see Section V.D), some of the studies used deprived animals. We have found no studies of extinction.

B. Amount of Reinforcement

1. Patterning Effects

Premack et al. (1964), using licking as the operant and wheel running as the reinforcer in rats, varied reinforcement duration from 2 to 20 sec on an FR 10 schedule. Postreinforcement pause duration was directly related to amount of reinforcement, which conflicts with some, but not all, food reinforcement studies.

2. Regulatory Effects

In the same study, number of responses per session was inversely related to reinforcement size, but compensation was never perfect and responding broke down altogether with the briefest reinforcements. The sessions were only 20 min long, so there may have been ceiling effects; and better compensation might have been obtained with an FR 1 schedule (see p. 163).

C. Fixed-Ratio Schedules

1. Patterning Effects

Premack et al. (1964) also tested rats on a series of FR schedules from 5 to 300, with licking as operant, and obtained normal steplike responding up to at least FR 80. Similar results were reported by Collier and Hirsch (1971) using

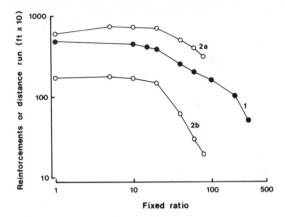

FIG. 6. Number of reinforcements (1 and 2a) or distance run (2b) per session, as a function of FR size, with wheel or treadmill running as reinforcer: data from (●) Premack *et al.* (1964); (○) Collier and Hirsch (1971).

lever pressing as operant; in both studies, however, postreinforcement pauses were unusually long, ranging from about 1 min at FR 1 to about 10 min at FR 60.

2. *Regulatory Effects*

The results of three experiments from the two studies cited above are shown in Fig. 6. In those of Collier and Hirsch, food-deprived rats lever pressed for access to a free-running wheel (Curve 2a) or a motor-driven treadmill (Curve 2b), and the animals were allowed to determine reinforcement duration since the apparatus remained switched on until running ceased. Compensation was complete up to about FR 20, which is roughly comparable to food-reinforced performance. The inferior initial compensation obtained by Premack *et al.* (1964) (Curve 1) may merely reflect their use of shorter sessions (20 min, as opposed to 2 hr in Collier and Hirsch's, 1971, experiments).

D. MOTIVATIONAL ASPECTS OF RUNNING

Three aspects of running account for most of the literature: its circadian rhythmicity; its relation to drives such as hunger, thirst, and sex; and its status as a consummatory behavior in its own right (for reviews see Munn, 1950; Baumeister *et al.*, 1964; Cofer and Appley, 1964; Gross, 1968; Hinde, 1970; Bolles, 1975). Circadian rhythmicity does not concern us, except in that it is evidence of internal control.

It is well known that running in rats increases with hunger (Richter, 1922, 1927), thirst (Hall, 1955), and estrus (Wang, 1923), and that it is inversely related to ambient temperature (Munn, 1950), but the interpretation of these findings is a matter of dispute. The enhanced activity of food-deprived animals has proved a particularly contentious issue, because one would intuitively expect conservation of energy to be more adaptive than expenditure. Early theorists suggested that increases in activity were an innate response to various physiological need states, and that they served to increase the animal's chance of finding the desired commodity (e.g., Sherrington, 1900; Wang, 1923), or to disperse the population from adverse environments (Wald and Jackson, 1944). However, the increase in activity was later shown to be limited mainly to the few hours preceding feeding on a regular deprivation schedule (Sheffield and Campbell, 1954; Amsel and Work, 1961; Bolles, 1963), and was greatly reduced by careful isolation from external disturbance (Campbell and Sheffield, 1953; Hall, 1956; Teghtsoonian and Campbell, 1960). This prompted the suggestion that hunger increases responsivity to external stimuli (especially stimuli associated with food), rather than that it increases activity directly for some biologically adaptive reason (Campbell and Sheffield, 1953; Campbell and Lynch, 1969).

In contrast to "responsivity" theories, "regulatory" theories suggest that running plays some role in the animal's overall energy economy. Again, a major aim has been to explain the counterintuitive increase in running induced by food deprivation. Brobeck (1945) suggested that running serves to maintain a normal body temperature in the face of starvation-induced hypothermia, but others (e.g., Andik et al., 1963; Collier et al., 1965; Collier and Levitsky, 1968; Leshner, 1971) propose that it is concerned with the maintenance of a certain balance of body composition or weight. The evidence is that running is closely related to degree of body weight loss (Collier and Levitsky, 1968); it is affected by various metabolic imbalances (Collier and Squibb, 1967; Leshner, 1971); and energy expenditure on running is conserved when wheel torque is varied (Collier and Leshner, 1967). The tendency to compensate for changes in FR size and amount of reinforcement also indicates conservation of energy expenditure (Collier, 1970). Collier proposes that when an animal is deprived of a necessary dietary constituent (or is exposed to low temperature), it undergoes voluntary body weight loss to a point at which average intake of the commodity in question equals average expenditure, and he suggests that the enhanced running of food-deprived rats is adaptive because it accelerates the process of weight loss, and helps the animal to stay at a reduced weight. His theory thus elegantly debunks the assumption that a deprived animal needs to conserve energy.

Variants of the same approach have been proposed by Morrison (1968) and Premack and Premack (1963). Morrison emphasizes that eating and digestion themselves require energy, and proposes that energy not spent eating must be accounted for by an increase in noneating activity. However, his argument rests on the assumption that the animal needs to conserve a certain ratio of energy loss while active to energy loss while resting or asleep, and it is not clear why this should be so. Premack and Premack suggest that time spent running increases in deprived animals to fill the time which would have been spent eating, and they ingeniously demonstrate that eating increases in rats deprived of access to running wheels.

Thus, there is reasonable support for regulatory theories in general, but substantial disagreement about what is being regulated, and even confirmed regulatory theorists admit that running is reactive in at least some circumstances (e.g., Collier and Squibb, 1967). We can therefore conclude with reasonable safety that deprivation-induced running, like eating, drinking, and thermoregulation, is subject to both internal and external control.

The question of whether running constitutes a consummatory activity in its own right arises because animals run vigorously in their home cages even when not subject to apparent physiological need, and also because running acts as a reinforcer. These findings, plus the fact that running increases over a few days or weeks when the animal is first allowed access to a wheel (Seward and Pereboom, 1955), have led to the suggestion that running is self-reinforcing (e.g., Gross, 1968). Presumably this means that running is reinforced by its own sensory consequences. If so, it is indirectly supported by an experiment showing that deermice prefer to run in square wheels or wheels provided with hurdles, rather than in conventional round ones (Kavanau and Brant, 1965). The authors of this study conclude that running is attractive because it allows the animal to perform elaborate acrobatic routines. Those who have watched deermice running will sympathize with this view, but it leaves open the question of why acrobatics should be important or enjoyable, and it is not applicable to less agile species. The postulation of an "activity drive" is no better because attempts to specify antecedent conditions, such as an effect of deprivation of running, have been unsuccessful (e.g., Bolles, 1975). And the notion that running is one index of a general activity drive has foundered in the face of evidence that different measures of activity correlate poorly (e.g., Anderson, 1937; Eayrs, 1954; Weasner et al., 1960).

De Kock and Rohn (1971) have speculatively offered various interpretations of running in social groups of rodents, such as that it substitutes for actual traversal of space in particular behavioral contexts. Similarly, it is often suggested that the stereotyped pacing seen in many caged animals (e.g., Hediger, 1950) is a substitute for normal locomotor activity. "Substitute" theories, however, seem unable to cope with the scale of the behavior: for example, Mongolian gerbils regularly run for 8-10 hr a night, and cover the equivalent of 12-15 miles (Roper, 1976b). It seems scarcely credible that they would travel comparable distances in the wild, and evidence from trapping (e.g., Fenyuk and Deyashev, cited in Elton, 1942) suggests that they do not. Furthermore, running virtually disappears in a seminatural but still confined environment (Roper and Polioudakis, 1977), suggesting that it is indeed an artifact of impoverished housing conditions, but not merely of limited space. It may eventually prove possible to explain these extraordinary amounts of running in terms of energy regulation, but it seems quite likely that running can become divorced from any regulatory function, so that it simply expands to fit the available time.

To conclude, a number of variables are known to affect running, but the factors that control it remain obscure. As with deprivation-induced running, internal and external factors are probably both important; and the search for a single theory of running (or worse, of activity) is probably doomed to failure.

VI. Nest Material as Reinforcer

A. Demonstrations that Nest Material Can Act as a Reinforcer

Nest material has been claimed to reinforce an arbitrary operant response in hamsters (Jansen *et al.*, 1969), rats (Oley and Slotnick, 1970), mice (Roper, 1973a, b), gerbils (Glickman, 1973), and zebra finches (Roper and Clarke, unpublished observations), and to reinforce learning of a position discrimination in canaries (Hinde and Steel, 1972). The animals were tested in their home cages for all or part of the day, since Jansen *et al.* (1969) report that hamsters failed to work for nest material in a Skinner box. Most of the rodent studies used normal animals tested at room temperature, and nest building was encouraged by removing the nest before testing. The studies by Jansen and co-workers and by Roper included controls showing that reinforced rate of responding exceeded that of a yoked subject, or exceeded operant level, and observation of the animals showed that they did use the material to build nests.

B. Acquisition and Extinction

Oley and Slotnick (1970) report that pregnant rats began to press a lever for nest material after the delivery of a few free reinforcements, without being shaped. Roper (1975a) observed equally rapid acquisition of a key-pressing response by female mice. In both studies the manipulandum was located very close to the paper dispenser, a procedure that results in faster acquisition and higher asymptotic response rates with food as reinforcer (Bremner and Trowill, 1962; Davidson *et al.*, 1971). When Roper increased the distance between the manipulandum and the dispenser by only 2.5 cm, acquisition was significantly retarded, and usually required several sessions of manual shaping.

Roper (unpublished observations) has consistently found that shaping is more difficult with nest material than with food, except when the distance between the manipulandum and paper dispenser is minimal. With nest material, requiring the animal to make a closer approximation to the desired response frequently results in it making one or two subcriterion responses, and then apparently losing interest in nest building altogether. With food, failure to obtain reinforcement results in enhanced activity in the region of the dispenser and manipulandum, from which activity the required response is easily shaped. The difference, which is perhaps analagous to (although more marked than) the failure of water to induce a frustration effect, cannot be easily ascribed to a low level of nest-building motivation, because mice respond extremely vigorously and persistently to material presented noncontingently (Roper, 1973a, b).

The preceding observations suggest that responding reinforced by nest material might show little resistance to extinction, but no comparative data are available.

C. Amount of Reinforcement

1. Patterning Effects

Roper (1973a, 1976a) varied the amount of paper reinforcement given to mice by varying either the length or the width of each paper strip, or the number of strips delivered. In one experiment, mice key pressed on an FR 1 schedule for 1 hr a day, and each reinforcement consisted of either a single strip 10 cm long, a single strip 20 cm long, or two separate strips 10 cm long. All strips were of the same width. There was some suggestion that the animals responded more vigorously for two separate strips than for single ones of either length, but response rates were obscured by large differences in the time spent detaching and manipulating strips of different length and number.

In a second experiment the mice worked on low FR schedules, and reinforcement consisted of a single strip of paper 10 cm long, but either 0.65 cm, 1.25 cm, or 2.5 cm wide. They responded at a higher rate for the wider strips, when differences in the time taken to detach each strip were taken into account. These results are not particularly convincing, but they suggest that differences in width of paper reinforcement affect responding in the usual manner, while differences in length have no effect.

2. Regulatory Effects

Roper found that neither length nor number of strips per reinforcement affected number of responses per session, so that the total amount of paper obtained (and the size of the nest) was directly proportional to amount of reinforcement. In the second experiment, number of responses and reinforcements was positively related to reinforcement width, a result opposite to those obtained with the other reinforcers considered thus far.

D. FIXED-RATIO SCHEDULES

1. Patterning Effects

Roper (1973b) required mice to key press for paper on a series of FR schedules, with the manipulandum 6.0 cm distant from the dispenser. Steplike responding was obtained at low ratios, and postreinforcement pause duration increased with FR size, but the pauses were unusually long (ranging from 15 sec at FR 1 to 1 min at FR 10), and strain appeared as early as FR 15. The highest ratio reached by any animal was FR 40.

In a second experiment (Roper, 1975a) the response key was located as close as possible to the dispenser. The mice again responded in a pause-and-run manner, but the pauses were shorter. Responding continued to a somewhat higher level, but the highest ratio reached by any animal (FR 60) was still low by the standards of food reinforcement (e.g., Smart, 1970). The only other published results on FR performance are those of Oley and Slotnick (1970), who reported typical responding up to at least FR 40 in pregnant rats.

2. Regulatory Effects

In the first study described above, Roper (1973b) obtained complete absence of compensation for increases in FR size (Fig. 7, Curve 1), but when the key was located closer to the dispenser, compensation occurred up to about FR 5 (Fig. 7, Curve 2). Thus, nest material resembles food only when response-reinforcer distance is minimal, even though the maximum distance used by Roper (6.0 cm) is not large by the standards of normal operant procedure.

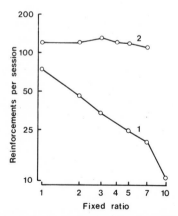

FIG. 7. Number of reinforcements per session as a function of FR size, with nest material as reinforcer for key pressing in mice: (1) key-reinforcer distance 6.5 cm; (2) key-reinforcer distance 4.0 cm. (Data from Roper, 1973a.)

3. Effects on Activities Other Than Operant Responding

To summarize, Roper's experiments show that a small decrease in distance between manipulandum and dispenser results in an increase in number of responses per session on an FR 1 schedule, an increase in the size of the ratio at which strain appears, a decrease in postreinforcement pause duration, an increase in response rate on an FR 1 schedule, and an increase in the degree of compensation for increases in FR size. Once again, then, we find that "patterning effects" and "regulatory effects" are correlated, and the question arises of whether they are causally related. Knowledge of the activities that occurred during the postreinforcement pause sheds some light on this problem.

In the first experiment, paper strips were initially delivered noncontingently. The mice usually "gathered" each strip and carried it into the nest box, and then returned immediately for another, but occasionally an animal might gather a number of strips in succession, and then carry them in a single bout. (The latter behavior was more efficient, because several strips could be carried in a single journey.) When 20 or 30 strips had been carried to the nest site, the animal would engage in a bout of building. Sequences of gathering, carrying, and building were repeated until the nest reached completion, except for periodic interruption by bouts of eating and other activities.

When an FR 1 schedule was introduced, there was an increase in the probability of carrying and building, and an increase in the duration of bouts of building. Probability and duration of building continued to increase with successively higher ratios, probability of carrying having reached unity at FR 1 or 2. Thus, the unusually long postreinforcement pauses seen in this experiment were filled by an increase in the frequency and duration of the activities normally elicited by presentation of nest material. A similar effect was observed by Oley and Slotnick (1970). However, in Roper's (1975a) second experiment, in which postreinforcement pauses remained comparatively short, the frequency and duration of building remained much lower. The difference between the two experiments cannot be attributed to postreinforcement behavior learned during acquisition, because exaggerated carrying and building developed in a group of animals trained with a small key-reinforcer distance, and then shifted to a large one.

4. Postreinforcement Building as Adjunctive Behavior

The postreinforcement building observed in the first experiment bears some resemblance to the "adjunctive behavior" sometimes observed when food is presented on intermittent schedules (see reviews by Staddon and Simmelhag, 1971; Falk, 1972; Segal, 1972). The prototypic example of adjunctive behavior is "polydipsia," which is postreinforcement drinking. It has been demonstrated mainly with interval schedules, and may develop to such an extent that the animal drinks more in a short experimental session than it would normally consume in a day (Falk, 1961, 1972). Falk suggests as criteria of adjunctive activities that they are schedule dependent, occur early in the postreinforcement pause, have no obvious value to the animal, and constitute an exaggerated version of a normal activity. The exaggerated building observed with nest material as reinforcer fulfills all these criteria.

More precise support for the analogy can be derived from experiments showing that building and drinking can be obtained on identical schedules, and that they bear a similar sequential relationship to the reinforcing activity. Roper (1973a) delivered paper noncontingently to mice, on a series of fixed-time schedules. Carrying and building increased as a function of interreinforcement interval, and their frequencies of occurrence were not significantly different from those obtained on FR schedules with equivalent reinforcement rates. Thus schedule-induced nest building, like polydipsia (see Falk, 1972), occurs on time-dependent schedules, does not require an instrumental contingency, and seems to be closely related to reinforcement rate. However, nonnesting behavior was significantly less with an operant requirement than without one, showing that it was not solely determined by reinforcement rate.

Conversely, Schaeffer and Diehl (1966) have shown polydipsia using FR schedules, in rats. Furthermore, drinking in rats is the most frequent postreinforcement activity other than lever pressing on a food-reinforced FR 1 schedule, even when animals are able to engage in a variety of other activities (Roper, unpublished observations). Thus, schedule-induced drinking and nest building both constitute increases in the activity that is most likely to follow the response immediately elicited by delivery of reinforcement, on an FR 1 schedule.

5. Conclusions

Paper- and food-reinforced responding show a similar pause-and-run pattern, a similar relation between pause duration and FR size, and a similar tendency to support postreinforcement activities that are stochastically related to the initial consummatory response. They differ quantitatively, however, with respect to pause duration, frequency of occurrence of adjunctive behavior (which was unity at FR 10 in the case of building, but only about 0.06 at the same ratio with food), and resistance to ratio strain. Furthermore, compensation for increases in FR size was markedly poorer with paper than with food. Can these quantitative differences be explained by saying that paper is a weaker reinforcer than food?

Some support for the latter view is provided by the finding that food-reinforced FR performance shows poor compensation for increases in FR size (Roper, 1975a), and prolonged postreinforcement pausing (Sidman and Stebbins, 1954; Ferster and Skinner, 1957; Collier et al., 1967) when deprivation level is low. Amount of schedule-induced drinking (Falk, 1972) and air licking (Mendelson and Chillag, 1971) is directly related to deprivation level, however. Similarly, pause duration is inversely related to amount of food reinforcement (Powell, 1969), while amount of polydipsia is directly related (Flory, 1971). Thus, we cannot explain both prolonged pausing and enhanced building by saying that nest material resembles food when deprivation level is low, or when amount of reinforcement is small.

An alternative approach is to point to the high levels of building and long pauses which occurred with paper on an FR 1 schedule. Thus, the frequency with which building followed carrying was about 0.5 (Roper, 1973b), whereas the frequency with which drinking followed eating was about 0.01 (Schaeffer and Diehl, 1966). In both cases, the frequency of occurrence of the activity in question had approximately doubled by FR 10, that is, *proportionate* increase in the frequency of the adjunctive activity was approximately the same. Although this quantitative comparison will not bear much weight, being based on sparse data from two different species, it suggests that the comparatively high frequency of building may merely reflect its frequency of occurrence in the baseline condition. Certainly this possibility is worth proper consideration before turning to less obvious differences between the two activities, such as that building directly involves the primary reinforcer, whereas drinking does not.

This analysis implies that incidence of adjunctive behavior determines post-reinforcement pause duration, which is not the view most commonly held. Thus, Falk (1972) suggests that pausing occurs on intermittent schedules because the animal learns that responses made immediately after delivery of reinforcement are never reinforced; and adjunctive behavior occurs merely to fill up this pause. In support of this view, it might be pointed out that pausing occurs when the animal is not given special facilities for adjunctive behavior. Even in the barren environment of the Skinner box, however, animals are able to engage in a wide variety of activities other than operant responding and eating, and there is evidence that these unrecorded activities do compete with the operant. Thus, pigeons have been shown to peck at a higher rate than normal on various intermittent schedules when they are physically restrained (Richardson and Loughead, 1974), or tested in a very small chamber (Skuban and Richardson, 1975), so as to prevent them from leaving the immediate vicinity of the key. Furthermore, M. J. Morgan (unpublished observations) and Roper (in preparation) have shown that responding by rats on interval schedules increases when opportunity to engage in various adjunctive activities is withdrawn. Finally, the fact that pause duration increases at low deprivation levels, whereas adjunctive behavior decreases, suggests that the latter is an active response to the thwarting of a strongly motivated consummatory activity (cf. McFarland, 1966), rather than a passive response to the inhibition of operant activity. Thus, there is some justification for arguing that prolonged pausing occurs with paper as reinforcer not because the reinforcer exerts weak control over the operant, but because activities inherent in the nest-building sequence compete with the operant.

Even this is not the whole story, because there remains the apparent distractibility of the mice during shaping, and the finding that disruption of nest building by nonnesting activities increased when a contingency was introduced. To try and explain these results, we shall turn to nest building as a motivational system.

E. Nest Building as a Motivational System

1. Deprivation

Roper (1973a) gave mice access to hoppers of paper strips for 2 hr a day in their home cages, and removed the previous day's nest 5 hr, 1 hr, or immediately before testing. He found a slight, but significant deprivation effect.

In a second experiment Roper (1973a) attempted to discover whether mice would adapt to a regular periodic schedule of access to nest material in the way that they adapt to a periodic schedule of access to food. Animals were allowed access to paper strips for 2 or 22 hr a day, and their nests were removed 2 hr before testing. The 2-hr group took no more material than did the 22-hr group in the same 2-hr period, even though the 22-hr group engaged in a substantial amount of extra nest building during the remaining 20 hr. The failure to obtain a difference in the first 2 hr could not be attributed to a simple ceiling effect. Since nest building also shows a diurnal rhythm (Oley and Slotnick, 1970; Roper, 1975b), it follows that the amount of material taken during a session of limited duration is strongly dependent upon the time of day at which the test is conducted. It might be concluded that the control of nest building differs fundamentally from that of feeding or drinking, but it is worth noting that some species (e.g., hamsters and guinea pigs) do not adapt well to periodic food-deprivation schedules (e.g., Kutscher, 1969).

2. Satiation

The accepted procedure of removing the nest prior to testing implies that the presence of a nest inhibits further nest building. This is certainly true, but evidence from a variety of field and laboratory studies indicates that the inhibition is sometimes incomplete (Hinde and Steel, 1972; Roper, 1976a). Roper allowed mice free access to hoppers of paper strips in cages with separate nest boxes, and measured the amount of paper removed from the hopper each day, the amount left in the main compartment of the cage, and the amount carried into the nest box. The nest was removed at the beginning of the experiment, but was then left to accumulate for two weeks. The amount of paper removed from the hopper showed no decline over the two weeks, even though none was taken into the nest box after the first few days. Thus, the presence of a completed nest seems to inhibit carrying, but not gathering (see also Glickman et al., 1967, and Rowell, 1959, for reports of similar behavior in gerbils and hamsters). Hinde and Stevenson (1969, 1970) suggest that gathering may be intrinsically reinforcing, but

Roper (1976a) found mice reluctant to key press for paper in the presence of a completed nest.

3. Value to the Animal

Nest building in nonreproducing rodents is primarily a thermoregulatory response, and Sealander (1952) has shown that deermice survive low temperatures more successfully when given access to nest material. During the reproductive cycle, nest building presumably also aids survival of the young. In normal laboratory conditions, on the other hand, adult rodents survive quite adequately without nests. Although it is not surprising that laboratory animals continue to engage in behavior that has adaptive significance only in the wild, nest material clearly has less immediate value (in some sense) to the laboratory animal than does food or water.

4. Other Factors

Nest building is inversely related to ambient temperature in various species of rodents, and is dependent upon hormonal state in females (see reviews by Lehrman, 1961; Rosenblatt, 1970; Moltz, 1971). It also shows diurnal rhythmicity (see above). Almost all investigators of nest building in rodents have reported extreme individual variability (e.g., Rowell, 1959; Richards, 1965; Lisk et al., 1969; Glickman, 1973).

5. Theoretical Considerations

Glickman (1973) suggests that paper is a weak reinforcer in gerbils (in the sense that it supports a low and variable operant response rate) because nest building depends more upon being elicited by external cues than upon being "driven" by internal ones. Thus, he implies that short-term control over operant behavior is poor because the animal does not "feel" need for nest material in the way that it "feels" hungry or thirsty. Hence, it has little to sustain its attention to nest building during periods of nonreinforcement.

Although we shall probably never know what animals feel, this argument does have some intuitive appeal. It would be foolish to deny that nest building depends on hormonal condition, temperature, time of day, and other "drive" variables (see above), but, on the other hand, many of the data indicate that certain nest building activities are unusually dependent upon the incentive value of the stimulus, at least in nonreproducing rodents. Thus, mice fail to adapt to a periodic schedule of access to material; gathering fails to satiate as long as a supply of material is freely available; amount of material obtained in an operant situation is, if anything, positively related to amount of reinforcement; compensation for increases in work requirement is poor; responding is unusually sensitive to increase in distance between manipulandum and paper dispenser; and nest building can come to occupy a very large proportion of the animal's time in relation to its apparent usefulness, provided that material is easily obtainable. Furthermore, Glickman's (1973) theory accounts for the fact that many of these anomalies are not apparent in the nest building of birds (Hinde, 1967; Hinde and Steel, 1966; Hinde and Steel, this volume). This would be expected, because the behavior is more closely related to hormonal conditions in birds than it is in nonreproducing rodents. Finally, Glickman's position does lead to suggestions for further research, though it is doubtful whether it is strong enough to yield unequivocal predictions. For example, it suggests that responding for paper should extinguish rapidly, and that operant performance should be improved by the addition of cues such as low temperature or visible presence of the material during the interreinforcement interval (Glickman, 1973, p. 233). Eventually, arguments about the relative importance of external versus internal control of motivated behavior may be superseded by physiological knowledge, or they may turn out to be completely misguided, but in the case of nest building they are probably more useful than simple statements about reinforcing strength.

VII. Aggression as Reinforcer

A. Demonstrations that Aggression Can Act as a Reinforcer

The opportunity to fight with, or display aggressively toward, a conspecific has been claimed to be a reinforcer for fighting cocks (Thompson, 1964), mice (Tellegen *et al.* 1969), rats (Dreyer and Church, 1970), and pigeons (Cole and Parker, 1971); predatory behavior in rats has also been claimed to be reinforcing (Van Hemel, 1972; see Polsky, 1975, for a review). The only systematic investigations of aggression as reinforcer, however, have used fish as subjects. Fish are popular primarily because aggression can be elicited by the visual image of a conspecific behind glass, or by a mirror image of the subject, thus simplifying the procedure and avoiding the possibility of actual fighting. Inasmuch as the reinforcing properties of aggressive behavior have been a matter of dispute, we shall review several studies using different instrumental responses, procedures, and species, and conclude this section by discussing whether aggression or some other motivation underlies the results.

1. Target Pressing

Target pressing has not been widely used, perhaps because it is difficult to condition in the Siamese fighting fish (*Betta splendens*). Hogan and Rozin (see Hogan, 1961) report that several days of hand shaping were insufficient to condition responding for food, and they finally resorted to placing a small worm behind clear plastic on the target. Using this method they trained seven bettas to

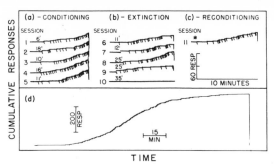

FIG. 8. Record of one betta responding for the visual presentation of another male betta. The recorder steps up and makes a downward stroke with each lever press. The figure at the beginning of each curve in A and B is the number of minutes that elapsed prior to the first press. In Session 11, the opaque screen was raised for the first 10 min; the fish's first response followed in 4 min. Panel D is the full 2.25-hr Session 14. (From Hogan, 1961.)

press a small piece of black plastic attached to a thin steel rod (see Hogan and Rozin, 1962), with white worms as the reinforcer. When the fish were pressing consistently, the sight of another fish was gradually substituted for the food, but this resulted in extinction in all but one subject. Training continued with the one exception for six days, followed by extinction for five days, and finally by reconditioning. Since the time to the first response was very variable, each session lasted for 10 min after the first press. The results are shown in Fig. 8. The response was conditioned, extinguished, and reconditioned in much the same way as it would have been for food, except that rate of pressing tended to increase toward the end of the session. This is the opposite of what happens when fish receive food reinforcement (Hogan, 1961). Figure 8(d) is a cumulative record of a single 2-hr session, which shows that the initial "warm-up" is followed by a typical satiation curve.

During conditioning, the fish approached and displayed at the lever before it pressed; when it finally made the response, it often charged at and hit the lever with much greater force than it had done for food. Both the display and the charge dropped out during extinction and reappeared during reconditioning. The display was still present after a two-month rest, and continued for another two months when the fish was tested several times weekly.

Sevenster (1968, 1973) reports success in training male sticklebacks (*Gasterosteus aculeatus*) to bite a rod with aggressive display as reinforcer, but he does not report the length or number of his training sessions.

2. *Swimming through a Ring or Tunnel*

Swimming through a ring or tunnel has been the most widely used response (Thompson, 1963, 1969; Hogan, 1967, 1978; Sevenster, 1968, 1973; Hogan *et al.*, 1970; Baenninger, 1970; Fantino *et al.*, 1972; Baenninger and Mattleman,

1973). Three variants of this response have also been used: swimming into either half of an E-shaped container (Turnbough and Lloyd, 1973); swimming into a particular unmarked part of the tank (Rhoad *et al.*, 1975); and swimming into an L-shaped tube (Rasa, 1971). Bettas were the subjects in all these studies except the one by Rasa, in which damsel fish (*Microspathodon chrysurus*) were used.

In all experiments, rate of responding rose reliably when the response was followed by the opportunity to see and display at a conspecific. Goldstein (1967) and Hogan (1967) used yoked subjects to control for the increase of general activity that occurs when the fish display, and Hogan also tested the fish in extinction after a 24-hr delay. Significant differences between experimental and control fish were found in all cases.

Most of the betta studies used a mirror image of the subject as the aggression-provoking stimulus. In addition, Thompson (1963) found a moving or stationary model to be less effective than a mirror image, and Rhoad *et al.* (1975) found a live fish behind glass, a mirror image, a moving model, and a stationary model to be increasingly less effective. Aggressive responses to these stimuli also wane increasingly fast (see p. 201), which suggests that the effectiveness of a stimulus as a reinforcer is proportional to the strength of the aggressive display that it provokes.

3. Swimming Down a Runway

Swimming speed in a runway has also been found to increase over trials when aggressive display is permitted in the goal box. Hogan (1961, 1967), using bettas as subjects, found similar results using a mirror image, a conspecific behind glass, and a fight with a conspecific as the reinforcer. Hogan used the opportunity to eat in the goal box as a control condition. In most cases, swimming for food was consistently faster and less variable than swimming for display, which raised the question of whether display was really reinforcing in the runway situation. Bols (1976) answered this question by using a control group that received no stimulus in the goal box. She found that swimming for display was consistently faster than swimming for nothing (see Fig. 12B, on p. 204). In fact, when the goal box was empty, most fish would not swim down the runway at all, and had to be pushed. Further, when fish were allowed to choose between an empty goal box and one containing a mirror, they chose the mirror about 80% of the time (see Fig. 12A).

4. Aggression or Curiosity?

Most of the authors cited above have assumed that instrumental responding is reinforced by aggressive behavior, but Johnson and Johnson (1973) have questioned this view. They provide evidence that opportunity to view a large variety of objects, including another fish, a turtle, a marble, and an empty chamber supported swimming through a tunnel equally well. They also report that although their fish often displayed at the various objects when first exposed to them, no stimulus evoked display by the end of the session, even though swimming through the tunnel continued. Interpretation of these data is difficult, however, because the number of responses per hour during a 4-hr experimental period was compared with the same measure during a subsequent 20-hr control period. The apparatus was presumably illuminated all the time, but the fish might still have been subject to daily activity rhythms: under conditions of 24-hr illumination, Hogan (1961) found that fish given continuous access to a mirror, attacks at which were automatically recorded, showed greatly attenuated performance during late evening and early morning hours.

More extensive studies by Bols (1977) have used paradise fish (*Macropodus opercularis*), dwarf gouramis (*Colisa lalia*), nondisplaying bettas, and a marble as stimulus objects, as well as displaying bettas and a mirror image. Some of these stimuli (though not the marble) supported swimming down the runway, but only those that reliably evoked aggressive display gave results similar to those of most previous studies. Rasa (1971) showed that a silver star did not support the response of entering an L maze. The fact that various investigators have found a correlation between rate of responding and amount of aggressive display evoked by the stimulus (see above) suggests that aggressive motivation plays an important role. But in cases where little or no display is evoked, or when the fish are closely confined (as was the case in the Johnson and Johnson, 1973, study), curiosity may be an additional factor.

B. ACQUISITION

Swimming through a ring, swimming in and out of an L maze, and rod biting generally increase abruptly after the first few reinforcements, but detailed data on acquisition are not available. Some individual bettas reach maximal rates of swimming through a ring within 15 min of their first reinforced response (Hogan, 1964, unpublished).

Over the course of days, different patterns of responding in bettas are reported by different investigators. Hogan (1967) and Baenninger (1970) reported the highest daily rate of responding on the first day or two of training, with a slow decline over the next several days, whereas Thompson (1963) reported a gradual increase in daily rate over almost two weeks of training. There is no obvious reason for this difference. Changes over days may be related to fluctuations in general aggressive motivation, but other factors are implicated by Baenninger and Mattleman (1973). They found that bettas would learn to swim through a ring to activate a mirror, even when another mirror was continuously present on the opposite wall of the aquarium. Their fish displayed less and less to the free mirror while they still responded vigorously to the earned one; that is, operant responding increased rapidly at the same time that display to the free mirror declined. Thus, changes in general level of aggression cannot account for the pattern of operant responding. As in most of the experiments cited above, operant responding also declined after a few days.

Swimming speed in the runway increases over the first 50–60 trials and then typically shows a decrease (Hogan, 1967, 1974; Bols, 1976; see Fig. 12B, p. 204). In all these experiments there have been food reinforcement control groups. Swimming speed for food increases at about the same rate as for a mirror for the first 20–30 trials, but then continues increasing at a higher rate than for a mirror. Even after 100 trials, swimming speed for food usually has not reached asymptote.

C. EXTINCTION

Many investigators have presented data on extinction, but each case seems to be different. After several days of continuous access to mirror reinforcement in a ring situation, during the first 24 hr of extinction, bettas showed a slight increase or no decline in responding (Baenninger, 1970), a decrease of 40–50% (Thompson, 1963; Baenninger and Mattleman, 1973), or a decrease of about 70% (Hogan, 1967). One damsel fish, in the L maze, showed a decrease of about 70% (Rasa, 1971). One stickleback, which had been reinforced for swimming through a ring for about 1.5 hr, showed a 30% decrease in response rate during 1 hr of extinction (Sevenster, 1973). The change in responding during extinction does not seem to be correlated with the absolute rate of responding at the end of training, and reasons for the great variability are not obvious.

In two cases in which extinction after food and after display were directly compared, responding declined significantly faster for display both in the runway (Hogan, 1967) and in the ring apparatus with 1-hr sessions (Hogan, 1978).

D. AMOUNT OF REINFORCEMENT

Amount of reinforcement can be varied in terms of the adequacy of the releasing stimulus, or in terms of the length of time for which a stimulus is presented. Thompson (1963) and Rhoad et al. (1975) found that the number of responses per session was directly related to the efficacy of the reinforcing stimulus, using 24-hr and 1-hr sessions, respectively. One problem with considering amount in terms of stimulus adequacy is that different stimuli may evoke different responses, and hence are not strictly comparable (see the discussion of discrepancy hypothesis below).

Using swimming through a ring as operant, Hogan et al. (1970) varied the duration of mirror presentation from 5 to 40 sec, and found no effect on number of responses per 2-hr or 8-hr session. In a similar study, Grabowski and Thompson (1968, unpublished results) varied the duration of mirror presentation from 15 to 120 sec. Number of responses per session decreased as a function of reinforcement duration. In this study, the absolute rate of responding was much higher than in the one by Hogan *et al.* (1970), and the time occupied by mirror presentation was a very significant portion of the 1-hr session. If only the time available for responding is considered, response rates for 15- and 30-sec mirror presentations were about the same, but response rates for 60- and 100-sec presentations rose sharply. These results are difficult to interpret because of the priming effect of mirror presentation (see below). A more sophisticated design would be needed to distinguish reinforcing and motivating effects (cf. Gallistel *et al.*, 1974). Leaving aside the theoretical problems of interpretation, however, the results show either no compensation, or negative compensation, for changes in amount of reinforcement. In this respect aggressive display resembles nest material, but differs from food, water, heat, and wheel running.

E.   FIXED-RATIO SCHEDULES

1. Patterning Effects

Grabowski and Thompson (1968), using bettas, report difficulty in maintaining responding beyond FR 4, for a 2-min mirror presentation. By arranging for intermediate responses to turn on colored lights, however, they obtained responding up to FR 24. When the stimulus lights were removed responding continued at FR 24, but at a lower level. Hogan *et al.* (1970) obtained responding up to FR 6 for a 20-sec mirror presentation, without any special training procedure.

In a study described more fully below, Hogan (1978), using bettas, varied the FR requirement and state of deprivation, with food or mirror as reinforcer. Two analyses of response patterning were made. First, the distribution of responding during the session was compared between reinforcers. On an FR 1 schedule with food as reinforcer, just over 70% of all responses were made during the first half of the 1-hr session; with mirror as reinforcer, only 57% were made during the first half-hour. Thus, the fish responded more evenly for the mirror. As the FR requirement was increased, the proportion of food responses in the first half-hour decreased to about 62%, while the proportion of mirror responses increased to about 62%. There was no difference between the deprived and the prefed/pre-exposed conditions with either reinforcer. Thus, the distribution of responding within sessions, and its interaction with the increase in FR size, was characteristic of the reinforcer and independent of the absolute rate of responding.

Interresponse times on the FR schedules were also analyzed, and the results are shown in Fig. 9. On FR 4, responding for food accelerated as reinforcement approached, in both the never prefed and the previously prefed fish, even though the interresponse times of the former were only about half those of the latter. Interresponse times for mirror reinforcement remained constant over the inter-reinforcement interval, and the absolute times were in between those of the two

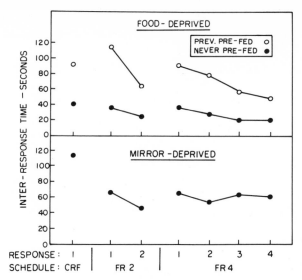

FIG. 9. Mean interresponse times between consecutive responses as a function of FR schedule.

food-reinforcement groups. Thus, fish respond for food differently from rats or pigeons on FR schedules, and they respond differently for food and display. Once again, the pattern of responding is characteristic of the reinforcer and independent of the absolute rate.

Thompson (1969) presents a cumulative record for a betta responding for mirror on FR 4. The fish responded at a rate of about 1 per min with no particular pattern of interresponse times, which is consistent with Hogan's (1978) results. Sevenster (1973) obtained a response rate of about 3 per min in a stickleback tested on a VR 3 schedule, but there was no systematic variation in interresponse times.

2. Regulatory Effects

Hogan et al. (1970) varied the FR requirement from 1 to 6 in an ascending order, with display or food as reinforcer. With display, the number of responses emitted in 12 hr remained constant over schedules, so that the number of reinforcements declined (Fig. 11, Curve 1). With food, the number of responses increased so that the number of reinforcements remained constant (see Fig. 3, Curve 6). Grabowski and Thompson (1968) found that number of responses increased from about 20 per hr on FR 1 to about 40 per hr on FR 24, which still constitutes extremely poor compensation.

Hogan (1978) varied both the FR requirement and the deprivation level, with both food and display as reinforcer. In the deprived condition, fish were allowed neither to display nor to eat for 24 hr; in the preexposed/prefed condition, they

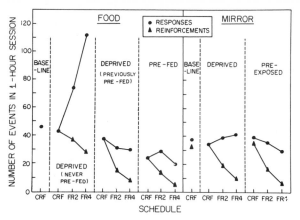

FIG. 10. Mean responses and reinforcements as a function of type of reinforcement, state of deprivation, and FR schedule.

were exposed to the mirror or given their normal daily intake of white worms during the half-hour before being tested. Preexposure to a mirror corresponds to priming (see below) so might be expected to increase responding. Fish were tested daily for both mirror and food in separate 1-hr sessions, and half the fish received the deprived condition first and half the preexposed/prefed condition. With the mirror as reinforcer, there was no compensation for increases in FR size, regardless of deprivation condition (see Fig. 10 and Fig. 11, Curve 2). The different number of responses in the studies shown in Fig. 11 reflects the difference between 12-hr and 1-hr sessions.

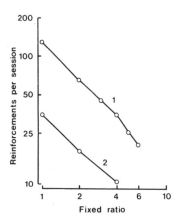

FIG. 11. Number of reinforcements per session as a function of FR size, with aggressive display as reinforcer in Siamese fighting fish. Data from (1) Hogan, Kleist and Hutchings (1970); (2) Hogan (1978), using fish preexposed to the aggression-eliciting stimulus.

The results for food are especially interesting (Fig. 10). Deprived fish that were never prefed showed good compensation for increases in FR size (cf. Hogan *et al.*, 1970), but fish that were prefed or previously prefed showed no compensation (cf. Roper, 1975a, using food as reinforcer in mice). Thus, by manipulating deprivation, it was possible to make degree of compensation for food similar to that for a mirror, but it has not yet been possible to manipulate display so as to obtain compensation as good as is normally obtained with food.

F. Aggression as a Motivational System

1. Deprivation and Satiation

Aggressive behavior in bettas does not undergo regular cyclical variation, except for apparent diurnal rhythms (see above). Confronted with the proper stimulus, most male fish show strong aggressive display throughout most of their lives. Nonetheless, there are both long- and short-term changes in the probability that a particular stimulus will evoke an aggressive response, and some of these changes are relevant to studies of aggression as a reinforcer.

Most studies of the waning of aggressive responses have been done in the context of habituation. Fish have been exposed to a stimulus (usually a mirror or a conspecific behind glass) continuously or intermittently, for various periods of time, and a number of display components have been measured. The results indicate that waning is erratic, that individual components of the display wane at different rates, and that complete cessation of display is rarely obtained, but the level of responsiveness does decrease with continuous or intermittent exposure over hours or days. In some studies, recovery of responsiveness has been investigated by isolating the fish for various periods after responsiveness has waned, and then retesting it. Some recovery occurs in the first day or two of isolation, but recovery is rarely complete even after 14 days (Hogan, 1961; Laudien, 1965; Clayton and Hinde, 1968; Peeke and Peeke, 1970; Figler, 1972).

Both the rate and the pattern of waning depend on the stimulus. Responses to a live displaying conspecific or to a mirror wane less rapidly than responses to nondisplaying conspecifics or to various models (Lissmann, 1932; Figler, 1972). As mentioned above, operant responding is supported by these stimuli in the same order. The rate of waning also depends on the size of the test container: fish tested in small containers respond for longer than fish tested in large ones (Goldstein, 1975; Hogan, Parker, and Macnaughton, unpublished observations).

Most studies suggest that the decrease of responsiveness is stimulus specific. The degree of specificity can be striking: Baenninger and Mattleman (1973) report that their fish responded differently to the same stimulus (a mirror), depending on its location in the tank. However, there does seem to be some lowering of general aggressive motivation, since continued presence of a rival in a neighboring territory can lead to reduced attacks on strangers, at least in sticklebacks (van den Assem and van der Molen, 1968; see also Klein *et al.*, 1976).

Several authors have speculated on the processes underlying waning of responsiveness. Sensory or central adaptation (Hogan, 1961) or response-specific decrements (Rasa, 1971) probably play some role, but they cannot account for all the data. Rhoad *et al.* (1975) have proposed that responsiveness may wane because the fish learns that displaying at a particular "intruder" does not drive it away, and this experience is aversive. In a somewhat similar vein, Bols (1976, 1977) suggests that the fish is able to correlate its own behavior with that of the stimulus, and that when the stimulus responds inappropriately (i.e., fails to respond like a normal fish), a discrepancy is registered. The larger the discrepancy or the longer it exists, the greater escape motivation is activated. The underlying assumption that a fish has an "expectation" of its rival's behavior is plausible, because Simpson (1968) has shown that the effects of the behavior of one fish on that of another are quite predictable.

The discrepancy hypothesis proposed by Bols is similar to the associative learning hypothesis proposed by Rhoad *et al.* (1975), in that both postulate that inappropriate consequences of behavior are aversive. However, Bols' explanation focuses on inappropriate consequences that arise during moment by moment interactions between a fish and its rival, whereas Rhoad and co-workers invoke inappropriate long-term consequences. Furthermore, Bols' hypothesis is essentially motivational (the behavior of the fish depends on the momentary level of the discrepancy), whereas Rhoad and co-workers imply that the effects of a stimulus depend primarily on interactions the fish has had with that stimulus on previous occasions. These hypotheses do not conflict with each other, but account for different aspects of waning.

The analysis of aggressive motivation so far suggests that the effects of deprivation and satiation, as operations, are fairly long term, and that they are based on complex interactions between behavior and its consequences, and between aggression and escape.

2. Priming

Lissmann (1932) suggests that different components of the fighting behavior of bettas require different levels of aggressive motivation for their occurrence. Approach, color changes, and fin spreading occur at low levels; lateral and frontal displays and tail beating occur at an intermediate level; and biting occurs at the highest level. Since this is the order in which the various component responses normally occur, it seems likely that the level of aggression increases during the first few minutes of an encounter. The increase in responsiveness that occurs with exposure to an aggression-provoking stimulus is not stimulus specific: the fish also respond more strongly to a thermometer and a finger (Hogan,

1961). Priming of aggressive motivation has also been demonstrated in other species of fish (e.g., Sevenster, 1961; Heiligenberg, 1974, 1976), and in mice (Tellegen *et al.*, 1969), and is probably important in other animals.

Priming may be responsible for the "warm-up" effect observed with target pressing (see Fig. 8), the priming stimulus being (by virtue of classical conditioning) the target itself. Target pressing may be difficult to condition in bettas because the level of aggression is not normally high enough to support biting, and priming would be expected to facilitate learning. Evidence that priming facilitates performance is provided by Bols (1976), who found that 10 min of prior exposure to a mirror coupled with short intertrial intervals led to faster swimming in a runway than did 2 min of exposure coupled with long intervals. Similarly, Rasa (1971) found that priming damsel fish with a dummy resulted in higher levels of performance in an L-maze apparatus.

If a short bout of aggressive display increases aggression, one would expect shorter interresponse times immediately after reinforcement, on an FR schedule. In fact, interresponse times for display reinforcement do not change with time since reinforcement (see Fig. 9). However, the latter result might represent summation of an expectation-of-reward process and a priming process. If this is so, normal FR patterning should occur with a time-out after reinforcement.

Priming also failed to have the expected effect in a different experiment (see Fig. 10). This may be because the priming bout was too short (cf. Bols, 1976); because it was presented too long before the session (cf. Rasa, 1971); or because the priming stimulus was presented in the same place as the reinforcing stimulus, whereas it was presented in a different place in all the experiments where priming was efficacious (cf. also Baenninger and Mattleman, 1973).

3. Relation of Aggressive Motivation to Other Behavior Systems

a. Escape. Ever since Tinbergen's (1952) classic paper on the causation of displays, and the extension of these ideas by Morris (1956), it has been widely recognized that most animal displays reflect the activation of more than one motivational system. In the case of displays associated with fighting behavior, aggressive (attack) and escape motivation are most often found to be important. In bettas, several investigators have noted that some fish may avoid a conspecific or a mirror, and Baenninger (1970) has shown that escape from a mirror is reinforcing after display has waned, but Bols (1976) has provided even more convincing evidence that some amount of escape is probably always present during aggressive display. She measured a number of behaviors in the runway including time motionless, turning away from the goal box (before entering it), and air gulping. Some of her results are shown in Fig. 12. The fish swam faster when there was food in the goal box (F–N group) than when there was a mirror there (M–N group), as shown in Fig. 12B. The reason for the difference was that the M–N group remained motionless longer (Fig. 12C) and turned away from the

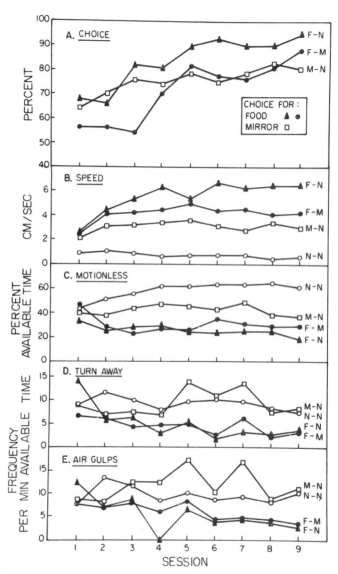

FIG. 12. Occurrence of various responses as a function of experimental condition (F = food; M = mirror; N = nothing) and number of trials (each session consisted of 10 trials). (From Bols, 1976.)

goal box more frequently (Fig. 12D). When the number of turns with respect to the time available for turning is calculated (as in Fig. 12), the mirror–nothing group had an even higher number than the nothing–nothing group. Since turning away is a direct measure of avoidance, it follows that avoidance was higher for the mirror than for nothing. (The frequent occurrence of air gulping in the mirror–nothing group is also consonant with the conclusion that aggressive display involves a conflict.) On the other hand, since the total swimming speed was faster for the mirror than for nothing, the mirror must have a much stronger attraction than nothing. It is especially interesting that in the food–mirror choice group, the fish chose food 80% of the time but swam significantly more slowly than the food–nothing choice group. (This is also true if swimming speeds are calculated only for the trials on which the fish chose food.) Thus, the aversive aspects of the mirror even interact with the attraction of food.

It seems likely that if the escape component could be minimized, responding for aggressive display might reach the same levels as responding for food. The differences in asymptotic level of responding for different stimuli in an operant situation (Thompson, 1963; Rhoad *et al.*, 1975) may reflect differences in escape motivation brought about by different degrees of discrepancy (Bols, 1977). On this view, asymptotic rate of responding is a measure of attack less escape motivation, while the long-term decline of responding would depend on associative learning.

b. Sex. In sticklebacks, the behavior in fighting situations seems to reflect the interaction of aggression primarily with sex, rather than with escape. Sevenster's (1968, 1973) analysis of rod biting for aggressive display shows that activation of the sexual system affects both the rate and the pattern of operant responding. The results of his experiments can be understood by assuming that sexual motivation inhibits responding based on aggressive motivation (see p. 211 below).

*c. Fear.** In a runway study in which male Bettas were given a choice between food and a mirror, Hogan (1974) found that the fish preferred food when they lived in the experimental apparatus during the experiment; but when they were transferred into the apparatus shortly before being tested, preference shifted toward the mirror. A preference for mirror was also found by Fantino *et al.* (1972), using a ring situation and transferring the fish each day. On the basis of both preference scores and swimming speeds, Hogan (1974) suggested that differential inhibition of hunger and aggression by fear of the unfamiliar environment is responsible for the preference shift.

4. Theoretical Considerations

a. Classical Conditioning. While swimming down the runway, or when approaching the tunnel, bettas are often seen to show gill cover erection and other

*For a discussion of the distinction between fear and escape, see Hogan (1965).

components of aggressive display. Sometimes the display appears to be directed at a particular part of the environment, but usually it just appears prior to the presentation of the mirror or other fish. These observations suggest that some form of classical conditioning has occurred (Hogan, 1961). Classical conditioning of the aggressive display in the betta has also been shown to occur quite readily to a weak electric shock (Adler and Hogan, 1963) and to a red light (Thompson and Sturm, 1965). In the experiment by Hogan and Rozin (see Hogan, 1961, and Fig. 8 above) it seems quite likely that the target had become a conditioned stimulus for aggressive responses: that is, the fish treated the target as if it were another fish. In the presence of the target, aggressive motivation would be primed, and the fish would finally attack the target. Responding would then accelerate as the level of aggression was raised. Conditioning would be maintained by pairing the sight of the target with a displaying fish after responding had begun. With this interpretation, one might want to conclude that instrumental conditioning had not occurred, and this raises the question of appetitive behavior.

b. *Appetitive Behavior.*   Do fish and other animals have appetitive behavior for aggression? Are they driven or lured to fight? Is aggression internally or externally controlled? This question can be asked for all the motivational systems we discuss, and we explore some general aspects of the question in Section X. Because of the great controversy surrounding the relation of internal factors to aggression (e.g., Lorenz, 1966; Montagu, 1968; see also discussion by Hinde, 1974, Chapter 16), however, it seems appropriate to make a few extra comments here.

Based on the evidence of classical conditioning cited above, it could be argued that in all the situations used to study instrumental conditioning, classical conditioning occurred instead. On this view, the approach response would be considered the initial response in a sequence of aggressive activities. Since gill cover erection requires a higher level of aggressive motivation than approach, it would not be at all necessary to see signs of obvious aggressive display in order to maintain that classical conditioning had occurred. Thus, one could hold the view that there is no appetitive behavior for aggression, and that aggression is always aroused by external stimuli. It should be noted, however, that a similar argument can be made for all the other reinforcers we have discussed. For example, we have already reviewed evidence (p. 183) that rats show little or no appetitive behavior when hungry unless stimuli are present that have been paired in the past with food. Also, several psychological theorists have taken the position that occurrence of all learned behavior depends on incentive motivation—that is, on expectation of reward aroused by stimuli previously associated with that reward (e.g., Bindra, 1969, 1974; Bolles, 1972). On this view, aggression is no different from any other reinforcer.

On the other hand, how an animal responds to a conditioned stimulus depends on its internal state, as shown by the experiments on priming. And the internal state depends not only on external priming influences, but also on internal, response-specific factors. At this point the argument becomes semantic, and one's opinion seems to be a matter of taste. One can say with Marler (1957) that, because inexperienced chaffinches never threaten or attack each other unless they find themselves, "by accident," very close to one another (i.e., they find themselves in the presence of aggression-arousing stimuli), they do not have appetitive behavior for aggression. Or one can say with Rasa (1971) that, because performance in the L maze in damsel fish depends on the level of aggressive motivation, they do have appetitive behavior for aggression. Some people might be tempted to argue that aggression is more externally motivated than other systems such as hunger (see Section X), but this argument is very similar to arguing about what percent of a particular behavior is innate and what percent learned (cf. Lehrman, 1970). In some contexts, these distinctions may have some value, but in others they can be completely misleading. The answer to the question about appetitive behavior for aggression then is that the fish are both driven and lured to fight, and that aggression is both internally and externally controlled. In studying aggression or any other motivational system, one must look for the factors controlling it in each particular situation.

VIII. SEX AS REINFORCER

There seems to be almost universal acceptance of the idea that the opportunity to engage in sexual behavior is reinforcing, at least in male animals; but the evidence on which this acceptance is based must be primarily introspective, because there are surprisingly few studies of instrumental learning in which sex was used as the reinforcer. Much of the experimental work has been devoted to understanding sex as a motivational system, rather than to instrumental learning. Therefore, information on the parameters of reinforcement we have been considering is often nonexistent. Nonetheless, we have included a section on sex because the few results that do exist point up especially well how the reinforcing aspects of sex can only be understood in the context of sexual motivation.

A. SEX AS REINFORCER FOR MALE RATS

Sexual behavior in male rats consists of various approach movements to the female followed by a series of mounts only, mounts with intromission (copulation), and finally an intromission with ejaculation (see Hart, 1968, for drawings of a sexual sequence). Typically, a male requires 8 or more intromissions before ejaculation occurs. Intromissions are brief, and there is an interval of about 40 sec between them. After ejaculation, an interval of about 5 min occurs before the male initiates sexual behavior again. In a single session a typical rat may achieve 5 or more ejaculations. In the second and subsequent ejaculatory series, the number of intromissions before ejaculation is about half the number required in the first series; the pause between ejaculatory series increases, however (Beach and Jordan, 1956b; Larsson, 1956; Brown et al., 1974; Sachs and Barfield, 1976; see also Bermant and Davidson, 1974, for a general review).

In the first "modern" study of sex as a reinforcer, Sheffield et al. (1951) showed that sexually active male rats (as determined by pretests) would traverse a runway and jump a small hurdle for the opportunity to copulate twice with a receptive female. Animals were given 2 trials a day every other day for 14 test days. The running speed reached asymptotic levels after 20 trials and was significantly higher than the running speed to another male. The running speed in both groups of active males was higher than in a group of sexually disinterested males running to a receptive female. It was observed that subjects running to another male often showed mounting on the goal-box male; analysis of the data showed a significant positive correlation between running speed and overt sexual activity in the goal box. Males in the study by Sheffield et al. (1951) never had the experience of ejaculation. A subsequent study by Beach and Jordan (1956a) showed that performance in a runway improved in the normal way when the subjects were allowed sufficient trials per session to achieve ejaculation. After castration, both running speed and sexual activity declined, but was reinstated by injections of androgen. Of interest in light of results from brain stimulation studies (see below) is the fact that in the normal rats, running time was almost twice as long for the first trial in each session as it was for the remaining trials. These results demonstrate that sexual behavior can serve as a reinforcer for the male rat.

Several other studies have investigated particular aspects of these results in more detail. Kagan (1955) showed that if male rats had experience with ejaculation, intromission without ejaculation led to increased running speeds for a few trials, but then performance declined. This result is very reminiscent of the behavior of Siamese fighting fish in the runway (see p. 197), and can also be understood in terms of a discrepancy hypothesis (see p. 202). Ware (1968) found similar effects of sexual experience. One particularly interesting result was that sexually inexperienced males actually ran significantly faster for a nonreceptive female reward than for copulation, with or without ejaculation. Whalen (1961) used male rats inexperienced with respect to ejaculation and showed that four intromissions supported better runway performance than one intromission, which was better than mounting only; all three groups selected the female over an empty goal box in a choice test. It seems likely that the difference between Whalen's and Ware's results with the nonreceptive female reward is due to the fact that

Whalen's subjects had all had copulatory experience. Finally, Schwartz (1956) used a lever-pressing situation to investigate recovery from sexual exhaustion and the relation between instrumental performance and subsequent sexual performance. He used a fairly elaborate shaping procedure and then tested his animals on a variable interval schedule with an average interval of just over 1½ min. Each reinforcement consisted of one intromission, and animals were allowed enough reinforcements to achieve ejaculation. The lever-pressing rate increased with days of recovery, but not significantly. There were, however, significant correlations between rate and several measures of sexual activity. The rate of lever pressing even in fully recovered animals was only about 2½ per minute, which is considerably below the normal rate of 50–60 per minute when pressing for food on a similar schedule (personal observation).

Several of these studies were concerned with what aspect of sexual behavior is actually reinforcing. The results support the statement that "social" contact, intromission only, and intromission with ejaculation are all reinforcing in sexually naive males. With sexual experience, however, only intromission with ejaculation remains a potent reinforcer.

Another concern of many authors is how sexual motivation can best be conceived. Beach (1956), for example, suggested that two relatively independent mechanisms were necessary to account for the sequence and timing of the male's behavior: a sexual arousal mechanism that increases the male's excitement until the copulatory threshold is attained, and an intromission and ejaculatory mechanism that is responsible for the patterning of copulatory behavior. Several elaborations and revisions of this model have been proposed (e.g., Whalen, 1966; Brown et al., 1974; see also Sachs and Barfield, 1976). A basic assumption of these models is that sexual behavior is primarily aroused by external (or fantasied) stimuli, and that concepts such as deprivation and satiation that are appropriate to hunger and thirst should be replaced by concepts such as recovery and exhaustion. This issue has arisen with respect to all the other motivational systems we have considered, and we return to it in Section X.

B. Sex as Reinforcer for Female Rats

A receptive female rat may approach and nuzzle a male, and, at his approach, may show characteristic darting movements; in response to his mounting and palpating her flanks, she assumes her lordosis posture which allows the male to penetrate (see Hardy and DeBold, 1972, for drawings of the lordosis posture).

Bermant (1961) and Bermant and Westbrook (1966) shaped estrous female rats to press a lever for sexual contact [i.e., a mount, an intromission (copulation), or an ejaculation] with a male rat. Shaping was fairly elaborate, and not all females acquired the response. Once trained, however, animals performed reliably. An FR 1 schedule was used and the time between each sexual contact and the next lever press was recorded. The results showed that the contact–response interval was directly related to the intensity of the sexual contact: after a mount, females responded in about 20 sec; after an intromission, in about 40 sec; and after an ejaculation, in about 2 min. Bermant and Westbrook point out that the operant behavior of males and females is in close synchrony after mounts and intromissions, but females are ready to return to sexual contact after an ejaculation much sooner than males. Peirce and Nuttall (1961) allowed estrous female rats to enter and leave an arena containing two or three active males and measured time to return to the arena after each kind of sexual contact. Their results were essentially similar to those of Bermant.

Several authors have questioned whether the above studies demonstrate a reinforcing effect of sexual contact. Hardy and DeBold (1972), for example, have suggested that the odor of a male rat may reinforce a receptive female (see below). A similar criticism was made by Bolles *et al.* (1968), who suggested that social contact rather than sexual contact might be responsible for maintaining lever pressing. Bolles and co-workers compared the running time, in an alley, of females either in estrus or in diestrus running to either a sexually active or a sexually inactive male. Females in diestrus did not run as fast as females in estrus, but there were no differences in running speed to active or passive males. Following the interpretation of the authors, these results have been cited as demonstrating that sexual contact is not reinforcing for females; but, in fact, these results are consonant with the interpretation that either social contact or sexual contact is reinforcing, or both are. In a subsequent study, Hill and Thomas (1973) found that females ran significantly faster to active than to passive males. They used experienced females, shorter intertrial intervals, and more training trials than Bolles *et al.* (1968). They conclude that *both* social and sexual sources of positive reinforcement are present in a typical mating situation.

As with sexual reinforcement for male rats, several authors have inquired which aspect(s) of the situation is actually reinforcing. In the case of female rats, this question is especially pertinent because the sexual situation has very obvious aversive aspects. Peirce and Nuttall (1961), for example, describe dramatic instances of escape behavior from the arena after copulation. They also point to the similarity between the female's approach–avoidance behavior and the behavior of rats, lever pressing for electrical stimulation of the brain, that press one lever to turn the stimulus on and then press another lever to turn it off (see p. 222 below). Hardy and DeBold (1972) review several other lines of evidence that copulatory stimuli are aversive to females. They suggest that "the reinforcing value of intromission for the female rat has been overrated," and that other stimulus qualities of the male may be responsible for reinforcement. Other stimulus qualities may well be important, but the results of Hill and Thomas (1973) indicate that intromission itself does have reinforcing effects. Further research using choice tests between sex and other reinforcers, and more sensitive measures of motivational strength at various points of the sexual sequence might help resolve some of these issues.

C. Courtship as Reinforcer for Fish and Pigeons

Sevenster (1968, 1973) has used the opportunity to court a female for 10 sec as a reinforcer for male sticklebacks. When the instrumental response was swimming through a ring, fish acquired the response rapidly and a minimum of shaping was required. The rate of responding, about 2 responses per min, was about the same as when an opportunity to fight a male was the reinforcer (see above, p. 194). When the instrumental response was biting a rod, however, more shaping was required and the response rate was only about 0.3 responses per min. This low rate was specific to the reinforcer, since biting the rod for an opportunity to fight occurred at the normal rate of 2 responses per min. Sevenster was able to show that the low rate had a dual cause: the rod became a substitute stimulus for a female (presumably through a process of classical conditioning; see p. 205); and a female normally inhibits biting. The pattern of responding in extinction was similar for all fish regardless of response or reinforcer.

Gilbertson (1975) did a similar experiment using male pigeons. The opportunity to court its mate for 13 sec was the reinforcer; the response required was pecking a standard pigeon key. Gilbertson found it impossible to shape the response: after several pairings of the key light with the female, the key light came to elicit courtship activities such as bowing and preening; but pecking the key did not occur. He finally succeeded by training the birds to peck a nearby key for food, after which they pecked the female-producing key, presumably due to stimulus generalization. The pattern of responding to the food key was essentially the same as Sevenster found to the ring or to the rod when fighting was the reinforcer (though pigeons responded at a higher rate than the fish), whereas responding to the female key was similar to responding to the rod when courtship was the reinforcer. Gilbertson suggests this similarity reflects similar causes: the female key becomes associated with the female, and the female normally inhibits pecking.

Magnitude of reinforcement has not been varied with these reinforcers, but Sevenster has used a variable-ratio (VR) 3 schedule with a few fish. Both these studies demonstrate very clearly how the species-characteristic structure of behavior can affect instrumental responding. We return to this point in Section X.

IX. Electrical Stimulation of the Brain as Reinforcer

Olds and Milner (1954) reported that rats, with electrodes implanted in various parts of the brain, would learn to press a lever that caused current to flow through the brain. This result was interpreted to mean that electrical stimulation of certain parts of the brain ("pleasure centers") could serve as a positive reinforcer for an instrumental response. Subsequent studies have confirmed the effect using Skinner boxes, runways, and mazes, a wide variety of species including monkeys and man, and various parameters of electrical stimulation. Many investigators have also tried to anatomically delimit the areas of the brain from which reinforcing effects are obtained. There have been several reviews and discussions of the literature, including those by Olds (1958), Trowill et al. (1969), Lenzer (1972), Gallistel (1973), and Rolls (1975).* Gallistel's review is the most extensive, and Rolls gives a more popular account, but each paper presents the material with emphases that reflect the theoretical bias of the author(s). In this section we shall consider only the literature that is relevant to a comparison between electrical stimulation of the brain and other reinforcers.

A. ACQUISITION

Acquisition of a lever-pressing response for electrical stimulation of the brain (ESB) is very rapid. Rats often learn to respond within 1 or 2 min of the first reinforced press (Olds, 1958, p. 316). Although some authors consider acquisition to be more rapid than with "conventional" reinforcers, Skinner (1938, p. 69) reported equally rapid acquisition of lever pressing in rats for food. High rates of responding for ESB may continue for hours or days, although both the rate and the persistence of responding depend on various physical parameters of the stimulation as well as the location of the electrode. With optimal physical parameters, the rate of responding often begins at asymptotic levels and remains stable for many sessions when animals are tested daily. Olds (1958), for example, reported stable responding in 2 rats for 15 daily 1-hr sessions. However, in another study, using apparently similar methods rats showed an increase in response rate over the first 9 daily 30-min sessions, followed by a slight decrease in responding from Day 10 to 15 (Seward et al., 1959). With continued access to stimulation for 16 hr or more, a gradual attenuation of responding occurred after several hours with some electrode placements, while with others, asymptotic performance continued for many hours, interrupted occasionally by a period of no responding at all. In general, the higher the rate of self-stimulation, the longer responding persists at asymptotic levels (Olds, 1958; Ray et al., 1968). In a recent study, Annau et al. (1974) have shown that rats which are allowed 24-hr access to ESB for many days will lever press at a very high rate for the first 3–12 hr, and then settle into a regular pattern of responding on subsequent days. The

---

*After our review was written, a book containing papers prepared for the First International Conference on Brain-Stimulation Reward appeared (Wauquier and Rolls, 1976). Many of these papers are relevant to our discussion.

pattern is very similar to the one seen for food under the same conditions. As in other studies, the absolute rate of responding depended on electrode placement and current level.

One peculiarity of lever pressing rewarded with ESB is that an animal often does not respond at the beginning of a session until the experimenter primes it, that is, administers a burst of stimulation. This phenomenon was reported in the original paper by Olds and Milner (1954), and has been reported frequently ever since. Nonetheless, not all rats require priming (e.g., Kent and Grossman, 1969), and these results have engendered considerable theoretical controversy. We shall return to this matter below.

Acquisition of a running response for ESB in a straight runway or maze is often similar to acquisition for food: running speed for both reinforcers increases to the same asymptotic levels over 20–30 trials (e.g., Olds, 1956). In some cases, however, rats run faster for ESB than for food (e.g., Olds, 1956) while in other cases rats run faster for food than for ESB (e.g., Wetzel, 1963). Asymptotic running speed for ESB depends on various parameters of the stimulation, while for food, it depends on degree of deprivation and amount or quality of reinforcement (see above, p. 161). These parameters, as well as other factors, are usually not considered, so direct comparisons of asymptotic speeds are seldom enlightening. Of more interest are comparisons between the effects produced by equivalent parametric variations.

The variable that has been studied most intensively is the interval between trials. Seward et al. (1960) showed that rats ran faster when trials occurred at 20-sec intervals than when they occurred at 15-min intervals. Further, running speed increased between the first and later trials within a session with the short intertrial interval, but showed no significant changes within a session with the long interval. Similar results were reported by Spear (1962), who used the same intervals as Seward et al. (1960), and by Gallistel (1966), who used 5-sec and 1-min intervals. In these and in several other studies, variability among subjects was high: some individual rats did not show the typical effects (see also Kent and Grossman, 1969).

Gallistel (1973, p. 195) has stated that it is difficult to find priminglike effects in the literature on natural rewards, and in a direct comparison of runway performance for ESB and for water, Gallistel (1967) found that the length of the intertrial interval did not affect the performance of thirsty rats for water. However, a subsequent study by Hunsicker and Reid (1974), using the same apparatus and some of the same rats that were used in a study of "priming" by Reid et al. (1973), showed that 24- or 48-hr water-deprived rats ran faster for water with 7-sec than with 95-sec intertrial intervals. Finally, Beninger and Milner (1977) compared runway performance for ESB, water, and sucrose solution using 5- and 60-sec intertrial intervals. For ESB, rats ran faster with the short interval; for water, speed was not affected by the interval; for sucrose, they ran faster with the long interval. One possible reason for the discrepant results for water in the various studies is the level of thirst. Hunsicker and Reid showed that the priming effect is deprivation dependent (it did not occur with 7- or 15-hr deprivation), and there are several indications that the rats used by Beninger and Milner were not highly motivated to work for water (even though their rats were 24-hr deprived). Whatever the reasons for these different results, however, it is clear that careful studies are needed in which parameters of deprivation and reinforcement magnitude are varied systematically for both reinforcers (cf. p. 172).

In the runway, as in the Skinner box, performance at the beginning of a session is often poorer than it was at the end of the previous session ("overnight decrement"). Although much of the evidence usually cited in support of this statement is not especially convincing, there is good evidence that priming at the beginning of a session or trial increases running speeds (e.g., Wetzel, 1963; Gallistel, 1969a), at least for some rats (Kent and Grossman, 1969). A recent experiment by Reid *et al.* (1973), which involved sending several rats to different laboratories for testing, found that all rats showed a "priming effect," although the magnitude of the effect was sometimes very small.

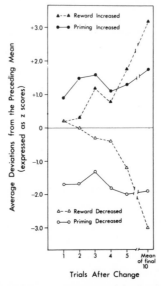

Fig. 13. The change in running speed as a function of the number of trials since a change in the amount of stimulation. The trial-by-trial deviations from the prechange means were normalized and then averaged. (From Gallistel *et al.*, 1974. Copyright 1974 by the American Psychological Association. Reproduced by permission.)

The effects of intertrial intervals and priming on runway performance for ESB seem, in many ways, to be motivational in nature rather than reinforcement effects responsible for learning. A paper by Gallistel et al. (1974) describes a paradigm that can be used to distinguish motivational and reward effects. The animal is primed with free stimulation before being put into the start box of a runway. In the goal box of the runway it receives stimulation as a reward for pressing a lever. The results of one such experiment, using rats as subjects, are shown in Fig. 13. Increasing or decreasing the priming stimulation caused an immediate change in performance on the first trial after the change, which remained constant over trials. In contrast, increasing or decreasing the reward stimulation resulted in a gradual change in performance over trials. The former effect can be considered a motivational effect, while the latter effect would seem to be a reward effect responsible for acquisition of the running response.

B.   EXTINCTION

Olds and Milner (1954) reported that bar pressing ceased abruptly when electrical stimulation was discontinued, though they presented no data to support their statement. (The two figures showing abrupt extinction are schematized, and the one figure showing actual data shows considerable responding in extinction. It is remarkable how often and how uncritically conclusions from many of these early studies are still cited.) Seward et al. (1959) showed that, after 15 30-min sessions of training with continuous reinforcement, responding dropped to about 20% of the final training level during the first 2 sessions of extinction, and remained at that level for a further 14 sessions of extinction. Other investigators have also shown that responding in extinction after continuous reinforcement may continue for 30 min or more (Trowill et al., 1969). One reason why the total amount of responding in extinction after ESB reward seems less than might be expected may be that there are thousands of reinforced responses in typical ESB studies. As Herberg (1963b) pointed out, overtraining a response with food reward leads to markedly lower resistance to extinction (see above, p. 162), and it might be expected that the same would be true with ESB reward. Unfortunately, however, there seems to be no proper study of overtraining with ESB. A second possible reason for rapid extinction after ESB training is that the animals used in many of the studies were not naive, and had presumably undergone extinction before. As both Herberg and Watkins (1966) and Deutsch and DiCara (1967) have shown, responses in extinction decline rapidly as a function of repeated extinction periods (but see Trowill et al., 1969, for a counterexample). This result is also typical of repeated extinction after food reward.

There are two studies in which extinction of a lever-pressing response for ESB was directly compared with extinction after a conventional reinforcer, either sugar water or water. One study was reported by Gibson et al. (1965). These authors pointed out that an important difference between most studies using ESB and conventional rewards is the temporal–spatial relation between the response and the reinforcement. In ESB studies, the animal receives the reward while it presses the lever, whereas in food or water studies, the animal must leave the lever to collect the food or water elsewhere. They arranged their experiment so that some rats had to press a lever and then received either ESB or sugar water by licking a nearby dipper, while others received one or the other reinforcer merely by licking the dipper. The rats that had to press the lever before collecting their reward showed more responses in a 30-min extinction test than those that merely collected their reward, but there were no differences in responding between ESB and sugar water rewarded rats in either condition.

The other study was reported by Quartermain and Webster (1968). They used a lever that incorporated a drinking cup on its upper surface. This arrangement was thus similar to that under which half of the Gibson *et al.* (1965) rats were tested. Unlike the Gibson *et al.* (1965) rats, all of which were hungry during training and extinction, only the rats tested with water were thirsty, and those receiving ESB had ad lib food and water. After 10 days of acquisition training, half the rats had a 30-min extinction session immediately following the last acquisition trial, while the other half were first returned to their home cages for 1 hr. All rats showed the same number of responses in the extinction session except the ESB rats with the 1-hr delay, which showed many fewer responses.

Quartermain and Webster (1968) and Deutsch and DiCara (1967) both criticize the Gibson *et al.* (1965) study on the grounds that their rats were hungry when being tested with ESB reward. That fact may account for the absolute rate of responding during extinction being somewhat higher than usual, since many studies have shown that food deprivation can increase responding in extinction (see below). However, the level of hunger cannot account for the fact that the rats that pressed the lever before collecting their reward, whether sugar water or ESB, showed more responses in extinction than the rats that merely collected their reward. In fact, Gibson *et al.* (1965) could not have made their conclusion about the importance of the temporal–spatial relation between the response and the reinforcement if all their rats had not been hungry! On the other hand, no one seems to have appreciated the fact that in Quartermain and Webster's study, fully satiated rats trained with ESB reward made just as many responses in extinction as did thirsty rats trained with water.

There is a series of studies reported by Deutsch and Howarth (1963) designed to test Deutsch's (1960) theory that extinction after ESB reward is due to the decay of drive effects caused by the brain stimulation. This theory will be discussed below (p. 224), but their results do seem to show that extinction of a lever-pressing response occurs more rapidly when the time interval between the end of training and extinction is increased from 0 to 10 sec. Their results are difficult to interpret since in their early studies they do not define their criteria for extinction, and the criteria they give later (Deutsch and Howarth, 1963, p. 450) are different from those used by most investigators. Nonetheless, it seems likely that drive decay effects do play a role in extinction (see Gallistel, 1973), though experiments analogous to the one by Gallistel *et al.* (1974) discussed above would be necessary to distinguish between motivational and reward effects in extinction. The study by Quartermain and Webster (1968) described above goes some way toward making such a distinction, and is usually cited as evidence that supports Deutsch's theory. It seems somewhat rash, however, to assume that effects of delays of seconds or a few minutes (Deutsch, Gallistel) are caused by the same mechanism as effects of delays of an hour (Quartermain).

Extinction of a running response for ESB in a maze was reported by Olds (1956) to be identical to extinction after food reward (all rats were hungry). This result is based on a reasonable experiment using eight rats, yet it is seldom cited in discussions of extinction after ESB.

C. AMOUNT OF REINFORCEMENT

The magnitude of ESB reward can be conceived either in terms of location of the electrode or in terms of intensity of stimulation. Using the rate of responding as the behavioral measure, several of the early studies of self-stimulation seemed to point to a fairly simple conclusion (e.g., Olds, 1958; Keesey, 1962): hypothalamic sites are more rewarding than forebrain sites, and more intense stimulation (up to a certain limit) is more rewarding than less intense stimulation. Unfortunately, however, rate and choice measures often lead to different conclusions (e.g., Hodos and Valenstein, 1962; Keesey, 1964; Ross, 1973). Further, motivational and reward effects of ESB may be confounded (Gallistel, 1969a). Both Valenstein (1964) and Gallistel (1973) gave detailed discussions of the problems involved in assessing reward magnitude with ESB.

The study by Annau *et al.* (1974), mentioned above, provides data analogous to data we have considered under the heading "regulatory effects" for other reinforcers. For many electrodes, these investigators found that number of responses per day increased directly as a function of current intensity. This is an example of negative compensation, and is similar to some of the results for nest material.

D. SCHEDULES OF REINFORCEMENT

The earliest study to report the use of ESB reward with intermittent schedules was by Sidman *et al.* (1955). They presented data on VI 16-sec and FR 7 and 8 schedules for two *cats*, and pointed out that responding was similar to responding for food. They presented no data whatsoever for rats, although they mentioned that rats were also used as subjects. They also stated that it was difficult to maintain responding on more demanding schedules, but gave no indication of what schedules they tried, how many animals or which species they used, etc. This study continues to be very widely cited in support of the claim that *rats* do not perform well on intermittent schedules for ESB reward!

A thorough and substantial study of intermittent schedules using ESB reward was published by Pliskoff *et al.* (1965), who state in their introduction:

> The lore of brain stimulation reinforcement research teaches that intermittent schedule performances are difficult to maintain. It is hard to estimate the degree to which that lore is the result of research on intermittent schedules, since "negative" results tend not to be published, and the degree to which its acceptance has discouraged such research. (p. 75)

Their results suggest that the latter reason is correct. They systematically investigated FI, FR, and VI schedules, as well as schedules involving differential reinforcement of low rates of responding, in 10 rats with electrode placements in both hypothalamic and forebrain regions of the brain. They used a procedure conceptually similar to the one used by Gibson *et al.* (1965): the rats responded on a permanent lever during the various schedules, but a second lever was introduced into the box when reinforcement was due. Responding on the second (retractable) lever produced the ESB reward. (This is a heterogeneous chain schedule, similar to those used by Carlisle, 1970, to study heat reinforcement; see p. 179.) Using this procedure, rats with hypothalamic electrodes maintained responding on FR schedules as high as 200, and the pattern and rate of responding on the various schedules were typical of responding for food. On the FR schedules, for example, postreinforcement pauses increased monotonically from FR 15 to FR 200. Gibson *et al.* (1965) presented data showing that responding on an FR 20 schedule for ESB reward was indistinguishable from responding for sugar water, and Trowill *et al.* (1969) were able to obtain typical responding on an FR 50 schedule using a single lever. These results all suggest that ESB reward from some electrode sites has many of the same properties as food reward.

Pliskoff *et al.* (1965) also reported that their rats with forebrain placements behaved differently: it was not possible to maintain responding on the higher FI and FR schedules, and both the rate and pattern of responding were atypical of responding for food. It is interesting to compare these results with those of Keesey and Goldstein (1968). These investigators used a progressive fixed-ratio procedure in which rats were required to emit increasingly more responses in order to obtain reinforcement. The highest levels of stable responding ranged from about FR 8 to FR 24 for the 6 rats tested. This is considerably less than levels of FR 120 and higher reached by rats that received sweet milk on a similar procedure (Hodos and Kalman, 1963). In the Keesey and Goldstein study, however, the 2 rats with forebrain placements were no different from the 4 rats with hypothalamic placements with respect to either rate or pattern of responding. Rats in the Pliskoff *et al.* (1965) study received 20 or more $^1/_5$-sec stimulations for each reward, whereas rats in the Keesey and Goldstein study received only 1 ½-sec stimulation. Thus, the large reward in the hypothalamus seems to be as effective a reinforcer as food, but the small reward is much less effective. On the other hand, the small reward in the forebrain leads to better performance (in terms of both rate and pattern of responding) than the large reward. These results clearly point up some of the difficulties involved in assessing reward magnitude, as discussed above.

The results from the studies reviewed above (and others, e.g., Brady and Conrad, 1960) would seem to show that with careful selection of parameters, it is no more difficult to get schedule control of behavior with ESB than with other reinforcers. It is therefore somewhat surprising that this issue continues to be controversial (e.g., Gallistel, 1973; Beninger et al., 1977).

E. MOTIVATION UNDERLYING ESB EFFECTS

1. Relation of ESB to Conventional Systems

One of the earliest concerns of investigators of the self-stimulation phenomenon was whether ESB excites cells that are normally involved in mediating the effects of conventional reinforcers such as food, water, and sex objects. In this section we shall consider some of the evidence that relates ESB effects to hunger, sex, and other motivational systems.

Early experiments by Olds (1958) showed that food deprivation resulted in higher rates of self-stimulation from particular electrode locations. Subsequent studies by Margules and Olds (1962) and Hoebel and Teitlebaum (1962) showed further that electrodes in the lateral hypothalamus that elicited feeding during stimulation also supported self-stimulation. Self-stimulation through these electrodes increased more when rats were food deprived than did self-stimulation through other electrodes that did not elicit feeding (Margules and Olds, 1962). Further, responding during 3-min extinction periods following lateral hypothalamic ESB reward was greater when rats were hungry than when they were satiated (Deutsch and DiCara, 1967). In an extensive series of studies, Hoebel (1968) showed that a wide variety of manipulations that are known to affect feeding affected self-stimulation rates in the same way. These effects were specific, moreover, to electrodes in the lateral hypothalamus. Hoebel (1968) concluded that "reward obtained by lateral hypothalamic self-stimulation appears to be a reward of eating" (p. 89).

Stimulation of electrodes in the lateral hypothalamus may elicit drinking instead of or as well as eating, and Mogenson and Stevenson (1966) showed that electrodes that elicited drinking also supported self-stimulation. Although drinking has not been studied as thoroughly as eating with respect to self-stimulation, the evidence clearly suggests that eating and drinking are independent, but similar systems (Wise, 1974).

Other studies have shown that self-stimulation on particular electrodes, usually in the posterior hypothalamus, is affected by a number of variables, including castration and androgen injections, in the same way that they affect sexual behavior (Olds, 1958; Herberg, 1963a; Caggiula, 1970). These variables did not affect self-stimulation on electrodes in the lateral hypothalamus (Caggiula, 1970), once again suggesting independent physiological systems.

Finally, it has been found that electrodes that elicit some other behaviors, including attack and exploration, also support self-stimulation (see Glickman, 1973, for a review). It might appear that all these results, taken together, provide very strong evidence for the proposition that ESB is rewarding because it taps into brain structures that mediate the effects of conventional reinforcers, and that particular electrode placements are related to particular motivational systems (see Hoebel, 1975). Unfortunately, other evidence brings this conclusion into question.

One kind of counterevidence is that a particular electrode may be associated with two or three different kinds of behavior at different times. Valenstein *et al.* (1968) implanted electrodes in the lateral hypothalamus, and tested rats for "stimulus-bound" behavior by stimulating them in the presence of food, water, and a piece of wood. If an animal showed consistent stimulus-bound eating in this situation, the food was removed and the animal stimulated again (with the same stimulus parameters). In most cases it would then either drink or gnaw, and the new response would be consistent on future trials. On the basis of these and similar data, Valenstein *et al.* (1968, 1970) argued that elicited activities might depend on a stimulation-induced general drive state rather than on stimulation of specific motivational pathways. After an extensive review of the literature, Wise (1974) concluded that most, if not all, of the examples of multiple behaviors elicited by the same electrode could be understood as controlled by anatomically overlapping, but functionally distinct neural circuits. We would like to point out here, that earlier experiments by von Holst and von Saint Paul (1960) also demonstrated that multiple behaviors could be elicited from a single electrode, and that von Holst and von Saint Paul also concluded that anatomically overlapping, but functionally distinct neural circuits were involved. Their paper has been consistently ignored by the brain stimulation "establishment," evidently on the grounds that lack of methodological detail makes interpretation of their data impossible (e.g., Roberts *et al.*, 1967). Nonetheless, many of the facts they reported were only "discovered" 10 years later, and many of their ideas have yet to be appreciated.

Other counterevidence for specific motivational systems is that electrodes ostensibly located in an area that should produce stimulus-bound behavior and support self-stimulation often do not. Investigators that implant electrodes in the lateral hypothalamus, for example, uniformly report that some, often large, percentage of their animals are noneaters and nonresponders. Wise (1974) has claimed that most cases of nonresponding are due to the inhibitory effects of "fear," on the grounds that reduction of fear by drugs or habituation changes almost all animals into responders. Thus, this evidence may actually support the notion of specific motivational systems.

The evidence that is most difficult to reconcile with the idea that ESB elicits specific natural drive states comes from studies in which two electrode sites or one electrode site and one natural drive are manipulated. Gallistel (1969b) used rats with two electrodes implanted in different parts of the brain–for example, one in the lateral hypothalamus and one in the posterior hypothalamus. Each electrode presumably stimulated a distinct motivational system. Rats were tested both in a runway and in a T maze. Gallistel reasoned that priming on one electrode (inducing Drive State A) would lead to faster running if the rat were rewarded with stimulation from the same electrode (i.e., reward appropriate to Drive A) than if it were rewarded with stimulation from the other electrode (i.e., reward appropriate to Drive B). And, if the rat were primed on one electrode, it would choose reward on the same electrode in the T maze. In fact, the results showed that running speed was not affected by the particular combination of priming stimulation and reward stimulation, and that priming on one electrode did not induce rats to choose that electrode in preference to the other electrode. In a subsequent study, Gallistel and Beagley (1971) also used rats with electrodes at two sites, and varied the level of hunger and thirst. They found stable drive-induced shifts in electrode preference, and suggest that this specificity of reinforcement effects can be reconciled with the previous lack of specificity of drive effects "by assuming that the reinforcement circuits are more anatomically segregated from each other than are the drive circuits" (Gallistel and Beagley, 1971, p. 204).

A second example is a runway experiment by Stellar and Gallistel (1975). They looked at the effects of hunger, and of priming with ESB, on running speed for ESB and for food. For ESB reward, both hunger and priming caused faster running; but for food reward, only hunger caused faster running, while priming actually inhibited running. These results are certainly not consistent with the assumption that priming leads to a state of hunger. On the other hand, in the experiment by Wetzel (1963) described above, deprived rats running for food, with electrodes in the same location as some of the electrodes in Stellar and Gallistel's rats, did not show any inhibitory effects of ESB priming. In fact, her rats actually showed a nonsignificant increase in running speed after priming. Stellar and Gallistel's study was exploratory in nature, and only four rats were used, each of which had several electrodes. Further, only one electrode in one rat produced stimulation-elicited eating. Previous evidence shows that only stimulation of the appropriate part of the brain leads to a presumed state of hunger, and it would seem necessary for the Stellar and Gallistel experiment to be repeated with more subjects implanted appropriately, before placing too much weight on their findings.

A potentially powerful method for investigating the motivational state associated with ESB is suggested by the work of Peterson *et al.* (1972). These authors conducted an autoshaping experiment in which a stimulus (a retractable lever) was presented just prior to either free food or free ESB. Their rats licked and gnawed at the lever when food was the unconditioned stimulus, but approached, sniffed, and explored when ESB was the unconditioned stimulus. If ESB elicits a specific drive state, one would expect to see the same responses occur in an autoshaping situation using ESB as occur when that drive state is elicited naturally. Peterson *et al.* (1972) noted that behaviors shown by a rat to the lever were often seen during ESB of the same rat. They did not specifically test for stimulation-elicited behavior, however, so it is not possible to say what drive state was most likely elicited by their electrodes. Similar experiments designed to investigate the problem of motivational states associated with ESB might, however, prove quite fruitful.

In conclusion, the large bulk of evidence favors the view that electrodes tap into functionally distinct neural circuits that normally mediate conventional motivational systems. Further work should be done, however, to see whether the apparent exceptions to this conclusion seriously undermine its validity.

2. Relation of ESB to Fear

With certain electrode placements, ESB has punishing rather than rewarding effects (Olds, 1958). With such placements, rats may self-stimulate two or three times, and never return to the lever again. Of more interest to the present discussion, however, is the fact that there are many places in the brain at which stimulation seems to have both rewarding and punishing effects. Bower and Miller (1958) showed, for example, that rats would press a lever to produce ESB, but would also learn to escape from continuously delivered stimulation from the same electrode. A number of investigators have suggested that this dual effect of stimulation may be responsible for many of the anomalous effects of ESB. Wetzel (1963) noted that 2 of the 9 rats in her primed group did not run well for ESB reward, while 2 of the 10 rats in her unprimed group ran as well as most of the primed animals. She speculated that the relative magnitude of rewarding and aversive aspects of ESB varies among subjects, and, further, that the rewarding component is greatest during or immediately after stimulation, but the aversive component is greatest sometime later. A very similar proposal was made by Kent and Grossman (1969), who also found that some rats needed priming to perform well, while others did not. Their "nonprimers" could be turned into "primers" by the addition of tail shock while the rats were pressing the lever for ESB. The proposal that the dual nature of stimulation may be responsible for some of the anomalous effects of ESB is quite plausible, since there is reasonably good correlation between areas of the brain from which dual effects have been reported, and areas from which some of the anomalous effects described above have been found.

The fact that ESB can have dual effects is especially interesting in view of similar dual effects of aggression and sex as rewards, and this point will be discussed later. For the moment we shall ask what mechanism underlies the dual effects of ESB. A number of authors have suggested that dual effects come about when current spreads from electrodes placed in rewarding structures to nearby aversive structures. As stimulation remains on, excitation of neurons occurs further and further from the electrode tip through a process of temporal summation, and the neighboring aversive neural systems become active (Stein, 1962). This would explain why animals terminate "rewarding" stimulation when they are given control over stimulus duration. Experiments reported by Valenstein (1964, Fig. 3), however, show that an explanation invoking temporal summation would require summation over a time interval of a minute or more. Valenstein considered this time interval too long, but he offered no alternative explanation. Recent work by Shizgal and Matthews (1977) suggests that lengthy temporal summation is a characteristic of certain systems, and thus supports Stein's proposal. It might also be possible to apply some form of Bols' (1976, 1977) discrepancy hypothesis (see p. 202) to this problem: aversive effects may arise because stimulation on some electrodes produces patterns of neural firing that are more "unnatural" or "unexpected" than stimulation on other electrodes. Thus, neural structures that mediate aversive events such as pain need not be involved at all.

Two other ways in which fear may be related to ESB can be mentioned briefly. First, Deutsch and Howarth (1963) have shown that some rats will run to and press a lever for ESB reward when they are frightened by an external stimulus. They hypothesize that the electrode must be in a structure, stimulation of which reduces fear. Second, as described above, Wise (1974) has shown that fear can inhibit responding for ESB generally.

F. THEORETICAL CONSIDERATIONS

Many of the problems in interpreting the results of ESB studies are similar to problems that arise with other reinforcers, and these are considered in Section X. In this section we discuss a problem that has been central to almost all the theorizing in the field, and in some ways is peculiar to ESB reward: Do the electrodes stimulate a unitary reward system, or do they stimulate a motivational system as well? Gallistel's (1973, 1975) extensive discussion of this issue should be consulted by anyone interested in the theory of brain stimulation and its relation to theories of learning in psychology. We shall make only a few specific points here.

Deutsch (1960) discussed the current ESB literature in terms of his general theory of behavior. He showed that the data fitted his theory well if it were assumed that the stimulating electrode excited both a motivational and a reward process at the same time. He pointed out that it should be possible to verify many of his suggestions independently, and, in fact, he subsequently carried out a number of experiments to test these ideas, some of which have been described above. Essentially he suggested that the electrode was making the animal hungry (assuming an appropriate placement), and rewarding it with food at the same time. Excitation of the motivational system or drive outlasted excitation of the reward system after stimulation ceased, but the drive also decayed within several seconds. Deutsch showed that insatiability, rapid extinction, overnight decrements, effects of intertrial intervals and priming, and poor performance on schedules of partial reinforcement could all be understood in this way. Several types of evidence have been put forward to support the notion that two separate systems are being stimulated: there are differential thresholds for the appearance of drive effects and reward effects (e.g., Coons and Cruce, 1968); drive and reward effects can be separated out in learning experiments (e.g., Gallistel et al., 1974; see Fig. 13); and studies of the refractory periods of the neurons being stimulated suggest that separate populations of neurons are responsible for the drive and the reward effects (see Gallistel, 1975, for a review). The evidence in support of separate systems is in fact very strong.

Although not denying that a drive may be excited by ESB, several other theorists have attempted to demonstrate that many of the anomalous effects of ESB reward can be explained in other ways. Trowill et al. (1969) have proposed an incentive model, and Lenzer (1972) an associative model, of rewarding brain stimulation. In both models it is ESB-produced stimuli, and/or environmental stimuli that have been associated with ESB reward, that are responsible for arousing behavior (i.e., lever pressing or running), rather than some drive state aroused by the stimulation. As compared with the Deutsch model, these models require only one neural system—although the one system has two functions! These other models do emphasize aspects of ESB experiments—such as training procedures, previous experience of the animals, and temporal–spatial relationship of the response and reward—that proponents of the Deutsch model tend to ignore, and thus promote a better understanding of all the factors that determine behavior. Consideration of both kinds of theory leads us to the same conclusion we drew for aggression reinforcement: animals are both driven and lured to self-stimulate, and self-stimulation is both internally and externally controlled. In studying self-stimulation, one must look for the factors controlling it in each particular situation.

In reviewing the ESB literature, we have been amazed at the tenacity and single-mindedness with which proponents of each theory maintain that their theory explains everything. Most of these theories originated in the context of whether ESB was the same as conventional reinforcers. If these authors were to review the properties of conventional reinforcers, we would be surprised to find anyone of them still proposing a single theory. Our review has shown that each of the apparent anomalies with ESB reward can be found with one or more "natural" reinforcers. Many of these cases have been mentioned in various places above, but a very brief summary may be useful here.

Persistence or lack of satiation is seen with heat (p. 177) and aggression (p. 196); rapid extinction compared to food has been demonstrated with water (p. 171) and aggression (p. 197); a very well-documented case of overnight decrement occurred with sex (p. 208); better performance with short intertrial intervals occurred with water (p. 213), aggression (p. 203), and sex (p. 210); and priming effects have been demonstrated with water (p. 170) and aggression (p. 203). Poor performance on schedules has been found, under some circumstances, with most reinforcers including nest building (p. 187) and aggression (p. 199); a particularly striking parallel between ESB and heat is seen in the good performance on certain FR chain schedules, but rather sporadic performance on normal FR schedules (pp. 179 and 218). It seems clear that there would be many more examples of "anomalies" with the various reinforcers we have reviewed, but the appropriate experiments have simply not been done.

The one reinforcer that may seem conspicuous by its absence is the conventional reinforcer—food. We shall point out in Section X the many ways that food is similar to other reinforcers. Here we can mention the well-trained, food-reinforced rat or pigeon used in class demonstrations. The animal remains quietly sitting in its cage until the demonstrator "primes" it with a free reinforcement; only then does it turn circles or raise its head or press the lever. At the conclusion of the demonstration, responding stops abruptly—"spontaneous extinction."

This summary shows that all the phenomena reported with ESB reward are also seen with other reinforcers, but it might still be argued that no one natural reinforcer shows all the anomalies. The appropriate answer is that no one ESB electrode shows all the anomalies either. The neural systems that underlie all the reinforcers we have discussed are known to be located in the parts of the brain in which reward effects with ESB have been found. These systems are anatomically overlapping, and any single electrode may stimulate one or more of them. Given the diverse effects that are found with natural reinforcers, it is not surprising that reward effects with ESB are also diverse, and are frequently difficult to replicate. It is clear that any theory of ESB reward will need to be broad enough to encompass all the results found with natural rewards. None of the theories proposed to date seems to fulfill this requirement.

X. GENERAL DISCUSSION

We shall begin the discussion by presenting a brief summary of the concept of a "behavior system," because we find it helpful in defining what is meant by a reinforcing or motivational system, and also in interpreting similarities and differences among reinforcers. We then summarize the evidence for similarities and differences in the ability of reinforcers to support learning and to support asymptotic learned responding. Next, we consider a number of generalizations that have been put forward in an attempt to explain and predict differences among reinforcers including the role of external versus internal factors, homeostatic versus nonhomeostatic systems, alternatives to behavioral compensation, "conservation" models of behavior, the "weak reinforcer" hypothesis, and the function of behavior. We then discuss the problem of whether it is possible to identify the aspect of a reinforcer that is reinforcing. Finally, we present our conclusions.

A. THE NATURE OF BEHAVIOR SYSTEMS

Lorenz (e.g., 1937) has proposed that each animal possesses a number of species-typical behavior patterns (*Erbkoordinationen*), the occurrence of which depends on the summation of a unique set of internal and external factors. These ideas are summarized in the well-known hydraulic model (Lorenz, 1939, 1950). Although this model has been criticized on many grounds (e.g., Hinde, 1960), both it and its derivatives (e.g., Tinbergen, 1950, 1952; von Holst and von Saint Paul, 1960; Sevenster, 1961; Kruijt, 1964; Baerends, 1970, 1975; Hogan, 1971; McFarland, 1971) share features that are relevant to understanding the differences and similarities among reinforcers. Not least of these is the distinction that they make between the structure underlying an activity, and its motivation.

First, all the models assume the existence of various structural units. These include response units of the type discussed by Lorenz (see also Barlow, 1968; Hinde, 1970), perceptual units such as releasing mechanisms (e.g., Baerends and Kruijt, 1973) and comparator mechanisms (von Holst and Mittelstaedt, 1950), and central coordinating and integrating units. Second, all the models suggest ways in which these units are connected with one another, ranging from the simple hierarchical scheme of Tinbergen (1950) to arrangements of much greater complexity (e.g., Baerends, 1970, 1975). Common to all models is the existence of coordinating units which control groups of response units, and which are controlled by perceptual units and by internal factors such as hormones and spontaneous neural activity (see, e.g., Roeder, 1975). The coordinating units are frequently given names such as sex, aggression, fear, hunger, etc., that is, they correspond to what psychologists term motivational states. An essential characteristic of the coordinating units is that they are defined primarily in terms of their connections with response, perceptual, and other coordinating units (i.e., in terms of their structure), and in terms of the factors that control them (i.e., in terms of motivation or causation), but *not* in terms of functions such as reproduction, maintenance of a territory, avoiding harm, providing nutrition, etc.* A behavior system can thus be defined as (1) an organization of perceptual, response, and coordinating units, (2) that acts as a unit in some situations. The first part of this definition is structural, the second motivational. Ideally, it might be desirable to have a purely structural definition, but at present we can only infer structure from causal analysis.

B. The Role of Reinforcement in Learning

1. Acquisition

Acquisition of an operant response such as lever pressing or swimming through a ring can occur very rapidly for all the reinforcers we have considered. Skinner (1936, 1938) has suggested that food or water reinforcement can support one-trial learning of a lever-press response in suitably pretrained animals, and the same may be true of all other reinforcers.

In some cases acquisition was noticeably difficult, but we attributed this to motivational rather than learning variables. For example, target pressing was difficult to shape with aggressive display as reinforcer in betta, but this seemed to be because the level of aggression was too low to elicit the operant. In other words, acquisition was retarded because the response could not occur in that behavioral context, not because it was insufficiently reinforced when it did occur (cf. Sevenster, 1973). Similarly, Roper suggested that the difficulty sometimes encountered in shaping key pressing for paper in mice was attributable to special motivational properties of the nest-building system. Loosely speaking, the animals seem to behave in these cases as if they know what to do to get the reinforcer, but cannot bring themselves to do it.

Acquisition of a running or swimming response in a straight alley or maze seems always to proceed more gradually: no matter how familiar the animal is

---

*Von Holst and von Saint Paul (1960) and Baerends (1970, 1975) refer to their models as *functional* organizations of behavior, and this may be somewhat confusing since we state that their models are *causal*. This terminological problem is related to the level of analysis. The concept of releasing mechanism, for example, is a functional concept at the physiological level: it is postulated that somewhere in the nervous system there must be an organization of neurons that is responsible for the properties attributed to releasing mechanisms. These properties could come about as a result of any of several different neural organizations. The actual neural organization is not of special interest in this case, only the functional properties of that organization. At the behavioral level, however, the concept of the releasing mechanism is a causal concept: it is postulated that activation of a particular releasing mechanism is one of the controlling (causal) factors for a certain behavior. It is possible to construct models of behavior using physiological units as de Ruiter (1963), for example, has done for the hunger system of the rat (see also de Ruiter *et al.*, 1974). Whether such physiological models are useful depends on the question being asked.

with the apparatus, several trials are required for response speed to reach asymptote (e.g., Gallistel *et al.,* 1974). The precise number of trials varies with apparatus, species, degree of pretraining, and so on, but there is no evidence that the nature of the reinforcer influences speed of acquisition directly. In the one case in which acquisition of a running response was directly compared with two reinforcers (food and water) and found to be different, the difference was attributed to the fine structure of the elicited behavior, and ultimately to a difference in deprivation level. Thus, acquisition was apparently retarded by competing response tendencies, and not by any response-strengthening inadequacy on the part of the reinforcer.

Until convincing counterevidence appears, it seems reasonable to conclude that the association of an instrumental response with its consequences occurs equally well with all reinforcers, and that observed differences in speed of acquisition result from motivational factors. Because acquisition is subject to so many variables, however, precise delineation of the factors responsible for deviant behavior is likely to require lengthy and painstaking analysis. At the moment such analysis seems unlikely to be undertaken, because the vast majority of work on operant behavior ignores learning altogether. This may be in part because the responses that are studied are learned very quickly, thus making acquisition rather uninteresting.

2. *Extinction*

The number of variables that influence extinction is perhaps even greater than the number that influence acquisition, making comparisons between reinforcers extremely difficult. In those cases in which a direct comparison has been attempted (food and water, food and aggression, food or water and ESB), either no differences were found, or the differences were attributed to motivational factors (though not simply to ''low'' or ''high'' motivation). Thus, as with acquisition, the process of learning that a response is no longer reinforced may proceed equally rapidly with all reinforcers, despite differences in performance with different reinforcers.

3. *Changes in Amount or Schedule of Reinforcement*

When amount or schedule of reinforcement is varied, operant responding changes over the course of several trials or sessions, and then stabilizes at a new level. This process of adjustment presumably involves learning that the conditions of reinforcement have changed. In cases in which adjustment to a new FR schedule was directly compared between reinforcers (food and nest material; food and aggressive display), it occurred within one session, even when the detailed pattern of responding differed between reinforcers (see below). Again, therefore, there is no evidence that rate of learning differs between reinforcers.

4. Learning and Motivation

The preceding conclusions (indeed, the entire organization of our paper) presuppose that learning and motivation (or, learning and performance) can be meaningfully distinguished. This is not always held to be so. For example, Bindra (1969) argues that response "selection" and response "facilitation" are indistinguishable aspects of the problem of motivation; and the current language of behaviorism attributes both the acquisition of a response and its continued occurrence to the single principle of reinforcement.

In terms of the concept "behavior system," we conceive of learning as a process that changes the connections between units (cf. Hogan, 1971; Gallistel, 1975). In this respect our conception clearly has much in common with traditional ideas of connectionism and response strengthening. However, we favor a more "cognitive" view of learning, believing that connections are not formed between the representations of stimuli and responses, or stimuli and stimuli, directly, but occur for the most part at a more complex or "central" level.* In particular, it seems likely that stimuli and responses often become associated with central coordinating mechanisms. This means, for example, that if a rat learns that lever pressing and the hunger system are associated, many of the causal factors that already affect the hunger system will now also affect lever pressing (cf. Skinner, 1938, p. 24; Miller, 1959, p. 276 ff.).

Thus, our conception of learning is ultimately a structural one. We have already pointed out that notions of the structure of behavior systems are based primarily upon behavioral data. The value of our distinction between learning and motivation must therefore be determined by the extent to which it helps us to analyze and understand behavior. We maintain that the distinction reflects a genuine and important problem in behavior, and that the atheoretical language of Skinnerism is unlikely to make this problem disappear.

C. THE ROLE OF REINFORCEMENT IN MAINTAINING LEARNED BEHAVIOR

1. Amount and Schedules of Reinforcement: Patterning Effects

With food as reinforcer, changes in amount of reinforcement produce diverse effects. Running speed, various measures of response rate, and postreinforcement pause duration sometimes increase, sometimes decrease, and are sometimes unaffected. Some of this variability reflects differences in the way amount

---

*Although a "cognitive" approach is not common among workers in instrumental learning, many recent accounts of classical conditioning or the relation of instrumental learning to classical conditioning have a heavily "cognitive" flavor (e.g., Bolles, 1972; Bindra, 1974; Mackintosh, 1974; Rescorla, 1978).

is varied, in species, or in the kind of food used, but much remains unexplained. With such a poor basis for comparison, little can be made of results with other reinforcers. For example, the finding that changes in the duration of aggressive display do not affect response rate in betta might or might not imply a difference from food reinforcement, depending on the studies that are cited in comparison. However, the fact that response rate is always inversely related to reinforcement size with heat as reinforcer reflects a clear difference in the nature of the motivational systems underlying thermoregulation and eating or drinking.

The patterns of responding induced by fixed-ratio schedules are more stable both within and between reinforcers, though data are sparse (few authors have bothered to include cumulative records when dealing with unusual reinforcers). With the exception of aggressive display, all the reinforcers considered by us induce the typical "pause and run" pattern of responding, at least under optimal conditions. With wheel running, nest material, and heat as reinforcer, postreinforcement pauses were unusually long at low ratios. With nest material this was attributed to the occurrence of a long chain of responses elicited by the reinforcer, and with heat to the properties of the motivational system. In the case of wheel running it remains unexplained.

With aggressive display as reinforcer in betta, Hogan found response rate to be slow and consistent throughout the interreinforcement interval. The absence of a distinct postreinforcement pause seems to be a species difference, because it also occurs with food (see Fig. 9). The failure of response rate to increase toward the end of the ratio run was attributed to the summation of priming and expectation-of-reward effects.

2. Amount and Schedules of Reinforcement: Regulatory Effects

In Section I, the Introduction, we discussed a number of ways in which changes in fixed-ratio size or in amount of reinforcement might affect number of responses made, and reinforcements obtained, per session. We proposed that animals might show greater or lesser tendencies to compensate for changes in these reinforcement parameters, and that the degree of compensation might vary between reinforcers. With food, water, heat, wheel running, and nest material as reinforcers, however, the degree of compensation varies with some or all of the following factors: amount or density of reinforcement, fixed-ratio size (as is shown by the nonlinearity of the curves), motivational level, distance between the manipulandum and the reinforcer dispenser, force required to make the operant response, and concurrent presence of an alternative reinforcer. Once again, then, apparent differences between reinforcers are frequently confounded with other variables.

Nevertheless, it is possible to present some tentative generalizations about compensation for increases in FR size. With liquid reinforcers compensation is poorer than with solid food, at least at low ratios. With nest material as reinforcer in mice, at normal temperatures, good compensation can only be obtained with a small key-dispenser distance. With heat as reinforcer, compensation falls off extremely rapidly at moderate fixed ratios, unless the animal is given control over reinforcement duration. With aggressive display as reinforcer it has as yet proved impossible to obtain any degree of positive compensation.

In the case of the food/water comparison two authors attempted to equate motivational level and incentive value, in addition to species and operant, and their results give reason to suppose that the difference in compensation is not trivial. With the other reinforcers compensation is poor in what might be considered standard test conditions, but can be improved by manipulating response and/or reinforcement parameters. Whether or not compensation can be obtained with aggressive display remains to be seen.

Data on compensation for changes in amount of reinforcement are sparser, and few conclusions can be drawn. In general, poor compensation for increases in FR size seems to be correlated with poor compensation for decreases in amount of reinforcement. Nest material may be unusual in that it induces negative compensation. Instances of zero compensation may merely indicate that amount of reinforcement was varied in an inappropriate manner.

D. COMPARING BEHAVIOR SYSTEMS

1. Internal versus External Control of Behavior Systems: Priming

There is evidence that external stimuli can play an important role in arousing all the behavior systems that we have discussed. Here we ask whether each system can be primed by external stimuli, and whether it is useful to classify systems according to whether they are primarily internally or externally aroused.

The definition of the term *priming* poses some problems. A stimulus can be said to prime a system (or a response) if the arousing effects of that stimulus outlast its presence. An immediate problem is that any stimulus has aftereffects, and a minimum criterion of persistence of these aftereffects would be entirely arbitrary. For example, priming effects of ESB generally last for 5–10 sec (p. 216); and brief presentations of a dummy have both short-term (1–2 min) and long-term (several days) effects on aggressiveness in cichlid fish (Heiligenberg, 1974). Each of these effects is consistent with the definition of priming, but they differ greatly in time course, and probably also in the mechanisms underlying them (e.g., neural or hormonal). Thus, priming is not a unitary phenomenon.

Another problem is whether the term priming should be confined to cases in which the priming stimulus is the reinforcing stimulus. For example, Gallistel (1973) suggests that food and ESB are different as reinforcers because food is not subject to priming effects. But ingestion of food is being compared with the overall effect of ESB, whereas the Deutsch–Gallistel analysis suggests that ESB has both a reinforcing effect and a motivating effect. To be consistent, food should be compared only with the reinforcing effect. Furthermore, the motivating and reinforcing neural circuits are presumably independent, and it is the motivating circuits that are supposedly responsible for the priming effects. The hunger system can be aroused by stimuli such as appetizing odors, and we have reviewed evidence that activity in hungry rats is increased by stimuli that normally precede feeding (see p. 183). There is no reason why the motivating circuits aroused by ESB should not be mimicking similar effects. Even in cases in which a reinforcing stimulus can be shown to have priming effects (e.g., water, or a conspecific for aggression or sex), it is by no means certain that the same property of the stimulus underlies both effects.

In light of these considerations, we suggest that the term "priming" be used synonymously with the phrase "motivating effects of stimuli" (see Hinde, 1970, Chapters 10 and 13). If one accepts this more general definition, it follows that each behavior system that we have considered can be primed. It is still possible to ask, though, whether different systems can be characterized by their degree of susceptibility to priming.

Tinbergen's (1951, p. 124) model of motivation suggests that each central coordinating mechanism summates the effects of various internal and external influences, to give the total "motivation" of the system. Early experiments by van Iersel (1953) and Baerends et al. (1955) support this hypothesis, as has more recent work (but see Houston and McFarland, 1976). With respect to the present argument, the important point in Tinbergen's model is that the effects of external and internal influences are indistinguishable, because one can substitute for the other.

All the systems we have considered are influenced by specific internal factors (e.g., animals generally do not eat unless hungry, nor engage in sexual behavior unless in an appropriate hormonal state). Furthermore, as discussed above, all are susceptible to the motivating effects of external stimuli. For most reinforcers, the state of the system aroused by the summation of internal and external factors seems to be grossly similar. For example, in the case of nest building, which some authors have suggested is primarily externally aroused in nonreproducing rodents, animals show behavioral compensation on FR schedules that is no less accurate than that observed with food as reinforcer, provided that external conditions are made as favorable as possible.

The one remaining difference between systems is that the highest possible levels of nest building, aggression, and sexual behavior do not seem attainable without priming, and these are all systems in which compensation is poor, and which are affected relatively little by deprivation. Poor compensation is also correlated with susceptibility to priming when comparing food and water. Whether this difference is of sufficient importance to justify using it as a basis for classification (Beach, 1956; Glickman, 1973) depends on the question being asked. The major theoretical problem is that differences in the effects of antecedent drive conditions are only quantitative.

2. Homeostatic versus Nonhomeostatic Systems

The concept of homeostasis is used by physiologists to describe a state of equilibrium brought about by the operation of negative feedback: any departure from equilibrium sets up the conditions that effect a return to equilibrium. A homeostatic motivational system is, by analogy, one in which a physiological change triggers consummatory behavior, which in turn counteracts the physiological change. (Note that this is not the same as saying that the system is internally aroused. Thermoregulation is a homeostatic system that is aroused largely by external stimulus changes.)

Shettleworth (1972, p. 13) suggests that homeostatic systems, such as feeding and drinking, should induce better behavioral compensation than nonhomeostatic ones, such as aggression or nest building. As we have already noted, however, all the systems that we have described (with the possible exception of wheel running) produce a "drive" to return to equilibrium conditions, and are to that extent homeostatic. On the other hand, all systems (with the possible exception of thermoregulation) are nonhomeostatic, in the sense that animals will seek out and maintain arousing stimuli. For example, Collier et al. (1972) argue that most eating behavior, under normal conditions, is controlled by nonregulatory factors, and Blass and Hall (1976) summarize evidence leading to a similar conclusion for drinking. We must conclude that all systems possess both homeostatic and nonhomeostatic characteristics. Depending on the question being asked, classifications based on homeostatic (drive reducing) versus nonhomeostatic (incentive) factors may be temporarily useful, but they are unlikely to survive experimental analysis.

3. Alternatives to Behavioral Compensation

In an attempt to explain the poor compensation observed with water and heat as reinforcers, we suggested that physiological mechanisms of compensation might supplant behavioral ones. This line of argument could also be used to account for the general finding that degree of compensation decreases as FR size increases. For example, with food as reinforcer, animals might be forced to increase the efficiency of their metabolism if food becomes sufficiently difficult to get.

Although there is evidence that mechanisms of physiological compensation do exist in at least some systems, these cannot account completely for the absence of behavioral compensation. The fact is that animals required to work for food or water on high ratios lose weight, and those required to work for heat become hypothermic, sometimes to a fatal degree. Furthermore, operant responding

ceases well before the point at which the energy required to obtain one reinforcement exceeds the energy provided by it (e.g., Notterman and Mintz, 1965).
Thus, the proposed alternative forms of compensation are less efficient than
behavioral compensation would be, and if this is so, why is behavioral compensation abandoned in their favor?

4. "Conservation" Models

An alternative approach is to deny that operant performance gives a true
picture of motivational regulation, and to postulate instead that operant responding breaks down for reasons of its own. This hypothesis is consistent with the fact
that patterning and regulatory measures of responding seem to covary. For
example, postreinforcement pauses become especially long, and breaks within
ratio runs begin to appear at about the point at which compensation approaches
zero or becomes negative. Thus, negative or zero compensation seems to correspond roughly with what is termed "ratio strain" in operant jargon. The fact that
responding becomes generally ragged, rather than merely declining in overall
rate, suggests that the responding itself is breaking down, and not the motivational
system associated with the reinforcer. In other words, a certain minimum density
of reinforcement might be required to sustain operant responding, regardless of
how much the animal needs the reinforcer.

Recognition that the operant response has its own controlling factors is for-
mally made by the "conservation" models of Timberlake and Allison (1974) and
Allison (1976), which are themselves elaborations of Premack's (1965) theory of
reinforcement. Allison's (1976) formulation is the most explicit with respect to
the problem of compensation, and predicts compensation curves of the general
form obtained with all reinforcers except aggressive display. Furthermore, different degrees of compensation can be accounted for by variations in a single
parameter k. Stated verbally, the model holds that degree of compensation depends on the difficulty of the response relative to the value of the reinforcer, so
that in theory complete compensation is only obtained if the response is infinitely
easy. The relative "difficulty" or "value" of the operant response and consummatory behavior can in theory be predicted from behavior in a baseline condition.

Allison's model may prove to be of considerable value in quantifying and
predicting certain differences between reinforcers, but it suffers a number of
defects. Some of these are empirical, and may not be insuperable. First, the
model is unable to account for cases of sustained zero compensation, of the kind
that occurs with aggressive display as reinforcer (see Fig. 11). Nor is it able to
account for the occurrence of negative compensation at high fixed ratios. Thus, it
sacrifices the intuitively attractive view that "ratio strain" is merely an advanced
case of declining compensation. Finally, it is questionable whether the "difficulty" of a response is transitive. If response A shows good compensation with
respect to response X, but poor compensation with respect to Y, the model seems

to predict that X will be preferred over Y in a choice situation. However, Hogan's work with Siamese fighting fish shows that aggressive display may be preferred to eating, even though it shows poorer compensation (see p. 205).

More fundamentally, Allison's model tends to gloss over the fact that compensation may be poor for completely different reasons in different reinforcers. It is in some ways satisfying to reduce different degrees of compensation to differences in a single mathematical constant, but this does not of course tell us how the differences come about.

5. The "Weak Reinforcer" Hypothesis

A number of authors have suggested that poor compensation is an attribute of "weak" reinforcers (see p. 169). One way of classifying reinforcers, therefore, would be to locate each at some point on a weak–strong continuum. Here we mention two problems inherent in setting up such a continuum.

Shettleworth (1972, p. 11) states: "The weak reinforcer hypothesis implies that the effects of a given amount of a weak reinforcer on several measures of learning are equivalent to those of some small amount of food or water, or to those of food or water for nearly satiated animals." It follows from this view that amount of reinforcement and motivational level should be interchangeable variables, whose effects on behavior are correlated. Unfortunately this is not the case. With food reinforcement, increases in amount of reinforcement or in deprivation level improve compensation for increases in FR size, but have opposite effects on resistance to extinction. One must therefore ask whether a particular reinforcer is weak in the sense of resembling a small amount of food, or in the sense of resembling food at a low deprivation level. And why should weakness be defined in either of these terms, when factors such as response force and distance between manipulandum and dispenser are also known to affect compensation? The notion of a weak–strong continuum assumes that there is a single intervening "incentive" variable, and this assumption was abandoned by psychologists some years ago in the face of overwhelming evidence to the contrary.

Conversely, different measures of performance often fail to correlate across reinforcers. With aggression and ESB as reinforcers, acquisition was as rapid as with food, and rate of responding on a CRF schedule was as high, but compensation for increases in FR size was considerably poorer. Similarly, hypothalamically obese animals behave like poorly motivated controls in some respects, but not in others, and it is simplistic to say that they find food weakly reinforcing (see p. 169). Our review suggests that each reinforcer is unique in its effects on different aspects of instrumental behavior. Consequently, any single-variable hypothesis will be inadequate.

6. Value of the Reinforcer to the Animal

In conjunction with her homeostatic–nonhomeostatic distinction, Shettleworth (1972, p. 13) implies that differences among reinforcing systems might reflect differences in the necessity of the reinforcers for survival. This suggestion has some intuitive appeal: it is true that animals need a certain average amount of food per day in order to survive, and Beach (1956) has stated that no one ever died for lack of sex. But arguments based on survival value can be misleading. In the first place, the correlation between physiological "need" and psychological "drive" is far from perfect. For example, inhaling carbon monoxide causes a depletion of oxygen in the blood to the point at which unconsciousness and death occur; yet there seems to be no drive state associated with carbon monoxide poisoning. Similarly, the drive state associated with lethally cold temperatures seems insufficient to maintain responding for heat, whereas some animals respond for locomotion as a reinforcer far in excess of apparent need for exercise.

A second problem with the survival argument is that a "necessary" commodity may suddenly become unnecessary. Goldfish, for example, normally regulate their food intake quite well, but sometimes they almost stop eating for a period of several weeks. During these anorexic periods, food deprivation has no effect on the fishes' behavior (Rozin, 1961). Similar changes in the effect of food deprivation on food intake are seen in hibernating rodents (Mrosovsky, 1971). There are reasons why food is not necessary for survival during these periods of anorexia, but behaviorally, the feeding system is different during such periods.

A third problem is that survival can be considered either in the short term or in the long term. Although Siamese fighting fish do not immediately expire if they are prevented from displaying to "rivals," they do not remain as healthy or live as long as those given regular exposure to an aggression-provoking stimulus (Hogan, personal observation). No one seems to have investigated whether animals given regular sexual experience live longer than virgins, but it would not be surprising to find that they do. And, on the other side of the coin, North Americans have been said to eat themselves to death: their life expectancy is reduced by overeating (Mayer, 1975).

Finally, it is not clear whether we are dealing with survival value in the experimental conditions, or in nature. In the laboratory rodent, neither wheel running nor nest building have any obvious survival value, yet their reinforcing properties are different. Nest building does have survival value in the wild, but so, we must presume, do the vast majority of other consummatory activities. Who is to say whether eating or maintaining a territory is more important for the survival of the individual?

Notions of the value of different reinforcers to the animal have also been suggested by an analogy between operant behavior and economic demand theory. As Lea and Roper (1977) point out, an analogy can be drawn between compensation for increases in FR size and the economist's "elasticity of demand." The demand function of a commodity is the amount purchased as a function of its price; similarly, the compensation function is the amount of a reinforcer obtained as a function of FR size. Demand is said to be "inelastic" if increases in price do not lead to a reduction in amount consumed, and this is equivalent to good compensation.

Economic theory predicts that elasticity will be greater (i.e., compensation less good) if there is a "substitutable" commodity on the market at a constant price, because this commodity will be bought instead. Lea and Roper showed that this prediction is borne out by rats working for food in a Skinner box. Because substitutability is an important (perhaps, if widely defined, sufficient) index of the value of the commodity to the purchaser, prediction of substitutability would enable prediction of elasticity of demand in at least some circumstances. Unfortunately, however, no sure method of predicting substitutability has yet been found (see Lancaster, 1966): economists, like behaviorists, have to rely on intuition to tell them that bread is more essential than caviar, and on empiricism to tell them that elasticity of demand for the former commodity will be less than for the latter.

E. WHAT IS REINFORCING?

In Section I, the Introduction, we mentioned the wide variety of events that have been claimed to be reinforcers, and pointed out that many studies of these events were undertaken to prove or disprove some particular theory of reinforcement. Most of these theories have been concerned with identifying what particular aspect of the train of events that occurs in a reinforcing situation actually constitutes the reinforcer. These theories can be placed in a 2×3 classification based on our discussion of behavior systems: homeostatic (drive-reduction) and nonhomeostatic (drive-induction) theories, on the one hand; and perceptual, central, and response theories, on the other hand.

Homeostatic theories of reinforcement have been the most prevalent, and Miller's (e.g., 1959) ideas have probably been the most influential in psychology. His theory could be characterized as a homeostatic central theory in that reinforcement is identified with the reduction of some central drive state (such as hunger or fear). Ethologists have proposed related theories, but have emphasized perceptual- or response-related reduction of drive. Lashley (1938) and Thorpe (1956), for example, have suggested that the perception of particular stimuli, such as a completed nest, can serve to reduce or terminate the drive state responsible for the nest-building behavior. Lorenz (1937) and Tinbergen (1951, p. 106) have suggested that the performance of particular responses, such as chewing and swallowing, can serve to reduce the "action-specific energy" associated with those responses. Lorenz and Tinbergen imply that it is factors associated with performance of the responses that is reinforcing, and not the reduction of some central drive state such as hunger. Nonetheless, the common thread in all these theories is that the reduction in some drive state is presumed to be the reinforcer.

Nonhomeostatic theories of reinforcement are more numerous than homeostatic theories, but they have generally been less influential since they stress the "pleasurable" aspects of reinforcement and identify an increase in stimulation as the reinforcing event. Pleasure is often considered an unscientific concept, and seeking stimulation often seems "unphysiological." Nonetheless, both pleasure and stimulus seeking have become more respectable in recent years, and these theories are now more widely held. Several nonhomeostatic stimulus theories have been proposed. Some emphasize that the hedonic quality of the reinforcer (e.g., the taste of the food) is crucial (e.g., Young, 1959; Pfaffmann, 1960), while others suggest that stimulus change of any kind is sufficient (e.g., Kish, 1966). Central theories have been proposed to explain the results of ESB (e.g., Olds, 1958), and response theories have emphasized the arousal of "consummatory" or "species-specific" behavior patterns (e.g., Sheffield, 1966; Glickman and Schiff, 1967).

The most difficult problem in deciding among the various theories is that the performance of a response brings about stimulus changes, the perception of a stimulus brings about response changes, and all such changes probably have both drive-reducing and drive-inducing effects. There have been a number of experimental efforts to separate these different effects, but proponents of most theories have been quite ingenious in devising explanations for the results of these experiments in terms of their own theory. Many of the problems involved in choosing a particular theory are similar to the problems we have discussed in Section X.D, and our conclusion here is similar to our conclusion there: all reinforcers share some characteristics of each theory. Given that each behavior system is unique (see below), it seems most likely that the aspect of a reinforcer that is responsible for reinforcement may well be different for each reinforcer. Further, in most cases, it also seems likely that stimulus, response, and drive effects will in some sense be additive. Finally, our review suggests that there is no way, a priori, to predict what events will serve as reinforcers.

The theories of reinforcement that we have mentioned above were all concerned with specifying the event that causes changes in connections among units of behavior—that is, the event that is responsible for learning as we have defined it. There is one other class of theories that we would consider to be more theories of motivation than theories of reinforcement, namely, the theories of Premack (1965), Timberlake and Allison (1974), and Allison (1976). These theories do not deal with relatively permanent changes in connections, but predict overall outcomes of behavior on the basis of the "strength" (motivation, causal factors) of the various responses they consider. Thus, if the probability of drinking is low (because the animal has had ad lib water) and the probability of eating is high (because the animal has been deprived), the animal will increase its rate of drinking if it must drink in order to get food. The rate of both drinking and eating in the contingency situation is affected by the levels of thirst and hunger, and changing those levels causes predictable changes in the rates of responding. As

Premack himself states, his theory is an "empirical" theory of reinforcement, and is therefore not really attempting to specify the nature of reinforcement in the same way as the other theories.

F. CONCLUSIONS: THE UNIQUENESS OF BEHAVIOR SYSTEMS

We have conceptualized behavior systems in terms of various structural units and the connections among them. The actual connections that exist at a given moment in a given individual depend upon the developmental history of that individual. It follows that each system in each member of each species must be structurally unique, because the developmental history of no two individuals is identical. Thus, even the hunger system of two rats will vary as a function of each animal's developmental history. The structure of the hunger system of a rat trained to lever press for food will differ from that of an untrained rat, and Allison (1976) has shown that even rats that have been exposed to identical contingencies of water reinforcement have different compensation coefficients (k). It is true, of course, that the developmental histories of two rats are likely to be more similar than those of a rat and a mouse, and we may therefore expect many features of the hunger system to be "species specific." Whether or not individual differences among rats are important depends on the question being asked, and on the level of precision required in the answer.

Species-specific differences between hunger systems mean, for example, that generalizations about responding for food on FR schedules in rats may not hold for other species. We have already pointed to a number of differences between rats and pigeons (p. 163), and between rats and Siamese fighting fish (p. 199). A somewhat similar line of argument has been put forward by Collier et al. (1972; see also Hirsch and Collier, 1974a), who suggest that certain features of operant responding will vary in different species according to ecological determinants of feeding behavior such as vegetation, rainfall, and the density of prey and predators. However, they do not seem to distinguish between causes and functions of behavior, and it is not always clear how a particular ecological variable would affect operant behavior. The physiological and behavioral mechanisms possessed by an animal are the direct determinants of its behavior, and ecological variables of the kind mentioned by Collier et al. (1972) are important only as selective factors during the course of evolution. In fact, the results of their experiments show that the operant behavior of rats and guinea pigs is remarkably similar, considering the differences in their ecological niches. These results further support our contention that arguments based on the functions of behavior may be misleading when applied to causal analysis.

There are also differences between groups within species: the organization of sexual behavior in male and female rats is different, and our review points to a number of sex differences in instrumental behavior, with sex as reinforcer. Many examples of species differences in instrumental behavior with other reinforcers are to be found in the preceding pages.

This diversity clearly limits the kinds of generalizations that can be made about reinforcers, and we are led to the disheartening conclusion that prediction of behavior can only be made after the reinforcer, the species, and the particular experience of the individual are known. Consideration of the survival value of various reinforcers does not invariably lead to good hypotheses of causal mechanisms, and the various theories of reinforcement that have been proposed are not very useful in predicting behavior in a practical sense with respect to a variety of reinforcers. Given the present state of knowledge, this means empirical determination in each case, and a ragbag of post hoc explanations for any differences that might arise. The limited kinds of generalizations that can be made are, we suggest, best expressed in motivational terms.

Acknowledgments

This paper was instigated by Roper's reaction to a paper by Hogan presented at the 14th International Ethological Conference in Parma in August, 1975. Hogan's data on aggressive behavior in fighting fish and Roper's data on nest building in mice seemed to be natural companions, and a review of these data together with a few comparisons with conventional reinforcers seemed a timely undertaking. The result is not what either of us had expected, but we both feel that our collaboration has been fruitful and that the paper is far better than it would have been had either of us tackled it alone.

Many people read part of the paper as it was being written, and we are especially grateful to R. J. Bols, C. R. Gallistel, G. Koob, and D. F. Sherry for their comments on particular sections. A few people read the whole manuscript: C. Beer, R. A. Hinde, A. J. Hogan-Warburg, S. E. G. Lea, J. S. Rosenblatt, S. J. Shettleworth, and D. van der Kooy. Their comments have led to many improvements in both logic and clarity. We would point out that some of these people disagree with some of our conclusions, but their input has helped us state our position more clearly. We also thank S. E. G. Lea for help with Fig. 3, R. J. Bols for allowing us to present her unpublished data in Fig. 12, and M. Cook for excellent secretarial assistance.

Preparation of this paper was supported in part by a grant from the National Research Council of Canada to Hogan and a Research Fellowship from Churchill College, Cambridge to Roper.

References

Adair, E. R. 1971. Displacements of rectal temperature modify behavioural thermoregulation. *Physiol. Behav.* **7**, 21–26.

Adair, E. R., and Wright, B. A. 1976. Behavioral thermoregulation in the squirrel monkey when response effort is varied. *J. Comp. Physiol. Psychol.* **90**, 179–184.

Adler, N. T., and Hogan, J. A. 1963. Classical conditioning and punishment of an instinctive response in *Betta splendens. Anim. Behav.* **11**, 351–354.

Allison, J. 1976. Contrast, induction, facilitation, suppression, and conservation. *J. Exp. Anal. Behav.* **25**, 185–198.

Amsel, A. 1958. The role of frustrative nonreward in noncontinuous reward situations. *Psychol. Bull.* **55**, 102–119.

Amsel, A. 1962. Frustrative nonreward in partial reinforcement and discrimination learning: Some recent history and a theoretical extension. *Psychol. Rev.* **69**, 306–328.

Amsel, A., and Roussel, J. 1952. Motivational properties of frustration: I. Effects on a running response of the addition of frustration to the motivational complex. *J. Exp. Psychol.* **43**, 363–368.

Amsel, A., and Work, M. S. 1961. The role of learned factors in "spontaneous" activity. *J. Comp. Physiol. Psychol.* **54**, 527–532.

Anderson, E. A. 1937. Interrelationship of drives in the male albino rat: I. Intercorrelations of measures of drives. *J. Comp. Psychol.* **24**, 73–118.

Andersson, B. 1966. The physiology of thirst. *In* "Progress in Physiological Psychology" (E. Stellar and J. M. Sprague, eds.), Vol. 1, pp. 191–207. Academic Press, New York.

Andik, I., Donhoffer, S., Farkas, M., and Schmidt, P. 1963. Ambient temperature and survival on a protein-deficient diet. *Br. J. Nutr.* **17**, 257–261.

Annau, A., Heffner, R., and Koob, G. 1974. Electrical self-stimulation of single and multiple loci: Long term observations. *Physiol. Behav.* **13**, 281–290.

van den Assem, J., and van der Molen, J. N. 1968. Waning of the aggressive response in the three-spined stickleback upon constant exposure to a conspecific. I. A preliminary analysis of the phenomenon. *Behaviour* **34**, 286–324.

Baenninger, R. 1970. Visual reinforcement, habituation, and prior social experience of Siamese fighting fish. *J. Comp. Physiol. Psychol.* **71**, 1–5.

Baenninger, R., and Mattleman, R. A. 1973. Visual reinforcement: Operant acquisition in the presence of a free mirror. *Anim. Learn. Behav.* **1**, 302–306.

Baerends, G. P. 1970. A model of the functional organisation of incubation behaviour in the Herring Gull. *In* "The Herring Gull and Its Egg" (G. P. Baerends and R. H. Drent, eds.). *Behaviour Suppl.* **17**, 261–312.

Baerends, G. P. 1975. An evaluation of the conflict hypothesis as an explanatory principle for the evolution of displays. *In* "Function and Evolution in Behaviour" (G. P. Baerends, C. Beer, and A. Manning, eds.), pp. 187–227. Oxford Univ. Press, London and New York.

Baerends, G. P., and Kruijt, J. P. 1973. Stimulus selection. *In* "Constraints on Learning" (R. A. Hinde and J. Stevenson-Hinde, eds.), pp. 23–49. Academic Press, London.

Baerends, G. P., Brouwer, R., and Waterbolk, H. T. 1955. Ethological studies on *Lebistes reticulatus* (Peters): I. An analysis of the male courtship pattern. *Behaviour* **8**, 249–334.

Baldwin, B. A. 1968. Behavioural thermoregulation in mice. *Physiol. Behav.* **3**, 401–407.

Baldwin, B. A., and Ingram, D. L. 1968. Factors influencing behavioral thermoregulation in the pig. *Physiol. Behav.* **3**, 409–415.

Barlow, G. W. 1968. Ethological units of behavior. *In* "Central Nervous System and Fish Behavior" (D. Ingle, ed.), pp. 217–232. Univ. of Chicago Press, Chicago.

Barofsky, I., and Hurwitz, D. 1968. Within ratio responding during fixed ratio performance. *Psychon. Sci.* **11**, 263.

Baumeister, A., Hawkins, W. F., and Cromwell, R. T. 1964. Need states and activity level. *Psychol. Bull.* **61**, 438–453.

Beach, F. A. 1956. Characteristics of masculine "sex drive". *In* "Nebraska Symposium on Motivation, 1956" (M. R. Jones, ed.), pp. 1–32. Univ. of Nebraska Press, Lincoln.

Beach, F. A., and Jordan, L. 1956a. Effects of sexual reinforcement upon the performance of male rats in a straight runway. *J. Comp. Physiol. Psychol.* **49**, 105–110.

Beach, F. A., and Jordan, L. 1956b. Sexual exhaustion and recovery in the male rat. *Quart. J. Exp. Psychol.* **8**, 121–133.

Beninger, R. J., and Milner, P. M. 1977. Effects of signaled and unsignaled brain stimulation, water and sucrose reinforcement of running behavior in rats. *J. Comp. Physiol. Psychol.* **91**, 1272–1283.

Beninger, R. J., Bellisle, F., and Milner, P. M. 1977. Schedule control of behavior reinforced by electrical stimulation of the brain. *Science* **196**, 547–549.

Berlyne, D. E. 1969. The reward value of indifferent stimulation. *In* "Reinforcement and Behavior" (J. T. Tapp, ed.), pp. 179–214. Academic Press, New York.

Bermant, G. 1961. Response latencies of female rats during sexual intercourse. *Science* **133**, 1771–1773.

Bermant, G., and Davidson, J. M. 1974. "Biological Bases of Sexual Behavior." Harper & Row, New York.

Bermant, G., and Westbrook, W. H. 1966. Peripheral factors in the regulation of sexual contact by female rats. *J. Comp. Physiol. Psychol.* **61**, 244–250.

Bindra, D. 1969. The interrelated mechanisms of reinforcement and motivation, and the nature of their influence on response. *In* "Nebraska Symposium on Motivation, 1969" (W. J. Arnold and D. Levine, eds.), pp. 1–33. Univ. of Nebraska Press, Lincoln.

Bindra, D. 1974. A motivational view of learning, performance, and behavior modification. *Psychol. Rev.* **81**, 199–213.

Blass, E. M. 1975. The physiological, neurological and behavioral bases of thirst. *In* "Nebraska Symposium on Motivation, 1974" (J. K. Cole and T. B. Sonderegger, eds.), pp. 1–47. Univ. of Nebraska Press, Lincoln.

Blass, E. M., and Hall, W. G. 1976. Drinking termination: Interactions among hydrational, orogastric and behavioral controls in rats. *Psychol. Rev.* **83**, 356–374.

Bligh, J. 1973. "Temperature Regulation in Mammals and Other Vertebrates." North-Holland Publ., Amsterdam.

Bolles, R. C. 1958. A replication and further analysis of a study on position reversal learning in hungry and thirsty rats. *J. Comp. Physiol. Psychol.* **51**, 349.

Bolles, R. C. 1963. Effects of food deprivation upon the rat's behavior in its home cage. *J. Comp. Physiol. Psychol.* **56**, 456–460.

Bolles, R. C. 1970. Species-specific defense reactions and avoidance learning. *Psychol. Rev.* **77**, 32–48.

Bolles, R. C. 1972. Reinforcement, expectancy, and learning. *Psychol. Rev.* **79**, 394–409.

Bolles, R. C. 1975. "Theory of Motivation. 2nd ed." Harper, New York.

Bolles, R. C., and Petrinovich, L. 1956. Body-weight changes and behavioral attributes. *J. Comp. Physiol. Psychol.* **49**, 177–180.

Bolles, R. C., Rapp, H. M., and White, G. C. 1968. Failure of sexual activity to reinforce female rats. *J. Comp. Physiol. Psychol.* **65**, 311–313.

Bols, R. J. 1976. Factors influencing the reinforcing value of aggressive display in the Siamese fighting fish, *Betta splendens*. Ph.D. thesis, Univ. of Toronto, Canada.

Bols, R. J. 1977. Display reinforcement in the Siamese fighting fish, *Betta splendens*: Aggressive motivation or curiosity? *J. Comp. Physiol. Psychol.* **91**, 233–244.

Bower, G. H., and Miller, N. E. 1958. Rewarding and punishing effects from stimulating the same place in the rat's brain. *J. Comp. Physiol. Psychol.* **51**, 669–674.

Brady, J. V., and Conrad, D. G. 1960. Some effects of limbic system self-stimulation upon conditioned emotional behavior. *J. Comp. Physiol. Psychol.* **53**, 128–137.

Bremner, F. G., and Trowill, J. A. 1962. A combined manipulandum–reinforcement arrangement. *J. Exp. Anal. Behav.* **5**, 339–341.

Brobeck, J. R. 1945. Effects of variations in activity, food intake and environmental temperature on weight gain in the albino rat. *Am. J. Physiol.* **143**, 1–5.

Brown, R., Freeman, S., and McFarland, D. J. 1974. Towards a model for the copulatory behaviour of the male rat. *In* "Motivational Control Systems Analysis" (D. J. McFarland, ed.), pp. 461–510. Academic Press, New York.

Bruce, R. H. 1935. A further study of the effect of variation of reward and drive upon the maze performance of rats. *J. Comp. Psychol.* **20**, 157–182.

Bruce, R. H. 1938. The effect of lessening the drive upon performance by white rats in a maze. *J. Comp. Psychol.* **25**, 225–248.

Budgell, P. 1971. Behaviour thermoregulation in the Barbary dove (*Streptopelia risoria*). *Anim. Behav.* **19**, 524–531.

Cabanac, M. 1972. Thermoregulatory behavior. *In* "Essays on Temperature Regulation" (J. Bligh and R. E. Moore, eds.), pp. 19–36. North-Holland Publ., Amsterdam.

Caggiula, A. R. 1970. Analysis of the copulation-reward properties of posterior hypothalamic stimulation in male rats. *J. Comp. Physiol. Psychol.* **70**, 399–412.

Campbell, B. A., and Sheffield, F. D. 1953. Relation of random activity to food deprivation. *J. Comp. Physiol. Psychol.* **46**, 320–322.

Campbell, G. A., and Lynch, B. 1969. Cortical modulation of spontaneous activity during hunger and thirst. *J. Comp. Physiol. Psychol.* **67**, 15–22.

Carlisle, H. J. 1966a. Heat intake and hypothalamic temperature during behavioral temperature regulation. *J. Comp. Physiol. Psychol.* **61**, 388–397.

Carlisle, H. J. 1966b. Behavioural significance of hypothalamic temperature-sensitive cells. *Nature (London)* **209**, 1324–1325.

Carlisle, H. J. 1968. Peripheral thermal stimulation and thermoregulatory behavior. *J. Comp. Physiol. Psychol.* **66**, 507–510.

Carlisle, H. J. 1969. Effect of fixed-ratio thermal reinforcement on thermoregulatory behavior. *Physiol. Behav.* **4**, 23–28.

Carlisle, H. J. 1970. Intermittent heat as a reinforcer for rats in the cold. *Physiol. Behav.* **5**, 861–866.

Carlisle, H. J. 1971. Behavioral temperature regulation in Cynomolgus and Pig-tailed macaques. *J. Physiol. (Paris)* **63**, 226–228.

Cizek, L. J. 1961. Relationship between food and water ingestion in the rabbit. *Am. J. Physiol.* **201**, 557–566.

Clayton, F. L., and Hinde, R. A. 1968. The habituation and recovery of aggressive display in *Betta splendens. Behaviour* **30**, 96–106.

Cofer, C. N., and Appley, M. H. 1964. "Motivation: Theory and Research." Wiley, New York.

Cole, J. M., and Parker, B. K. 1971. Schedule-induced aggression: Access to an attackable target bird as a positive reinforcer. *Psychon. Sci.* **22**, 33–35.

Collier, G. 1970. Work: A weak reinforcer. *Trans. N.Y. Acad. Sci.* **32**, 557–576.

Collier, G., and Hirsch, E. 1971. Reinforcing properties of spontaneous activity in the rat. *J. Comp. Physiol. Psychol.* **77**, 155–160.

Collier, G., and Jennings, W. 1969. Work as a determinant of instrumental performance. *J. Comp. Physiol. Psychol.* **68**, 659–662.

Collier, G., and Knarr, F. 1966. Defense of water balance in the rat. *J. Comp. Physiol. Psychol.* **61**, 5–10.

Collier, G., and Leshner, A. I. 1967. An invariant in mouse running wheel behavior. *Psychon. Sci.* **8**, 9–10.

Collier, G., and Levitsky, D. 1967. Defense of water balance in rats: Behavioral and physiological responses to depletion. *J. Comp. Physiol. Psychol.* **64**, 59–67.

Collier, G., and Levitsky, D. A. 1968. Operant running as a function of deprivation and effort. *J. Comp. Physiol. Psychol.* **66**, 522–523.

Collier, G., and Squibb, R. L. 1967. Diet and activity. *J. Comp. Physiol. Psychol.* **64**, 409–413.

Collier, G., Squibb, R. L., and Jackson, F. 1965. Activity as a function of diet: I. Spontaneous activity. *Psychon. Sci.* **3**, 173–174.

Collier, G., Levitsky, D., and Squibb, R. L. 1967. Instrumental performance as a function of the energy content of the diet. *J. Comp. Physiol. Psychol.* **64**, 68–72.

Collier, G., Hirsch, E., and Hamlin, P. E. 1972. The ecological determinants of reinforcement in the rat. *Physiol. Behav.* **9**, 705–716.

Coons, E. E., and Cruce, J. A. F. 1968. Lateral hypothalamus: Food current intensity in maintaining self-stimulation of hunger. *Science* **159**, 1117–1119.

Corbit, J. D. 1970. Behavioral regulation of body temperature. *In* "Physiological and Behavioral Temperature Regulation" (J. D. Hardy, A. P. Gagge, and J. A. Stolwijk, eds.), pp. 777–801. Thomas, Springfield, Ill.

Davidson, A. B., Davis, D. J., and Cook, L. 1971. A rapid technique for training key-pressing in rats. *J. Exp. Anal. Behav.* **15**, 123–127.

Deutsch, J. A. 1960. "The Structural Basis of Behavior." Univ. of Chicago Press, Chicago.

Deutsch, J. A., and DiCara, L. 1967. Hunger and extinction in intracranial self-stimulation. *J. Comp. Physiol. Psychol.* **63**, 344–347.

Deutsch, J. A., and Howarth, C. I. 1963. Some tests of a theory in intracranial self-stimulation. *Psychol. Rev.* **70**, 444–460.

Dreyer, P. I., and Church, R. M. 1970. Reinforcement of shock-induced fighting. *Psychon. Sci.* **18**, 147–148.

Eayrs, J. T. 1954. Spontaneous activity in the rat. *Br. J. Anim. Behav.* **2**, 25–30.

Eisman, E., Linton, M., and Theios, J. 1960. The relationship between response strength and one parameter of the hunger drive. *J. Comp. Physiol. Psychol.* **53**, 359–363.

Elliott, M. H. 1929. The effect of change of 'drive' on maze performance. *Univ. Calif. Publ. Psychol.* **4**, 185–188.

Elton, C., 1942. "Voles, Mice and Lemmings—Problems in Population Dynamics." Oxford Univ. Press, London and New York.

Epstein, A. N., and Milestone, R. 1968. Showering as a coolant for rats exposed to heat. *Science* **160**, 895–896.

Falk, J. L. 1961. Production of polydipsia in normal rats by an intermittent food schedule. *Science* **133**, 195–196.

Falk, J. L. 1972. The nature and determinants of adjunctive behavior. *In* "Schedule Effects: Drugs, Drinking and Aggression" (R. M. Gilbert and J. D. Keehn, eds.), pp. 148–173. Univ. of Toronto Press, Toronto.

Fantino, E., Weigele, S., and Lancy, D. 1972. Aggressive display in the Siamese fighting fish (*Betta splendens*). *Learn. Motiv.* **3**, 457–468.

Felton, M., and Lyon, D. O. 1966. The post-reinforcement pause. *J. Exp. Anal. Behav.* **9**, 131–134.

Ferster, C. B., and Skinner, B. F. 1957. "Schedules of Reinforcement." Appleton, New York.

Figler, M. H. 1972. The relation between eliciting stimulus strength and habituation of the threat display in male Siamese fighting fish, *Betta splendens*. *Behaviour* **42**, 63–96.

Findley, J. D. 1959. Behavior output under chained fixed-ratio requirements in a 24-hr experimental space. *J. Exp. Anal. Behav.* **2**, 258.

Fitzsimons, J. T. 1971. The physiology of thirst: A review of the extraneural aspects of the mechanisms of drinking. *In* "Progress in Physiological Psychology" (E. Stellar and J. M. Sprague, eds.), Vol. 4, pp. 119–201. Academic Press, New York.

Flory, R. K. 1971. The control of schedule-induced polydipsia: Frequency and magnitude of reinforcement. *Learn. Motiv.* **2**, 215–227.

Gallistel, C. R. 1966. Motivating effects in self-stimulation. *J. Comp. Physiol. Psychol.* **62**, 95–101.

Gallistel, C. R. 1967. Intracranial stimulation and natural reward: Differential effects of trial spacing. *Psychon. Sci.* **9**, 167–168.

Gallistel, C. R. 1969a. The incentive of brain-stimulation reward. *J. Comp. Physiol. Psychol.* **69**, 713–721.

Gallistel, C. R. 1969b. Self-stimulation: Failure of pretrial stimulation to affect rats' electrode preference. *J. Comp. Physiol. Psychol.* **69**, 722–729.

Gallistel, C. R. 1973. Self-stimulation: The neurophysiology of reward and motivation. *In* "The Physiological Basis of Memory" (J. A. Deutsch, ed.), pp. 175–267. Academic Press, New York.

Gallistel, C. R. 1975. Motivation as central organizing process: The psychophysical approach to its functional and neurophysiological analysis. *In* "Nebraska Symposium on Motivation, 1974" (J. K. Cole and T. B. Sonderegger, eds.), pp. 183–250. Univ. of Nebraska Press, Lincoln.

Gallistel, C. R., and Beagley, G. 1971. Specificity of brain stimulation reward in the rat. *J. Comp. Physiol. Psychol.* **76**, 199–205.

Gallistel, C. R., Stellar, J. R., and Bubis, E. 1974. Parametric analysis of brain stimulation reward in the rat: I. The transient process and the memory-containing process. *J. Comp. Physiol. Psychol.* **87**, 848–859.

Garcia, J., McGowan, B. K., and Green, K. F. 1972. Biological constraints on conditioning. *In* "Classical Conditioning II: Current Research and Theory" (A. H. Black and W. F. Prokasy, eds.), pp. 3–27. Appleton, New York.

Gibson, W. E., Reid, L. D., Sakai, M., and Porter, P. B. 1965. Intracranial reinforcement compared with sugar-water reinforcement. *Science* **148**, 1357–1359.

Gilbertson, D. W. 1975. Courtship as a reinforcement for key pecking in the pigeon, *Columba livia*. *Anim. Behav.* **23**, 735–744.

Glickman, S. E., 1973. Responses and reinforcement. *In* "Constraints on Learning" (R. A. Hinde and J. Stevenson-Hinde, eds.), pp. 207–241. Academic Press, London.

Glickman, S. E., and Schiff, B. B. 1967. A biological theory of reinforcement. *Psychol. Rev.* **74**, 81–109.

Glickman, S. E., Fried, L., and Morrison, B. A. 1967. Shredding of nesting material in the Mongolian gerbil. *Percept. Mot. Skills* **24**, 474.

Goldstein, S. R. 1967. Mirror image as a reinforcer in Siamese fighting fish: A repetition with additional controls. *Psychon. Sci.* **7**, 331–332.

Goldstein, S. R. 1975. Observations on the establishment of a stable community of adult male and female Siamese fighting fish (*Betta splendens*). *Anim. Behav.* **23**, 179–185.

Goodrich, K. P. 1960. Running speed and drinking rate as functions of sucrose concentration and amount of consummatory activity. *J. Comp. Physiol. Psychol.* **53**, 245–250.

Grabowski, J. G., and Thompson, T. 1968. Effects of visual reinforcement duration and fixed ratio schedules on operant behavior of Siamese fighting fish. Paper presented at Meeting of the Amer. Psychol. Assn., San Francisco.

Gross, C. G. 1968. General activity. *In* "Analysis of Behavioral Change" (L. Weiskrantz, ed.), pp. 91–106. Harper & Row, New York.

Grossman, S. P. 1967. "Physiological Psychology." Wiley, New York.

Guttman, N. 1953. Operant conditioning, extinction and periodic reinforcement in relation to concentration of sucrose used as reinforcing agent. *J. Exp. Psychol.* **46**, 213–224.

Hall, J. F. 1955. Activity as a function of a restricted drinking schedule. *J. Comp. Physiol. Psychol.* **48**, 265–266.

Hall, J. F. 1956. The relation between external stimulation, food deprivation, and activity. *J. Comp. Physiol. Psychol.* **49**, 339–341.

Hamilton, C. L., and Brobeck, J. R. 1964. Hypothalamic hyperphagia in the monkey. *J. Comp. Physiol. Psychol.* **57**, 271–278.

Hardy, D. F., and DeBold, J. F. 1972. Effects of coital stimulation upon behavior of the female rat. *J. Comp. Physiol. Psychol.* **78**, 400–408.

Hart, B. L. 1968. Sexual reflexes and mating behavior in the male rat. *J. Comp. Physiol. Psychol.* **65**, 453–460.

Hediger, H. 1950. "Wild Animals in Captivity." Butterworth, London.

Heiligenberg, W. 1974. Processes governing behavioral states of readiness. *In* "Advances in the Study of Behavior" (D. S. Lehrman, J. A. Rosenblatt, R. A. Hinde, and E. Shaw, eds.), Vol. 5, pp. 173–200. Academic Press, New York.

Heiligenberg, W. 1976. The interaction of stimulus patterns controlling aggressiveness in the cichlid fish *Haplochromis burtoni*. *Anim. Behav.* **24**, 452–458.

Herberg, L. J. 1963a. Seminal ejaculation following positively reinforcing electrical stimulation of the rat hypothalamus. *J. Comp. Physiol. Psychol.* **56**, 679–685.

Herberg, L. J. 1963b. Determinants of extinction in electrical self-stimulation. *J. Comp. Physiol. Psychol.* **56**, 686–690.

Herberg, L. J., and Watkins, J. 1966. The effect of overtraining and repeated extinction on speed of extinction in electrical self-stimulation. *Quart. J. Exp. Psychol.* **56**, 75–77.

Hill, T. E., and Thomas, T. R. 1973. The role of reinforcement in the sexual behavior of the female rat. *Physiol. Behav.* **11**, 911–913.

Hinde, R. A. 1960. Energy models of motivation. *Symp. Soc. Exp. Biol.* **14**, 199–213.

Hinde, R. A. 1967. Aspects of the control of avian reproductive development within the breeding season. *Proc. Int. Ornithol. Congr.* **14**, 135–153.

Hinde, R. A. 1970. "Animal Behaviour: A Synthesis of Ethology and Comparative Psychology." McGraw-Hill, New York.

Hinde, R. A. 1974. "Biological Bases of Human Social Behaviour." McGraw-Hill, New York.

Hinde, R. A., and Steel, E. A. 1966. Integration of the reproductive behaviour of female canaries. *Symp. Soc. Exp. Biol.* **20**, 401–426.

Hinde, R. A., and Steel, E. A. 1972. Reinforcing events in the integration of canary nest-building. *Anim. Behav.* **20**, 514–525.

Hinde, R. A., and Stevenson, J. G. 1969. Sequences of behavior. *In* "Advances in the Study of Behavior" (D. S. Lehrman, R. A. Hinde, and E. Shaw, eds.), Vol. 2, pp. 267–296. Academic Press, New York.

Hinde, R. A., and Stevenson, J. G. 1970. Goals and response control. *In* "Development and Evolution of Behavior" (L. R. Aronson, E. Tobach, D. S. Lehrman, and J. S. Rosenblatt, eds.), pp. 216–237. Freeman, San Francisco.

Hinde, R. A., and Stevenson-Hinde, J. 1973. "Constraints on Learning." Academic Press, London.

Hirsch, E., and Collier, G. 1974a. The ecological determinants of reinforcement in the Guinea pig. *Physiol. Behav.* **12**, 239–249.

Hirsch, E., and Collier, G. 1974b. Effort as determinant of intake and patterns of drinking in the Guinea pig. *Physiol. Behav.* **12**, 647–655.

Hodos, W., and Kalman, G. 1963. Effects of increment size and reinforcement volume on progressive ratio performance. *J. Exp. Anal. Behav.* **6**, 387–392.

Hodos, W., and Valenstein, E. S. 1962. An evaluation of response rate as a measure of rewarding intracranial stimulation. *J. Comp. Physiol. Psychol.* **55**, 80–84.

Hoebel, B. G. 1968. Inhibition and disinhibition of self-stimulation and feeding: Hypothalamic control and postingestional factors. *J. Comp. Physiol. Psychol.* **66**, 89–100.

Hoebel, B. G. 1975. Brain reward and aversion systems in the control of feeding and sexual behavior. *In* "Nebraska Symposium on Motivation, 1974" (J. K. Cole and T. B. Sonderegger, eds.), pp. 49–112. Univ. of Nebraska Press, Lincoln.

Hoebel, B. G., and Teitlebaum, P. 1962. Hypothalamic control of feeding and self-stimulation. *Science* **135**, 375–376.

Hogan, J. A. 1961. Motivational aspects of instinctive behavior in *Betta splendens*. Ph.D. thesis, Harvard University, Cambridge, Mass.

Hogan, J. A. 1965. An experimental study of conflict and fear: An analysis of behavior of young chicks toward a mealworm. Part I. The behavior of chicks which do not eat the mealworm. *Behaviour* **25**, 45–97.

Hogan, J. A. 1967. Fighting and reinforcement in the Siamese fighting fish (*Betta splendens*). *J. Comp. Physiol. Psychol.* **64**, 356–359.

Hogan, J. A. 1971. The development of a hunger system in young chicks. *Behaviour* **39**, 128–201.

Hogan, J. A. 1974. On the choice between eating and aggressive display in the Siamese fighting fish (*Betta splendens*). *Learn. Motiv.* **5**, 273–287.

Hogan, J. A. 1978. Control of fixed-ratio responding for eating and aggressive display by deprivation and preexposure in the Siamese fighting fish (*Betta splendens*). Unpublished manuscript.

Hogan, J. A., and Rozin, P. 1962. An improved mechanical fish-lever. *Am. J. Psychol.* **75**, 307–308.

Hogan, J. A., Kleist, S., and Hutchings, C. S. L. 1970. Display and food as reinforcers in the Siamese fighting fish (*Betta splendens*). *J. Comp. Physiol. Psychol.* **70**, 351–357.

von Holst, E., and Mittelstaedt, H. 1950. Das Reafferenzprinzip. *Naturwissenschaften* **37**, 464–476. (See also: von Holst, E. 1954. Relations between the central nervous system and the peripheral organs. *Anim. Behav.* **2**, 89–94.)

von Holst, E., and von Saint Paul, U. 1960. Vom Wirkungsgefüge der Triebe. *Naturwissenschaften* **47**, 409–422. (Trans.: On the functional organisation of drives. *Anim. Behav.* **11**, 1–20. 1963.)

Houston, A., and McFarland, D. 1976. On the measurement of motivational variables. *Anim. Behav.* **24**, 459–475.

Hull, C. L. 1933. Differential habituation to internal stimuli in the albino rat. *J. Comp. Psychol.* **16**, 255–273.

Hull, C. L. 1943. "Principles of Behavior." Appleton, New York.

Hunsicker, J. P., and Reid, L. D. 1974. "Priming effect" in conventionally reinforced rats. *J. Comp. Physiol. Psychol.* **87**, 618–621.

van Iersel, J. J. A. 1953. An analysis of the parental behaviour of the three-spined stickleback (*Gasterosteus aculeatus* L.). *Behaviour Suppl. 3.*

Jansen, P. E., Goodman, E. D., Jowaisas, D., and Bunnell, B. N. 1969. Paper as a positive reinforcer for acquisition of a bar-press response by the golden hamster. *Psychon. Sci.* **16**, 113–114.

Johnson, R. N., and Johnson, L. D. 1973. Intra- and interspecific social and aggressive behaviour in the Siamese fighting fish, *Betta splendens*. *Anim. Behav.* **21**, 665–672.

Kagan, J. 1955. Differential reward value of incomplete and complete sexual behavior. *J. Comp. Physiol. Psychol.* **48**, 59–64.

Kavanau, J. L., and Brant, D. H. 1965. Wheel-running preferences of Peromyscus. *Nature (London)* **208**, 597–598.

Keesey, R. E. 1962. The relation between pulse frequency, intensity, and duration and the rate of responding for intracranial stimulation. *J. Comp. Physiol. Psychol.* **55**, 671–678.

Keesey, R. E. 1964. Duration of stimulation and the reward properties of hypothalamic stimulation. *J. Comp. Physiol. Psychol.* **58**, 201–207.

Keesey, R. E., and Goldstein, M. D. 1968. Use of progressive fixed-ratio procedures in the assessment of intracranial reinforcement. *J. Exp. Anal. Behav.* **11**, 293–301.

Keesey, R. E., and Kling, J. W. 1961. Amount of reinforcement and free-operant responding. *J. Exp. Anal. Behav.* **4**, 125–132.

Kemp, F. D. 1969. Thermal reinforcement and thermoregulatory behaviour in the lizard *Dipsosaurus dorsalis*: An operant technique. *Anim. Behav.* **17**, 446–451.

Kent, E., and Grossman, S. P. 1969. Evidence for a conflict interpretation of anomalous effects of rewarding brain stimulation. *J. Comp. Physiol. Psychol.* **69**, 381–390.

Killeen, P. 1969. Reinforcement frequency and contingency as factors in fixed-ratio behavior. *J. Exp. Anal. Behav.* **12**, 391–395.

Kimble, G. A. 1961. "Hilgard and Marquis' Conditioning and Learning," 2nd ed. Appleton, New York.

King, B. M., and Gaston, M. G. 1973. The effects of pretraining on the bar-pressing performance of VMH-lesioned rats. *Physiol. Behav.* **11**, 161–166.

King, B. M., and Gaston, M. G. 1976. Factors influencing the hunger and thirst motivated behavior of hypothalamic hyperphagic rats. *Physiol. Behav.* **16**, 33–41.

Kintsch, W. 1962. Runway performance as a function of drive strength and magnitude of reinforcement. *J. Comp. Physiol. Psychol.* **55**, 882–887.

Kish, G. B. 1966. Studies of sensory reinforcement. *In* "Operant Behavior: Areas of Research and Application" (W. K. Honig, ed.), pp. 109–159. Appleton, New York.

Klein, R. M., Figler, M. H., and Peeke, H. V. S. 1976. Modification of consummatory (attack) behavior resulting from prior habituation of appetitive (threat) components of the agonistic sequence in male *Betta splendens* (Pisces, Belontiidae). *Behaviour* **58**, 1–25.

Kling, J. W., and Schrier, A. M. 1971. Positive reinforcement. *In* "Woodworth and Schlosberg's Experimental Psychology" (J. W. Kling and L. A. Riggs, eds.), pp. 615–702. Holt, New York.

Knarr, F. A., and Collier, G. 1962. Taste and consummatory activity in amount and gradient of reinforcement functions. *J. Exp. Psychol.* **63**, 579–588.

de Kock, L. L., and Rohn, I. 1971. Observations on the use of the exercise-wheel in relation to the social rank and hormonal conditions in the bank vole (*Clethrionomys glareolus*), and the Norway lemming (*Lemmus lemmus*). *Z. Tierpsychol.* **29**, 180–195.

Kraeling, D. 1961. Analysis of amount of reward as a variable in learning. *J. Comp. Physiol. Psychol.* **54**, 560–565.

Kristt, D. A., and Sechzer, J. A. 1969. Behavioral thermoregulation at high environmental temperatures: Effect of variation in intensity of heat stimulus and magnitude of reinforcement. *Psychon. Sci.* **16**, 1–2.

Kruijt, J. P. 1964. Ontogeny of social behaviour in Burmese Red Junglefowl. *Behaviour Suppl. 12*.

Kutscher, C. L. 1969. Species differences in the interaction of feeding and drinking. *Ann. N.Y. Acad. Sci.* **157**, 539–552.

Kutscher, C. L. 1974. Strain differences in drinking in inbred mice during ad libitum feeding and food deprivation. *Physiol. Behav.* **13**, 63–70.

Lancaster, K. 1966. A new approach to consumer theory. *J. Polit. Econ.* **74**, 132–157.

Larsson, K. 1956. "Conditioning and Sexual Behavior in the Male Albino Rat." Almqvist and Wiksell, Stockholm.

Lashley, K. S. 1938. Experimental analysis of instinctive behavior. *Psychol. Rev.* **45**, 445–471.

Laudien, H. 1965. Untersuchungen über das Kampfverhalten der Männchen von *Betta splendens* Regan (Anabantidae, Pisces). *Z. Wiss. Zool.* **172**, 134–178.

Lea, S., and Roper, T. J. 1977. Demand for food on fixed-ratio schedules as a function of the quality of concurrently available reinforcement. *J. Exp. Anal. Behav.* **27**, 371–380.

Leeming, F. C. 1968. Response rate as a function of magnitude and schedule of heat reinforcement. *J. Exp. Psychol.* **76**, 74–77.

Lehrman, D. S. 1961. Hormonal regulation of parental behavior in birds and infra-human mammals. *In* "Sex and Internal Secretions" (W. C. Young, ed.), pp. 1268–1382. Williams & Wilkins, Baltimore, Maryland.

Lehrman, D. S. 1970. Semantic and conceptual issues in the nature–nurture problem. *In* "Development and Evolution of Behavior" (L. R. Aronson *et al.*, eds.), pp. 17–52. Freeman, San Francisco.

Le Magnen, J. 1971. Advances in studies on the physiological control and regulation of food intake. *In* "Progress in Physiological Psychology" (E. Stellar and J. M. Sprague, eds.), Vol. 4, pp. 204–261. Academic Press, New York.

Lenzer, I. I. 1972. Differences between behavior reinforced by electrical stimulation of the brain and conventionally reinforced behavior: An associative analysis. *Psychol. Bull.* **78**, 103–118.

Leshner, A. I. 1971. The adrenals and the regulatory nature of running wheel activity. *Physiol. Behav.* **6**, 551–558.

Levy, N., and Seward, J. P. 1969. Frustration and homogeneity of rewards in the double runway. *J. Exp. Psychol.* **81**, 460–463.

Lisk, R. D., Pretlow, R. A., and Friedman, S. M. 1969. Hormonal stimulation necessary for elicitation of maternal nest-building in the mouse (*Mus musculus*). *Anim. Behav.* **17**, 730–737.

Lissmann, H. W. 1932. Die Umwelt des Kampffisches (*Betta splendens* Regan). *Z. Vgl. Physiol.* **18**, 65–108.

Logan, F. A. 1960. "Incentive: How the Conditions of Reinforcement Affect the Performance of Rats." Yale Univ. Press, New Haven, Conn.

Logan, F. A. 1964. The free behavior situation. *In* "Nebraska Symposium on Motivation, 1964" (D. Levine, ed.), pp. 99–128. Univ. of Nebraska Press, Lincoln.

Logan, F. A., and Spanier, D. 1970. Relative effect of delay of food and water reward. *J. Comp. Physiol. Psychol.* **72**, 102–104.

Lorenz, K. 1937. Über die Bildung des Instinktbegriffes. *Naturwissenschaften* **25**, 289–300, 307–318, 324–331.

Lorenz, K. 1939. Vergleichende Verhaltensforschung. *Zool. Anz. Suppl. 12*, 69–102.

Lorenz, K. 1950. The comparative method in studying innate behaviour patterns. *Symp. Soc. Exp. Biol.* **4**, 221–268.

Lorenz, K. 1966. "On Aggression." Methuen, London.

Lowe, C., Davey, G. C. L., and Harzem, P. 1974. Effects of reinforcement magnitude on interval and ratio schedules. *J. Exp. Anal. Behav.* **22**, 553–560.

Macdonald, G. E., and de Toledo, L. 1974. Partial reinforcement effects and type of reward. *Learn. Motiv.* **5**, 288–298.

McFarland, D. J. 1966. On the causal and functional significance of displacement activities. *Z. Tierpsychol.* **23**, 217–235.

McFarland, D. J. 1971. "Feedback Mechanisms in Animal Behaviour." Academic Press, London.

Mackintosh, N. J. 1974. "The Psychology of Animal Learning." Academic Press, London and New York.

Margules, D. L., and Olds, J. 1962. Identical "feeding" and "rewarding" systems in the lateral hypothalamus of rats. *Science* **135**, 374–375.

Marler, P. 1957. Studies of fighting in chaffinches. 4. Appetitive and consummatory behaviour. *Br. J. Anim. Behav.* **5**, 29–37.

Mayer, J. 1975. "A Diet for Living." McKay, New York.

Mendelson, J., and Chillag, D. 1971. Schedule-induced air licking in rats. *Physiol. Behav.* **6**, 603–605.

Miller, N. E. 1959. Liberalization of basic S–R concepts: Extensions to conflict behavior, motivation, and social learning. *In* "Psychology: A Study of a Science" (S. Koch, ed.), Vol. 2, pp. 196–292. McGraw-Hill, New York.

Miller, N. E., Bailey, C. J., and Stevenson, J. A. F. 1950. Decreased 'hunger' but increased food intake resulting from hypothalamic lesions. *Science* **112**, 256–259.

Mogenson, G. J., and Stevenson, J. A. F. 1966. Drinking and self-stimulation with electrical stimulation of the lateral hypothalamus. *Physiol. Behav.* **1**, 251–254.

Moltz, H. 1971. The ontogeny of maternal behavior in some selected mammalian species. *In* "The Ontogeny of Vertebrate Behavior" (H. Moltz, ed.), pp. 263–313. Academic Press, New York.

Montagu, M. F. A. (ed.), 1968. "Man and Aggression." Oxford Univ. Press, London and New York.

Morris, D. 1956. The function and causation of courtship ceremonies. *In* "L'instinct dans le Comportement des Animaux et de L'homme" (P. P. Grasse, ed.), pp. 261–284. Fondation Singer Polignac, Paris.

Morrison, S. D. 1968. The constancy of the energy expended by rats on spontaneous activity, and the distribution of activity between feeding and non-feeding. *J. Physiol.* **197**, 305–323.

Mrosovsky, N. 1964. The performance of dormice and other hibernators on tests of hunger motivation. *Anim. Behav.* **12**, 454–469.

Mrosovsky, N. 1968. The adjustable brain of hibernators. *Sci. Am.* **218**(3), 110–118.

Mrosovsky, N. 1971. "Hibernation and the Hypothalamus." Appleton, New York.

Munn, N. L. 1950. "Handbook of Psychological Research on the Rat." Houghton, Boston, Mass.

Neuringer, A. J. 1967. Effects of reinforcement magnitude on choice and rate of responding. *J. Exp. Anal. Behav.* **10**, 417–424.

Notterman, J. M., and Mintz, D. E. 1965. "Dynamics of Response Control." Wiley, New York.

Novin, D., Wyrwicka, W., and Bray, G. A. (eds.), 1976. "Hunger: Basic Mechanisms and Clinical Implications." Raven, New York.

Olds, J. 1956. Runway and maze behavior controlled by basomedial forebrain stimulation in the rat. *J. Comp. Physiol. Psychol.* **49**, 507–512.

Olds, J. 1958. Self-stimulation of the brain. *Science* **127**, 315–324.

Olds, J., and Milner, P. 1954. Positive reinforcement produced by electrical stimulation of septal area and other regions of the rat brain. *J. Comp. Physiol. Psychol.* **47**, 419–427.

Oley, N. N., and Slotnick, B. M. 1970. Nesting material as a reinforcement for operant behavior in the rat. *Psychon. Sci.* **21**, 41–43.

Omwake, L. 1933. The activity and learning of white rats. *J. Comp. Psychol.* **16**, 275–285.

Peeke, H. V. S., and Peeke, S. C. 1970. Habituation of conspecific aggressive responses in the Siamese fighting fish (*Betta splendens*). *Behaviour* **36**, 232–245.

Peirce, J. T., and Nuttall, R. L. 1961. Self-paced sexual behavior in the female rat. *J. Comp. Physiol. Psychol.* **54**, 310–313.

Peterson, G. B., Ackil, J. E., Frommer, G. P., and Hearst, E. S. 1972. Conditioned approach and contact behavior toward signals for food or brain-stimulation reinforcement. *Science* **177**, 1009–1011.

Petrinovich, L., and Bolles, R. 1954. Deprivation states and behavioral attributes. *J. Comp. Physiol. Psychol.* **47**, 450–453.

Pfaffmann, C. 1960. The pleasures of sensation. *Psychol. Rev.* **67**, 253–268.

Pliskoff, S. S., Wright, J. E., and Hawkins, T. D. 1965. Brain stimulation as a reinforcer: Intermittent schedules. *J. Exp. Anal. Behav.* **8**, 75–88.

Polsky, R. H. 1975. Hunger, prey feeding, and predatory aggression. *Behav. Biol.* **13**, 81–93.

Powell, R. W. 1969. The effect of reinforcement magnitude upon responding under fixed-ratio schedules. *J. Exp. Anal. Behav.* **12**, 605–608.

Premack, D. 1965. Reinforcement theory. *In* "Nebraska Symposium on Motivation, 1965" (D. Levine, ed.), pp. 123–180. Univ. of Nebraska Press, Lincoln.

Premack, D., and Premack, A. J. 1963. Increased eating in rats deprived of running. *J. Exp. Anal. Behav.* **6**, 209–212.

Premack, D., Schaeffer, R. W., and Hundt, A. 1964. Reinforcement of drinking by running: Effect of fixed ratio and reinforcement time. *J. Exp. Anal. Behav.* **7**, 91–96.

Pubols, B. H., Jr. 1960. Incentive magnitude, learning, and performance in animals. *Psychol. Bull.* **57**, 89–115.

Quartermain, D., and Webster, D. 1968. Extinction following intracranial reward: The effect of delay between acquisition and extinction. *Science* **159**, 1259–1260.

Rasa, O. A. E. 1971. Appetence for aggression in juvenile damsel fish. *Z. Tierpsychol. Beih.* **7**.

Ray, O. S., Hine, B., and Bivens, L. W. 1968. Stability of self-stimulation responding during long test sessions. *Physiol. Behav.* **3**, 161–165.

Regal, P. J. 1971. Long term studies with operant conditioning techniques of temperature regulation patterns in reptiles. *J. Physiol. (Paris)* **63**, 403–406.

Reid, L. D., Hunsicker, J. P., Kent, E. W., Lindsay, J. L., and Gallistel, C. R. 1973. Incidence and magnitude of the 'priming effect' in self-stimulating rats. *J. Comp. Physiol. Psychol.* **82**, 286–293.

Rescorla, R. A. 1978. Some implications of a cognitive perspective on Pavlovian conditioning. *In* "Cognitive Processes in Animal Behavior" (S. Hulse, H. Fowler, and W. K. Honig, eds.). Erlbaum Assoc., Hillsdale, N.J. In press.

Rhoad, K. D., Kalat, J. W., and Klopfer, P. 1975. Aggression and avoidance by *Betta splendens* toward natural and artificial stimuli. *Anim. Learn. Behav.* **3**, 271–276.

Richards, M. P. M. 1965. Aspects of maternal behaviour in the golden hamster. Ph.D. thesis, Univ. of Cambridge, England.

Richardson, W. K., and Loughead, T. E. 1974. The effect of physical restraint on behavior under the differential-reinforcement-of-low-rate schedule. *J. Exp. Anal. Behav.* **21**, 455–461.

Richter, C. P. 1922. A behavioristic study of the activity of the rat. *Comp. Psychol. Monogr.* **1**, 1–55.

Richter, C. P. 1927. Animal behavior and internal drives. *Quart. Rev. Biol.* **2**, 307–343.

Robbins, D. 1969. Effect of duration of water reinforcement on running behavior and consummatory activity. *J. Comp. Physiol. Psychol.* **69**, 311–316.

Roberts, W. W., Steinberg, M. L., and Means, L. W. 1967. Hypothalamic mechanisms for sexual, aggressive, and other motivational behaviors in the opossum, *Didelphis virginiana. J. Comp. Physiol. Psychol.* **64**, 1–15.

Roeder, K. D. 1975. Feedback, spontaneous activity, and behaviour. *In* "Function and Evolution in Behaviour" (G. P. Baerends, C. Beer, and A. Manning, eds.), pp. 55–70. Oxford Univ. Press, London and New York.

Rolls, E. T. 1975. "The Brain and Reward." Pergamon, Oxford.

Roper, T. J. 1973a. The organisation of nest-building in female mice. Ph.D. thesis, University of Cambridge, England.

Roper, T. J. 1973b. Nesting material as a reinforcer for female mice. *Anim. Behav.* **21**, 733–740.

Roper, T. J. 1975a. Nest material and food as reinforcers for fixed-ratio responding in mice. *Learn. Motiv.* **6**, 327–343.

Roper, T. J. 1975b. Diurnal rhythms in the nest-building behaviour of female mice. *Behaviour* **52**, 95–103.

Roper, T. J. 1976a. Self-sustaining activities and reinforcement in the nest-building behaviour of mice. *Behaviour* **59**, 40–58.

Roper, T. J. 1976b. Sex differences in circadian wheel running rhythms in the Mongolian gerbil. *Physiol. Behav.* **17**, 549–551.

Roper, T. J., and Poliondakis, M. 1977. The behaviour of Mongolian gerbils in a semi-natural environment, with special reference to ventral marking, dominance and sociability. *Behaviour* **61**, 207–237.

Rosenblatt, J. S. 1970. Views on the onset and maintenance of maternal behavior in the rat. *In* "Development and Evolution of Behavior" (L. R. Aronson *et al.,* eds.), pp. 489–518. Freeman, San Francisco.

Ross, A. R. 1973. A simple method for determining the relative reward value of electrical brain stimulation. *Physiol. Behav.* **11**, 399–401.

Rowell, T. E. 1959. Maternal behaviour in the golden hamster. Ph.D. thesis, University of Cambridge, England.

Rozin, P. 1961. Some aspects of regulatory behavior in the goldfish, *Carassius auratus.* Ph.D. thesis, Harvard University, Cambridge, Mass.

Rozin, P. 1968. The use of poikilothermy in the analysis of behavior. *In* "The Central Nervous System and Fish Behavior" (D. Ingle, ed.), pp. 181–192. Univ. of Chicago Press, Chicago.

Rozin, P., and Kalat, J. W. 1971. Specific hungers and poison avoidance as adaptive specializations of learning. *Psychol. Rev.* **78**, 459–486.

Rozin, P., and Mayer, J. 1961a. Regulation of food intake in the goldfish. *Am. J. Physiol.* **201**, 968–974.

Rozin, P., and Mayer, J. 1961b. Thermal reinforcement and thermoregulatory behavior in the goldfish, *Carassius auratus. Science* **134**, 942–943.

Rozin, P. N., and Mayer, J. 1964. Some factors influencing short-term food intake in the goldfish. *Am. J. Physiol.* **206**, 1430–1436.

de Ruiter, L. 1963. The physiology of vertebrate feeding behaviour. *Z. Tierpsychol.* **20**, 498–516.

de Ruiter, L., Wiepkema, P. R., and Veening, J. G. 1974. Models of behavior and the hypothalamus. *In* "Progress in Brain Research—Vol. 41: Integrative Hypothalamic Activity" (D. F. Swaab and J. P. Schadé, eds.), pp. 481–507. Elsevier, Amsterdam.

Sachs, B. D., and Barfield, R. J. 1976. Functional analysis of masculine copulatory behavior in the rat. *In* "Advances in the Study of Behavior" (J. S. Rosenblatt *et al.,* eds.), Vol. 7, pp. 91–154. Academic Press, New York.

Satinoff, E. 1964. Behavioral thermoregulation in response to local cooling of the rat brain. *Am. J. Physiol.* **206**, 1389–1394.

Schaeffer, R. W., and Diehl, J. C. 1966. Collateral water drinking in rats maintained on FR food reinforcement schedules. *Psychon. Sci.* **4**, 257–258.

Schwartz, M. 1956. Instrumental and consummatory measures of sexual capacity in the male rat. *J. Comp. Physiol. Psychol.* **49**, 328–333.

Sealander, J. A. 1952. The relationship of nest protection and huddling to survival of *Peromyscus* at low temperature. *Ecology* **33**, 63–71.

Segal, E. F. 1972. Induction and the provenance of operants. *In* "Reinforcement: Behavioral Analyses" (R. M. Gilbert and J. R. Millenson, eds.), pp. 1–34. Academic Press, New York.

Seligman, M. E. P. 1970. On the generality of the laws of learning. *Psychol. Rev.* **77**, 406–418.

Seligman, M. E. P., and Hager, J. L. 1972. "Biological Boundaries of Learning." Appleton, New York.

Sevenster, P. 1961. A causal analysis of a displacement activity (Fanning in *Gasterosteus aculeatus* L.). *Behaviour, Suppl. 9.*

Sevenster, P. 1968. Motivation and learning in sticklebacks. *In* "The Central Nervous System and Fish Behavior" (D. Ingle, ed.), pp. 233–245. Univ. of Chicago Press, Chicago.

Sevenster, P. 1973. Incompatibility of response and reward. *In* "Constraints on Learning" (R. A. Hinde and J. Stevenson-Hinde, eds.), pp. 265–283. Academic Press, London.

Seward, J. P., and Pereboom, A. C. 1955. A note on the learning of "spontaneous" activity. *Am. J. Psychol.* **68**, 139–142.

Seward, J. P., Uyeda, A., and Olds, J. 1959. Resistance to extinction following cranial self-stimulation. *J. Comp. Physiol. Psychol.* **52**, 294–299.

Seward, J. P., Uyeda, A. A., and Olds, J. 1960. Reinforcing effect of brain stimulation on runway performance as a function of interval between trials. *J. Comp. Physiol. Psychol.* **53**, 224–228.

Seybert, J. A., and Gerard, I. C. 1976. Acquisition and extinction effects of partial reinforcement under conditions of thirst motivation. *Bull. Psychon. Soc.* **8**, 590–592.

Seybert, J. A., Gerard, I. C., Lawrence, T., Nash, S. W., and Williams, C. L. 1976. Effects of schedule and magnitude of reinforcement under conditions of thirst motivation. *Learn. Motiv.* **7**, 559–570.

Shanab, M. E., Melrose, S., and Young, T. 1975. The partial reinforcement effect sustained through blocks of continuous water reinforcement. *Bull. Psychon. Soc.* **6**, 261–264.

Sheffield, F. D. 1966. A drive induction theory of reinforcement. *In* "Current Research in Motivation" (R. N. Haber, ed.), pp. 98–111. Holt, New York.

Sheffield, F. D., and Campbell, B. A. 1954. The role of experience in the "spontaneous activity" of hungry rats. *J. Comp. Physiol. Psychol.* **47**, 97–100.

Sheffield, F. D., Wulff, J. J., and Backer, R. 1951. Reward value of copulation without sexual drive reduction. *J. Comp. Physiol. Psychol.* **44**, 3–8.

Sherrington, C. S. 1900. Cutaneous sensation. *In* "Textbook of Physiology" (E. A. Schaeffer, ed.). Macmillan, New York.

Shettleworth, S. J. 1972. Constraints on learning. *In* "Advances in the Study of Behavior" (D. S. Lehrman, R. A. Hinde, and E. Shaw, eds.), Vol. 4, pp. 1–68. Academic Press, New York.

Shettleworth, S. J. 1975. Reinforcement and the organization of behavior in Golden hamsters: Hunger, environment and food reinforcement. *J. Exp. Psychol.: Anim. Behav. Processes* **1**, 56–87.

Shizgal, P., and Matthews, G. 1977. Electrical stimulation of the rat diencephalon: Differential effects of interrupted stimulation on on- and off-responding. *Brain Res.* **129**, 319–333.

Sidman, M., and Stebbins, W. C. 1954. Satiation effects under fixed-ratio schedules of reinforcement. *J. Comp. Physiol. Psychol.* **47**, 114–116.

Sidman, M., Brady, J. V., Boren, J. J., Conrad, D. G., and Schulman, A. 1955. Reward schedules and behavior maintained by intracranial self-stimulation. *Science* **122**, 830–831.

Silverstone, T. (ed.), 1976. "Appetite and Food Intake." Dahlem Konferenzen, Berlin.

Simpson, M. J. A. 1968. The display of the Siamese fighting fish, *Betta splendens. Anim. Behav. Monogr.* **1**, 1–73.

Singh, D. 1974. Role of preoperative experience on reaction to quinine taste in hypothalamic hyperphagic rats. *J. Comp. Physiol. Psychol.* **86**, 674–678.

Skinner, B. F. 1932. On the rate of formation of a conditioned reflex. *J. Gen. Psychol.* **7**, 274–286.

Skinner, B. F. 1936. Thirst as an arbitrary drive. *J. Gen. Psychol.* **15**, 205–210.

Skinner, B. F. 1938. "The Behavior of Organisms." Appleton, New York.

Skuban, W. E., and Richardson, W. K. 1975. The effect of the size of the test environment on behavior under two temporally defined schedules. *J. Exp. Anal. Behav.* **23**, 271–275.

Smart, J. L. 1970. Trial-and-error behaviour of inbred and F_1 hybrid mice. *Anim. Behav.* **18**, 445–453.

Smith, M. F., and Smith, K. V. 1939. Thirst-motivated activity and its extinction in the cat. *J. Gen. Psychol.* **21**, 89–98.

Snyder, H. L. 1962. Saccharine concentration and deprivation as determinants of instrumental and consummatory response strengths. *J. Exp. Psychol.* **63**, 610–615.

Spear, N. E. 1962. Comparison of the reinforcing effect of brain stimulation on Skinner box, runway, and maze performance. *J. Comp. Physiol. Psychol.* **55**, 679–684.

Staddon, J. E. R., and Simmelhag, V. L. 1971. The superstition experiment: A reexamination of its implications for the principles of adaptive behavior. *Psychol. Rev.* **78**, 3–43.

Stein, L. 1962. An analysis of stimulus-duration preference in self-stimulation of the brain. *J. Comp. Physiol. Psychol.* **55**, 405–414.

Stellar, J. R., and Gallistel, C. R. 1975. Runway performance of rats for brain-stimulation or food reward: Effects of hunger and priming. *J. Comp. Physiol. Psychol.* **89**, 590–599.

Stevenson-Hinde, J. 1973. Constraints on reinforcement. *In* "Constraints on Learning" (R. A. Hinde and J. Stevenson-Hinde, eds.), pp. 285–296. Academic Press, London.

Tapp, J. T. (ed.), 1969. "Reinforcement and Behavior." Academic Press, New York.

Teghtsoonian, R., and Campbell, B. A. 1960. Random activity of the rat during food deprivation as a function of environment. *J. Comp. Physiol. Psychol.* **53**, 242–244.

Teitelbaum, P. 1957. Random and food-directed activity in hyperphagic and normal rats. *J. Comp. Physiol. Psychol.* **50**, 486–590.

Teitelbaum, P. 1961. Disturbances in feeding and drinking behavior after hypothalamic lesions. *In* "Nebraska Symposium on Motivation, 1961" (M. R. Jones. ed.), pp. 39–65. Univ. of Nebraska Press, Lincoln.

Teitelbaum, P. 1971. The encephalization of hunger. *In* "Progress in Physiological Psychology" (E. Stellar and J. M. Sprague, eds.), Vol. 4, pp. 319–350. Academic Press, New York.

Tellegen, A., Horn, J. M., and Legrand, R. G. 1969. Opportunity for aggression as a reinforcer in mice. *Psychon. Sci.* **14**, 104–105.

Thach, J. S. 1970. Modulation of food and water intake by size of fixed ratio. *Proc. Annu. Conv. Am. Psychol. Assn.* **5**, 755–756.

Thompson, T. I. 1963. Visual reinforcement in Siamese fighting fish. *Science* **141**, 55–57.

Thompson, T. I. 1964. Visual reinforcement in fighting cocks. *J. Exp. Anal. Behav.* **7**, 45–49.

Thompson, T. I. 1969. Aggressive behaviour of Siamese fighting fish. *In* "International Symposium on the Biology of Aggressive Behaviour " (S. Garattini and E. B. Sigg, eds.), pp. 15–31. Excerpta Medica, Amsterdam.

Thompson, T. I., and Sturm, T. 1965. Classical conditioning of aggressive display in Siamese fighting fish. *J. Exp. Anal. Behav.* **8**, 397–403.

Thorpe, W. H. 1956. "Learning and Instinct in Animals." Harvard Univ. Press, Cambridge, Mass.

Timberlake, W., and Allison, J. 1974. Response deprivation: An empirical approach to instrumental performance. *Psychol. Rev.* **81**, 146–164.

Tinbergen, N. 1950. The hierarchical organization of nervous mechanisms underlying instinctive behaviour. *Symp. Soc. Exp. Biol.* **4**, 305–312.

Tinbergen, N. 1951. "The Study of Instinct." Oxford Univ. Press, London and New York.

Tinbergen, N. 1952. "Derived" activities; their causation, biological significance, origin and emancipation during evolution. *Quart. Rev. Biol.* **27**, 1–32.

Trowill, J. A., Panksepp, J., and Gandelman, R. 1969. An incentive model of rewarding brain stimulation. *Psychol. Rev.* **76**, 264–281.

Turnbough, P. D., and Lloyd, K. E. 1973. Operant responding in Siamese fighting fish (*Betta splendens*) as a function of schedule of reinforcement and visual reinforcers. *J. Exp. Anal. Behav.* **20**, 355–362.

Valenstein, E. S. 1964. Problems of measurement and interpretation with reinforcing brain stimulation. *Psychol. Rev.* **71**, 415–437.

Valenstein, E. S., Cox, V. C., and Kakolewski, J. W. 1968. Modification of motivated behavior elicited by electrical stimulation of the hypothalamus. *Science* **159**, 1119–1121.

Valenstein, E. S., Cox, V. C., and Kakolewski, J. W. 1970. Reexamination of the role of the hypothalamus in motivation. *Psychol. Rev.* **77**, 16–31.

Van Hemel, P. E. 1972. Aggression as a reinforcer: Operant behavior in the mouse-killing rat. *J. Exp. Anal. Behav.* **17**, 237–245.

Wald, G., and Jackson, B. 1944. Activity and nutritional deprivation. *Proc. Nat. Acad. Sci. USA* **30**, 255–263.

Wang, G. H. 1923. Relation between "spontaneous" activity and oestrous cycle in the white rat. *Comp. Psychol. Monogr.* **2**, (Serial No. 6).

Ware, R. 1968. Development of differential reinforcing values of sexual responses in the male albino rat. *J. Comp. Physiol. Psychol.* **65**, 461–465.

Warner, L. H. 1928. A study of thirst behavior in the white rat by means of the obstruction method. *J. Genet. Psychol.* **35**, 178–192.

Wasserman, E. A. 1973. Pavlovian conditioning with heat reinforcement produces stimulus-directed pecking in chicks. *Science* **181**, 875–877.

Wauquier, A., and Rolls, E. T. (eds.), 1976. "Brain-Stimulation Reward." North-Holland Publ., Amsterdam.

Weasner, M. H., Finger, F. W., and Reid, L. S. 1960. Activity changes under food deprivation as a function of recording device. *J. Comp. Physiol. Psychol.* **53**, 470–474.

Weiss, B. 1957. Thermal behavior of the subnourished and pantothenic-acid-deprived rat. *J. Comp. Physiol. Psychol.* **50**, 481–485.

Weiss, B., and Laties, V. G. 1960. Magnitude of reinforcement as a variable in thermoregulatory behavior. *J. Comp. Physiol. Psychol.* **53**, 603–608.

Weiss, B., and Laties, V. G. 1961. Behavioral thermoregulation. *Science* **133**, 1338–1344.

Wetzel, M. C. 1963. Self-stimulation aftereffects and runway performance in the rat. *J. Comp. Physiol. Psychol.* **56**, 673–678.

Whalen, R. E. 1961. Effects of mounting without intromission and intromission without ejaculation on sexual behavior and maze learning. *J. Comp. Physiol. Psychol.* **54**, 409–415.

Whalen, R. E. 1966. Sexual motivation. *Psychol. Rev.* **73**, 151–163.

Wickens, D. D., Hall, J., and Reid, L. S. 1949. Associative and retroactive inhibition as a function of the drive stimulus. *J. Comp. Physiol. Psychol.* **42**, 398–403.

Wike, E. L., and Farrow, B. J. 1962. The effects of magnitude of water reward on selective learning and habit reversal. *J. Comp. Physiol. Psychol.* **55**, 1024–1028.

Wise, R. A. 1974. Lateral hypothalamic electrical stimulation: Does it make animals 'hungry'? *Brain Research* **67**, 187–209.

Wright, J. W. 1976. Effect of hunger on the drinking behaviour of rodents adapted for mesic and xeric environments. *Anim. Behav.* **24**, 300–304.

Young, P. T. 1959. The role of affective processes in learning and motivation. *Psychol. Rev.* **66**, 104–125.

Subject Index

A

B